ELECTRON TUBES IN INDUSTRY

Electron Tubes in Industry

by **KEITH HENNEY**

Editorial Director, *Electronics*
Editor, *The Radio Engineering Handbook*
Author, *Principles of Radio*

and **JAMES D. FAHNESTOCK**

Associate Editor, *Electronics*

THIRD EDITION

McGRAW-HILL BOOK COMPANY, INC. 1952
NEW YORK   TORONTO   LONDON

VIII

28179

Electronic devices are in evidence in virtually all branches of industry today. In fact, many people credit the electron tube with responsibility for the high standard of living currently enjoyed by the civilized world.

As a result of the electronic revolution that has taken place within the last twenty years, it has become necessary for persons engaged in nonelectronic branches of industry to come in contact with electron-tube terms and techniques. The steel-mill operator depends on tubes to perform many critical operations; the worker depends on electronic instruments to check his work. Doctors use tubes to take much of the guesswork out of their diagnoses. Mining and drilling engineers rely on tubes to locate and evaluate underground mineral deposits. Even at home electronics is playing an important part in the form of television for entertainment, and in such luxuries as automatic garage-door openers, burglar alarms, and so on. It is indeed difficult to imagine a person today who is not in some way affected by some form of electronic circuitry, either directly or indirectly.

The purpose of this book is to provide industrial personnel— engineers and technicians—with enough fundamentals to permit them to talk intelligently about electronics, to know what can be expected of electronic devices and what their limitations are, and to help them visualize new applications. In presenting these fundamentals, practical tried and tested circuits are used as examples. Many of these circuits have already found successful application in industry, and sufficient information is presented to enable the reader to evaluate each circuit with his own requirements in mind. These circuits and techniques will be directly applicable to many new industrial jobs.

The complicated theoretical aspects of electron-tube technology have purposely been held to a minimum to prevent clouding the reader's mind with superfluous information. Extensive references are provided for the reader who requires more advanced or more detailed information. Most of these references cite original works in the literature that approach the subject at a level that should be useful to the readers of this book.

The authors are indebted to the many engineers who have taken time to describe their developments in the literature. Without this unselfish flow of information, a great deal of wasteful duplication of effort and reinvention would retard progress in this youthful but important industry.

KEITH HENNEY

JAMES D. FAHNESTOCK

NEW YORK, N. Y.
August, 1952

CONTENTS

CHAPTER 1

BASIC CIRCUIT ELEMENTS

All electronic devices are constructed around a few basic components. It is the proper combination of these basic elements that makes possible the wonders of electronics. Properly arranging the basic components into circuits gives man almost complete and practically instantaneous control over the movement of electrons, which is the basis of the electrical and electronic industries.

Resistance. Present-day knowledge indicates that certain materials have, in their cores, electrons which are relatively free to move from one atom to another; and certain other materials have so few such free electrons that virtually no exchange of electrons takes place. *Conductors*, therefore, exhibit relatively little resistance to electron movement, and *insulators* resist such movements.

Each electron represents a known and fixed amount of what we call "electricity," and when enough electrons move from one point to another, we say a measurable electric current "flows." One ampere, for example, is the electrical engineer's word for the flow of 6.28 million million million electrons between two points in one second of time.

Voltage, Current, Power. What makes electrons move from one point to another? Since each electron is really a pinch of *negative* electricity, it will be attracted toward any *positively* charged body and repulsed by any negatively charged body. The difference in charge between two points in a circuit—by whatever cause this difference is produced—is the motive force in the circuit which makes the electrons move. Our term for this charge difference is *potential* or *voltage.*

Voltage, current, and resistance—the fundamental characteristics of the electric circuit—are related by Ohm's law, which states that E volts will cause the movement of I amperes through R ohms. Thus,

$$I = \frac{E}{R} \quad \text{or} \quad E = IR \quad \text{or} \quad R = \frac{E}{I}$$

In other words, one ampere of current will flow through a material whose resistance is one ohm if a potential difference of one volt is applied across the material. This condition is illustrated in Fig. 1A, where the potential difference (voltage) is supplied by a battery.

If two 1-ohm resistances are used instead of a single unit, the current that flows will be ½ amp, as in Fig. 1B, and one-half of the applied voltage will appear across each resistor. The current in this case can be increased to 1 amp by doubling the applied voltage.

In moving from one place to another, electrons bump into other atomic building blocks—this is the essence of the resistance which impedes electron movement. Heat is produced by these collisions and this heat is a measure of the power required to move the electrons against the resistance. Numerically the power is

$$P = I^2R \quad \text{or} \quad \frac{E^2}{R} \quad \text{or} \quad IE$$

where P is the power in watts, I the current in amperes, R the resistance in ohms, and E the voltage in volts.

Direction of Current Flow. When a battery forces current through a resistance, the voltage "dropped" across the resistance can be measured with a voltmeter. In making voltage measurements (or current measurements) care must be taken to observe the proper polarity. The positive terminal of a meter must always be placed nearest the point which is toward the positive terminal of the battery, as shown in Fig. 1. Otherwise the needle will move backward.

Alternating Current. In a-c circuits the voltage and current are continually changing in direction and amplitude. Since the instantaneous voltage varies, the instantaneous current will vary in exact time phase in a resistive circuit, and this value of current can be obtained by using Ohm's law, provided the instantaneous value of voltage is used. The heating effect, or power consumption, in a resistive circuit, on the other hand, depends upon values of current and voltage which are somewhat less than the maximum or peak value. Actually the heating effect for sinusoidal voltages and currents must be obtained by multiplying the maximum values of current and voltage by 0.707 to obtain the *rms* value.

Thus an rms current of 1 amp of alternating current will produce the same heating effect as 1 amp of direct current when flowing through identical resistances.

Most a-c current and voltmeters read directly in rms values.

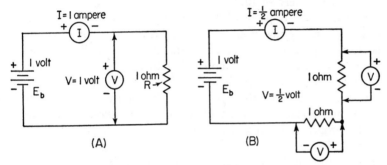

FIG. 1. Basic circuits containing series resistance and a d-c voltage source illustrate the application of Ohm's law.

Resistance is only one of the several factors which affect the flow of electrons in circuits. It is the only impeding influence of a d-c circuit. But when one deals with a-c circuits, other factors enter the picture and must be taken into account when figuring currents and voltages.

Nonlinear Resistors. Resistors, devices which possess resistance in usable form, are obtainable in many shapes, sizes, and forms, some of which do not obey Ohm's law; that is, the resistance they possess is not independent of the current through them, or the voltage across them, or the temperature at which they operate. A *rectifier*, for example, may be considered as a resistor which passes current only if that current flows in a certain direction, and a rectifier may be employed as a one-way type of resistor.

A *varistor* is a device whose resistance is highly sensitive to voltage or temperature. It is made up of metallic compounds of several sorts, copper oxide and silicon carbide being typical examples. Thyrite (silicon carbide) has a very steep characteristic indicating that at normal voltage the resistance is very high but that if the voltage rises appreciably, the resistance may drop to a very low value. It may be used, therefore, as a protective device across points where high voltage surges may occur.

Thermistors have high negative temperature coefficients; that is, their resistance decreases with increases in temperature. They are useful in temperature measurement and control.

It should be noted that all resistors have some temperature coefficient, positive or negative, but these variations of resistance may be extremely small.

Inductance. A piece of No. 20 copper wire 100 ft long will have a d-c resistance of about 1 ohm. If this same length of wire is wound up in the form of a coil, its resistance to direct current remains the same, but its opposition to the flow of alternating current increases. The higher the frequency of the alternating current, the greater the opposition offered by the coil. This phenomenon is due to an effect known as *inductance*. Inductance is the property of a coil that tends to resist any *change* in the current flowing through it. It is caused by the magnetic field that is established around any current-carrying wire. At the moment the current starts flowing, the field is established in the form of invisible concentric lines of force extending outward from the wire. As the current increases, these lines of force move out from the wire and generate a voltage in any wires lying in their path. In a coil, adjacent turns lie directly in the path of these lines of force. The polarity of the voltage induced in these turns is such that it tends to oppose the original current change. Once the current is established at some constant value, the effect of inductance disappears, because the lines of force are now stationary, and no opposing voltage, or back emf, is generated.

Inductance in a D-C Circuit. Consider the basic circuit shown in Fig. 2. If only resistance were involved, the current would immediately rise to its final value as soon as SW_1 was set to position A. However, the presence of inductance L changes the situation. When the battery is connected in the circuit, the current rises slowly because of the inductance effect. This is illustrated by the curves representing resistance voltage V_R, coil voltage V_L, and circuit current I with respect to the time when SW_1 is first connected to points A and B. When SW_1 is switched

to position *B*, the current that has been flowing in the circuit
will not drop to zero immediately, but will decrease as shown in
the curves (*I*).

It will be noticed that the voltage across the coil is maximum
at times when the value of the current is changing most rapidly.
This is stated mathematically by the equation

$$e = L \frac{di}{dt}$$

where *e* is the instantaneous voltage in volts, *L* the inductance of
the coil in henrys, and *di/dt* represents the rate at which the
current is changing at the instant the voltage is measured.

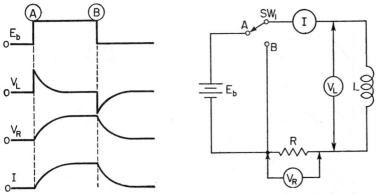

FIG. 2.   Transient effects in a circuit containing resistance and inductance.
When *SW*₁ is moved to position *A*, the battery voltage is impressed across
the coil and its resistance.   When *SW*₁ is moved to position *B*, the battery is
disconnected and the inductance is shorted.

When the steady flow of current through a coil is suddenly
interrupted by opening a switch in series with the coil, the
inductance tends to maintain this current flow.   So rapidly is
the current changing when the circuit is interrupted that the coil
voltage is very large—large enough, in fact, to cause electrons to
actually jump between the opening contacts of the switch in the
form of a spark as the circuit is broken.   This voltage may be
many times the voltage that was originally applied to the circuit.
The high voltage that is generated when a switch is opened in a
circuit containing considerable inductance is known as the *inductive kick*.   In designing such circuits, care must be taken to see

that switch contacts and coil insulation are sufficient to withstand these high surges of voltage.

Inductance in an A-C Circuit. When an inductance is placed
in a circuit containing an a-c voltage source, the effect of the
inductance is, again, to oppose changes in current flow. But in
this case the current is constantly changing, and so is the

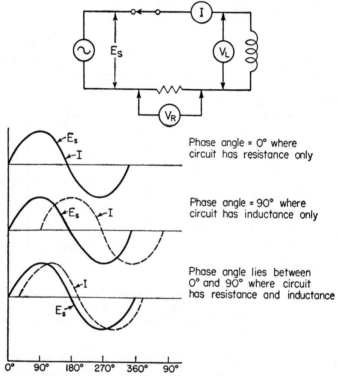

Phase angle = 0° where
circuit has resistance only

Phase angle = 90° where
circuit has inductance only

Phase angle lies between
0° and 90° where circuit
has resistance and inductance

Fig. 3.   In an a-c circuit containing only inductance, the voltage maximum
occurs 90 deg before the current maximum.

opposition to the current flow. The result is that the maximum
values of current and voltage do not occur at the same instant,
but in fact the maximum value of the current is delayed behind
the maximum of voltage. In a circuit containing inductance
only—no resistance—this time delay amounts to one-quarter
cycle of the alternating current, or 90 deg. If resistance as well
as inductance is in the circuit (Fig. 3), the time lag, or phase,

between current and voltage is less than 90 deg. The angle may be determined by the vector diagram shown in Fig. 4A.

The effect of inductance upon the flow of current is called *inductive reactance* and may be calculated from

$$X_L = 2\pi f L$$

where X_L is the reactance in ohms, f is the frequency in cycles per second, and L is the inductance in henrys.

The effect of a combination of resistance and inductance is called an *impedance* (Z) and is calculated as shown in Fig. 4A. It will be noted that the combined effect is always less than the direct sum of the resistive and the reactive effects. Thus if a

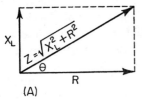
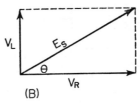

(A)   (B)

Fig. 4. Inductive reactance (X_L) and resistance (R) are combined vectorially to produce the combined effect, impedance (Z).

1-ohm resistor and a 1-ohm reactance are placed in a circuit, the combined effect is 1.41 ohms.

In using Ohm's law in a-c circuits containing both resistance and reactance, the impedance must be employed to find the current if the voltage is known. Thus,

$$I = \frac{E}{Z}$$

where

$$Z = \sqrt{R^2 + X^2}$$

Capacitance. Another element of a-c circuits is *capacitance*. It is possessed by a condenser, or capacitor, made up of two or more conductors separated from each other by an insulator. Two sheets of aluminum separated by a sheet of glass, for example, constitute a condenser. If such a device is connected to a battery, one of the plates to the positive terminal and the other to the negative battery terminal, any free electrons existing on the condenser plate connected to the positive battery terminal will move through the connecting circuit toward the battery, attracted by the positive charge there. This movement of electrons constitutes an electric current. Note, however, that no electrons actually move *through* the glass plate of the con-

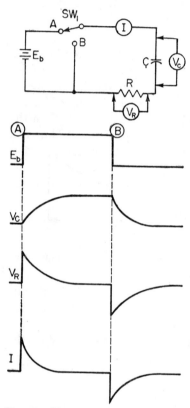

denser. In a circuit in which such a condenser exists, it is not necessary for electrons to move through the barrier imposed by the dielectric of the condenser to make it possible for current to flow in the external circuit.

Since electrons have now left one plate of the condenser, there is an unbalance or potential across the condenser, one plate having more electrons than the other. This unbalance in electrons constitutes a voltage, and it can be measured with appropriate apparatus. The more electrons that leave one of the plates, or the more that arrive at the other plate (from the battery), the greater will be the measurable voltage across the condenser.

Capacitance in a D-C Circuit. In Fig. 5, when the switch is moved to position A, electrons move through the connecting circuit, the condenser begins to charge, and a voltage begins to appear across the condenser. As more electrons move through the circuit and more voltage appears across the

Fig. 5. Transient effects in a circuit containing resistance and capacitance. When SW_1 is moved to position A, the condenser begins charging from battery. When SW_1 is moved to position B, condenser begins discharging through the resistance.

condenser the circuit current decreases, indicating that the voltage across the condenser opposes the flow of current. It is, in fact, of opposite polarity to that of the battery and acts like another battery in series with the original battery but so connected that it opposes the effect of the original battery.

The condenser voltage continues to rise until the voltage across it is equal to the battery voltage, and at this point current ceases to flow—the two voltages are exactly equal and opposite in effect. It is now fully charged. If the battery were removed and if there were no possible paths for the electrons to move through, the voltage across the condenser would exist forever.

The fundamental property of a condenser is its capacitance, and this property resists any change in voltage across its terminals. It acts like a storage device in that the number of electrons on its two sets of plates may be radically different so that potential energy is thereby stored in the device.

Time is required to change the voltage across a condenser and the length of time required to change the voltage and the amount of energy that can be stored in the condenser depends upon the capacitance.

The way in which a condenser reacts to the application of an external voltage is shown in the curves of Fig. 5. When the circuit is first completed by closing SW_1 to point A, the voltage across the condenser, V_c, rises slowly toward the value of the charging source E_b. The initial flow of current in the circuit may be very large; only the series resistance impedes the movement of electrons. But the current decreases as more and more voltage appears across the condenser.

Now if SW_1 is changed to position B, there will again be an initial rush of electrons from the plate which has too many through the circuit to the plate which has too few, and a heavy current flows. As the condenser discharges, the current through the circuit decreases and ultimately stops altogether.

Capacitive Reactance. A condenser, like an inductance, impedes the flow of current in an a-c circuit. This impeding effect is due to its reactance, the value of which may be obtained from

$$X_c = \frac{1}{2\pi f C}$$

where X_c is the reactance in ohms, f is the frequency in cycles per second, and C is the capacitance in farads.

In an inductive circuit the effect of the inductance (inductive reactance) is *directly* proportional to the inductance and the frequency. In a capacitive circuit the effect (capacitive reactance) is *inversely* proportional to the capacitance and the frequency. Thus,

$$I = \frac{E}{X_c} = 2\pi f C E$$

Because a condenser resists any change in voltage across its terminals, there is a time lag between the maximum values of

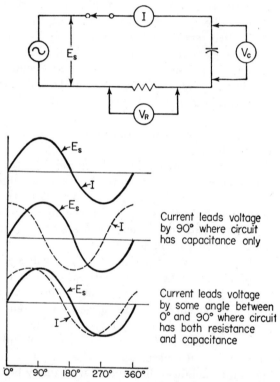

Fig. 6. In a circuit containing capacitance and resistance, voltage maximums lag current maximums by some phase angle between 0 and 90 deg.

voltage and current. In an a-c circuit containing capacitance only, the maximum value of voltage lags behind the maximum value of the current by one-quarter cycle or 90 deg. If the circuit contains resistance as well as capacitance, as shown in Fig. 6, the time lag or phase between the maximum values of voltage and current will be less than 90 deg and the actual value can be obtained from the vector diagram in Fig. 7.

Inductance and Capacitance Compared. Both inductance and capacitance impede the flow of current. Both slow up the attainment of final values of current or voltage. But their effects upon electric circuits are opposite in many ways.

The reactance of an inductor *increases* with frequency; that of a capacitor *decreases* with frequency. The *current* through an inductor cannot be changed instantaneously; the *voltage* across a capacitor cannot be changed instantly. In a circuit containing inductance and resistance in series, the *voltage* across the inductance at the moment the battery is connected to it is a maximum,

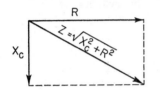 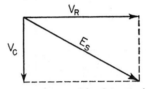

Fig. 7.   Capacitive reactance and resistance are combined vectorially to obtain impedance. In this case, however, the reactance is drawn downward instead of upward as in the case of the inductive reactance example of Fig. 4.

the current a minimum; in a capacitive circuit the *current* at the first instant is maximum and voltage across the capacitor is a minimum.

In an a-c circuit the current maximum lags behind the voltage maximum (in time) if the circuit is inductive; if it is capacitive the current maximum is ahead of the voltage maximum.

Resonance. Since the effects of inductance and capacitance are opposite in nature in many ways, very interesting results may be obtained by combining them in an a-c circuit. Figure 8 shows a simple circuit containing L, C, and R and a source of a-c voltage. The values of reactance are correct for only one frequency, and the phase relationships and voltages are also good for this frequency only. Note that the capacitive reactance nullifies part of the effect of the inductive reactance. The latter is larger, however, and the circuit is still inductively reactive so that the current lags behind the voltage.

At some frequency the effects of an inductance and a condenser in a circuit will be equal but of opposite nature so that their reactances cancel out. This is known as the resonant frequency which is determined as follows:

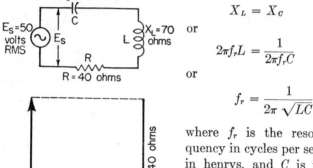

$$X_L = X_c$$

or

$$2\pi f_r L = \frac{1}{2\pi f_r C}$$

or

$$f_r = \frac{1}{2\pi \sqrt{LC}}$$

where f_r is the resonant frequency in cycles per second, L is in henrys, and C is in farads. The actual reactance in such a circuit at any particular frequency is the difference between the inductive and the capacitive reactances. This is obtained arithmetically, subtracting one from the other. To obtain the impedance in such a circuit the net reactance is first obtained, and this reactance is combined with the resistance vectorially. Thus in a circuit containing L, C, and R:

Inductive reactance:

$$X_L = 2\pi fL$$

Capacitive reactance:

$$X_C = \frac{1}{2\pi fC}$$

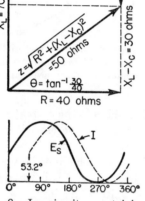

FIG. 8. In circuits containing resistance, capacitance, and inductance, the reactances counterbalance each other's effect or may cancel completely each other's effect.

Net reactance:

$$X_L - X_c$$

Impedance:

$$\sqrt{R^2 + (X_L - X_c)^2}$$

Series Resonance. Since the current in a series circuit containing R, L, and C varies with frequency, and since at some

frequency the inductive and capacitive reactances are equal, so
that each cancels the effect of the other, at this frequency the
current under the impetus of a given a-c voltage is a maximum.
At all other frequencies the current is less than this resonant
value.   Since at resonance the current is a maximum and is
greater than if either L or C were omitted, the other remaining
in the circuit, the voltage across any of the components is highest
at resonance.

As a matter of fact the voltage across either reactance at
resonance may be considerably higher than the voltage applied

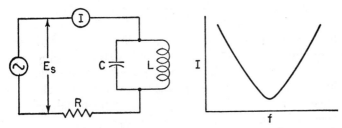

Fɪɢ. 9.   Current to a parallel resonant circuit is less at the resonant frequency than at other frequencies.

to the complete circuit.   This increase in voltage is a function
of the ratio of the reactance to the resistance, X/R, and if the
resistance of the circuit is low, the reactive voltages may become
as much as 100 times more than the total applied voltage.
This ratio is known as the Q of the circuit.

If the frequency of the applied voltage is lower than the resonant frequency of the circuit, the capacitive reactance will be
greater than the inductive reactance, and the circuit will act
like a capacitive circuit.   If the frequency is above resonance,
the circuit will be, in effect, an inductive circuit since the inductance will have a greater effect upon the current than does the
condenser.   At resonance the only thing that limits the flow of
current is the circuit resistance.

Parallel Resonant Circuit.   Conditions in a circuit in which
the condenser and the inductance are shunted across each other
and in series with the applied voltage (Fig. 9) are somewhat
different than in a series circuit.   Now as the resonant frequency
is approached from either direction, the effective impedance of
the parallel circuit increases so that the current taken from the

applied voltage source decreases and becomes a minimum at resonance. If, however, an ammeter is inserted in either the capacitive or the inductive branch of the circuit, it will be found that current higher than that taken from the source is flowing. This current may be many times higher than the source current; in fact the ratio of the two currents is a function of the reactance divided by the resistance of the branch of the circuit in which the ammeter is placed. This ratio, Q, may be equal to 100 or more, and so if the source supplies 1 amp to the parallel-tuned circuit, there may be 100 amp flowing through the coil and condenser; and the lower the resistance the greater will be the current.

Resonant circuits are "frequency selective"; that is, the effects they produce depend upon frequency. If the resistance is low, the effect as a function of frequency is very marked so that only a slight "mistuning" of the circuit away from resonance may produce a wide current variation in a series circuit or a wide voltage variation across a parallel circuit.

Resonant circuits are employed because of their frequency sensitivity, and many industrial applications of such circuits are to be found.

RC Circuits. Combinations of resistance and capacitance are found in nearly all industrial electronic circuits. They are of extreme utility and it is quite important to know how such circuits work. Let us study in more detail the action of the circuit shown in Fig. 5.

When the switch SW_1 is thrown to position A, electrons will move from the upper plate of the condenser to the positive terminal of the battery. Current will flow. At the instant the switch is closed there is no voltage on the condenser and, therefore, the entire battery voltage will appear across R. The current that will flow at this instant is E/R. The current is high, the voltage across R is high, and the voltage across C is zero.

As electrons continue to be attracted toward the positive terminal of the battery, the condenser assumes a charge; that is, a voltage appears across it. This voltage opposes the battery voltage and reduces the flow of current. The voltage across R must be the battery voltage minus the condenser voltage and must be equal at each instant to IR. As the charge on the condenser increases, less and less current flows because more and more opposing voltage is built up across the condenser. The current flow, therefore, decreases and finally stops. At this point there will be no voltage across R (no current flowing through it) and the full battery voltage appears across C. If the circuit is now broken, a voltmeter placed across C will indicate a voltage equal to that of the battery.

Condenser Discharge. Continuing with the detailed analysis, if SW_1 is switched to position B, the condenser will act like any source of voltage—it will push electrons around the circuit. They will attempt to leave the plate which is oversupplied and go through the circuit to the plate which has too few. This represents a flow of current and this current must flow through the resistance and produce a voltage drop there. At every instant this current flow must equal E/R where E is the condenser voltage at this instant. As the electrons flow through the circuit, they equalize the disparity of charge on the two plates. As this equalization proceeds, less and less voltage appears on the condenser and less and less current will flow. Finally there will be just as many electrons on one plate as on the other and the condenser will have no voltage. It will be discharged. The current in this discharge circuit will be in a direction opposite to that flowing on charge as shown by the time-constant curves.

Time Constant. The time required for a condenser to charge or discharge is proportional to the product of R and C. If the voltage is high, the finally charged condenser will have a high voltage and more energy will be stored in it, but it will take just as long to charge it to 100 volts from a 100-volt supply as to 1,000 volts from a 1,000-volt supply if C and R are the same in the two cases.

The product of R and C is an important factor in circuits consisting of R and C. This product is known as the *time constant* of the circuit and represents the actual time required to charge a condenser to 63 per cent of the value of the applied charging voltage or to discharge the condenser to 37 per cent of its charged value. The rate of charge or discharge is exponential, starting out high and becoming less and less, but not linearly. Any small portion of the curve representing charge or discharge is almost linear, however, and may be usefully employed in many cases where a linear change in voltage is required. Since the rate of change is exponential, the final value is theoretically reached only in an infinitely long time. For practical purposes the final value may be assumed to have been attained in $5RC$

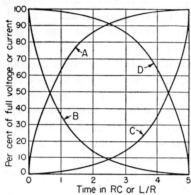

seconds, where C is in farads and R is in ohms.

Time-constant   Chart. Problems in RC circuits may be solved easily with a universal time-constant chart, as shown in Fig. 10 where curve A represents the rate of charge and curve B the rate of discharge. Suppose, for example, a resistor of 20,000 ohms is to be used with a condenser that is to charge to one-fifth of its

Fig.   10.   Universal   time-constant chart. A shows capacitor charging current, and B shows condenser discharge current. C shows current build-up in inductance, and D shows decay of current in an inductive circuit.

final   value   in   100   microseconds.   How   large   must the condenser be?

Using curve A it is found that one-fifth or 20 per cent of the final value is attained in approximately $0.2RC$ seconds. Since $0.2RC$ represents 100 microseconds, RC will represent 500 microseconds.   Thus,

$$RC = 500 \times 10^{-6} \text{ second}$$
$$R = 20,000 \text{ ohms}$$
$$C = \frac{500 \times 10^{-6}}{20,000} = 0.025 \times 10^{-6} \text{ farad}$$
$$= 0.025 \text{ microfarad}$$

Time Relations in RC Circuits. The statement will be found in many descriptions of RC circuits that the charge in a condenser cannot be changed instantly. This is correct so long as there is resistance in the circuit, and there is always some resistance. The voltage across the condenser, therefore, tends to remain fixed for a time determined by the value of R and C. When a voltage is suddenly impressed across an RC circuit, the voltage already across C tends to remain constant and the whole of the new voltage appears across the resistor. As the condenser charges, however, the voltage across C must change in accordance with the flow of current.

Consider the series circuit RC in Fig. 11A. The switch has been connected to the 50-volt battery long enough for the condenser to be fully charged to 50 volts. Current flow has ceased, and no voltage appears across R. If the switch is moved to the 150-volt battery, the voltage applied to the series RC

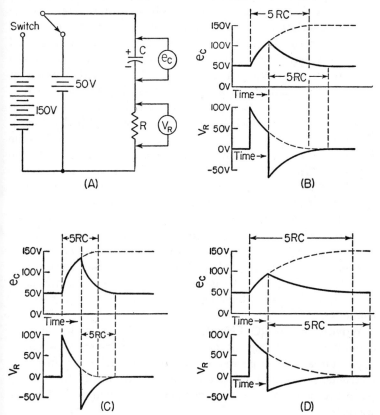

Fig. 11. Effect of increasing the battery voltage in an RC circuit from 50 to 150 volts after the condenser has been fully charged to the lower voltage.

circuit suddenly rises to 150 volts. Since the charge in the condenser cannot change instantaneously, the 100-volt change in voltage must appear across R. This voltage drop occurs as a result of the rush of charging current that flows when the higher voltage is impressed across the circuit.

If the switch is held in the 150-volt position for a length of time equal to 5RC, the condenser will be charged to that voltage for all practical purposes. If, however, the switch is returned to the 50-volt position before such a time interval has elapsed, the condenser will not have sufficient time to charge fully.

For example, let us assume that the switch is returned to the 50-volt position at a time such that the condenser has charged approximately 0.6 of the change in voltage, or 60 volts. At the instant of switching, 60 volts will appear across the resistor to make up for the difference in applied voltage (now 50 volts) and the voltage across the condenser (110 volts) which cannot change instantaneously. Now the condenser is the main source of voltage, being higher in voltage than the battery. The current is thus referred to as *discharge* current, and it flows in a direction opposite to that in which the charging current originally flowed. The voltage drop across the condenser gradually approaches the 50-volt value, current flow gradually diminishes (as does the voltage drop across R) and finally ceases, again, in a time approximately equal to $5RC$. Thus studying the voltages appearing across the two elements separately, curves like those shown in Fig. 11 can be drawn. If the voltage is held constant but the value of R or C *decreased*, the curves would be changed as shown in Fig. 11C. Here the charge and discharge curves are steeper. If R or C is *increased* in value, the curves will differ as shown in Fig. 11D. Here the charge and discharge curves are more gradual, and less voltage change actually occurs across the condenser.

Waveforms in RC Circuits. Frequently it is desirable to employ pulses of current or voltage. For instance, when an operation is to be triggered, or set off, at a particular time, it is convenient to initiate that operation electronically by a sharp pulse rather than by a slow-rising voltage, such as half a sine wave.

Pulses may conveniently be formed by the use of RC networks. A sharp pulse of voltage may be formed by the simple circuit shown in Fig. 12A. The time constant of the RC combination is made very short so the condenser charges very rapidly. When a voltage is applied to the input, the initial surge of current is very large, but it dies down rapidly as the condenser charges. The voltage across the resistor has the form of a sharp pulse.

This short-time-constant type of circuit, with the voltage taken across the resistor, is called a *differentiating circuit*. The voltage that appears across the resistor is actually the time derivative of the input voltage. In other words, the output voltage across the resistor is proportional to the rate of change of current in the circuit. If the time constant is long and the output voltage is taken from across the condenser (Fig. 12C), the waveform will represent the integral of the input voltage. This type of circuit effectively *integrates* any voltage applied to its input. If a series of sharp pulses is applied to the circuit, the output

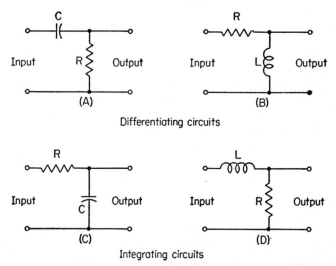

Differentiating circuits

Integrating circuits

FIG. 12. Differentiating (*A* and *B*) and integrating (*C* and *D*) circuits. Integrating circuits are characterized by long time constants, while differentiating circuits have short time constants compared with the period of the applied wave.

across the condenser will be proportional to the time integral of the signal. In effect, the circuit distributes the pulses of voltage evenly, filling in the valleys and cutting off the peaks, and the output represents a time average of the input signal.

Inductances may be used in integrating and differentiating circuits, with suitable circuit modifications, as indicated in Fig. 12*B* and 12*D*. The usual application of differentiating circuits is to convert a voltage waveform, such as a square wave, into a series of sharp pulses—one pulse for every cycle of the square wave. In practice, some auxiliary circuits must be used in conjunction with the differentiating circuit to achieve this end.

Thus a wide variety of modifications of voltage and current waveforms can be achieved by proper combinations of condensers, inductances, and resistors. Most electronic circuits depend on these tricks in one form or another. Television depends to a very great extent on circuits of this type for the synchronization and timing of the scanning of an electron beam in a receiver with the beam in the camera equipment at the transmitter. Radar depends almost entirely on the creation and proper timing of pulses of r-f power, which have as their beginning a source of voltage of some convenient waveform that is converted into pulses by appropriate circuitry. Other applications of R, L, and C circuits will become evident in subsequent chapters on specific applications.

Inductor Applications. Where alternating current is to be limited to a certain value, a low-resistance inductor may be employed. In this manner there is little power lost in the inductor resistance (and hence little temperature rise) while the current is "impeded" or limited by the inductive reactance of the coil.

A transformer is a two-winding inductor, which has very useful properties. In conformity with the natural property of inductance, when the current through one winding is increasing, an increase in voltage occurs across the other. When the current through the "primary" is constant, zero voltage appears across the "secondary." Therefore, if direct current flows through the primary, there will be no direct voltage across the secondary, and no direct current will flow through any apparatus connected to the secondary.

The transformer, therefore, can be employed to separate alternating and direct currents. That is, if a circuit contains both alternating and direct currents and if alternating current only is desired in another circuit, a transformer may be used to connect these two circuits together. Direct current will not flow from primary to secondary, and the second circuit is isolated from direct current in this manner.

If a sine wave of current flows through the primary, a sine wave of voltage appears across the secondary, but these voltages and currents are not in phase because of the inductive effect, resistance losses in the windings, and other causes. The transformer, therefore, may be employed as a phase-shifting device.

Since the same current change will produce a higher induced voltage through a coil of many turns than through a coil of few turns, the transformer may be (and usually is) employed to raise or lower voltages and currents without essential change in waveform. If the secondary has a higher number of turns than the primary, the voltage across the secondary will be higher than that across the primary, although the current through the secondary will be less. The product of I and E in each circuit must be equal since the transformer cannot increase the power taken from the primary source. Actually the secondary power ($I \times E$) is less than the primary power because of inherent transformer losses.

Up to a certain point, increasing the current through a coil produces corresponding increase in voltage across it; but after this certain point is reached, the core material "saturates" and further increase in current does not produce a corresponding voltage increase. A saturable-core reactor, therefore, is one in which the nonlinear relation between current and magnetization is employed. These devices have very important applications in electronics.

For example, let us place three windings upon a single iron core. Two of them correspond to the conventional primary and secondary. Through the third winding we will force a variable direct current. Since the secondary voltage is a function of the condition of the core material, it is evident that the secondary voltage will be a function of the direct current flowing through the third winding since this current has a pronounced effect upon the core condition.

Such a transformer may act as a current amplifier; that is, a small change in the direct current may produce a very great change in the alternating current flowing in the secondary circuit. This alternating current may be rectified with the result that a small change in the magnetizing direct current will change radically the secondary-circuit direct current. The system now is a magnetic amplifier and as such has very great importance.

Combinations of nonlinear circuit elements and magnetic amplifiers will undoubtedly replace many electron tubes in future industrial and communication applications. The amplifiers can be made quite small, light in weight, and stable in character- istics; since they have no moving parts and, unlike vacuum tubes,

require no filament heating power, the possibilities for application
are very great.

REFERENCES

Alpert, N., Linear Thyratron Control Circuit, *Electronics*, April, 1948,
p. 92.

Blow, T. C., Design Chart for Single Layer Inductance Coils, *Electronics*,
February, 1943, p. 91.

Blow, T. C., Solenoid Inductance Calculations, *Electronics*, May, 1942,
p. 63.

Caverly, Don P., "Primer of Electronics and Radiant Energy," Mc-
Graw-Hill Book Company, Inc., New York, 1952.

Developments in the Electrical Industry during 1935, *General Electric
Review*, January, 1936, p. 57.

Dreyer, J. F., Jr., Factors Determining Industrial Tube Life, *Electronic
Industries*, December, 1945, p. 94.

Electron Tubes . . . How They Work, *General Electric Review*, November, 1943, p. 612.

Graphical Symbols, *Electronics*, April, 1943, p. 84.

Hanna, C. R., Design of Reactances and Transformers Which Carry
Direct Current, *Journal of the American Institute of Electrical
Engineers*, February, 1927, p. 128.

Hanopol, L., Capacitor Discharge Chart, *Electronics*, August, 1938, p. 32.

Hesse, H. R., Six-place L-C Product Table, *Electronics*, June, 1938, p. 31.

Hull, A. W., Electronic Devices as Aids to Research, *Physics*, June, 1912.

Industrial Tube Characteristics, *Electronics*, June, 1942, p. 53.

Industrial Tube Terminology, *Electronics*, September, 1938, p. 29.

Kallman, H. E., Nonlinear Circuit Element Applications, *Electronics*,
August, 1946, p. 130.

Kellogg, E. W., Time Delay in Resistance-capacity Circuits, *Electronics*,
February, 1938, p. 26.

Kramer, A. W., Electron Tube Principles, *Instruments*, January, 1945,
p. 12, and February, 1945, p. 82.

Lee, R., Iron-core Components in Pulse Amplifiers, *Electronics*, August,
1943, p. 115.

Lee, R., Reactors in D-C Service, *Electronics*, September, 1936, p. 18.

McArthur, E. D., Electronics and Electron Tubes, *General Electric
Review*, beginning in March, 1933.

Maintaining Electron Tubes Used in Industrial Service, *Electronic
Industries*, March, 1938, p. 9.

Massaut, P. H., Distributed Capacitance of Single-layer Coils, *Electronics*, March, 1938, p. 32.

May, J. C., H. J. Reich, and J. G. Skalnik, Thyratron Phase-control
Circuits, *Electronics*, July, 1948, p. 107.

Ohman, G. P., Square-wave Differentiating Circuit Analysis, *Electronics*, August, 1945, p. 132.

Stansbury, C., Factors Affecting Adoption of Electronic Control in Industry, *Electrical World*, Jan. 26, 1934.

Stokley, James, "Electrons in Action," McGraw-Hill Book Company, Inc., New York, 1946.

Teachman, A. E., Equivalent Resistance Chart, *Electronics*, August, 1938, p. 32.

Vance, P. A., Saturable Reactors for Load Control, *General Electric Review*, August, 1947, p. 17.

White, W. C., Electron Tube Terminology, *Electronics*, December, 1942, p. 42.

Zeluff, Vin, and John Markus, "What Electronics Does," McGraw-Hill Book Company, Inc., New York, 1948.

CHAPTER 2

FUNDAMENTALS OF TUBES

Electron-tube technology differs from that with which the average electrical engineer is familiar in that it is essentially low-power, low-current technology.   Electron-tube circuits, in general, involve currents of the order of thousandths of amperes up to amperes and powers of the order of milliwatts to watts.   Only in high-power radio transmitters and in electronic heating and welding does the power controlled by tubes approach the order of kilowatts.   The industrial electronics expert must deal with circuits of low or high power, at low or high efficiency, with all manner of waveforms and with circuits of extreme simplicity or great complexity.   In general, however, the man coming to apply tube apparatus for the first time must get used to working with small currents and low powers.

Today there are hundreds of different types of tubes.   In general, however, they all have at least three things in common. Every tube must have a source of electrons, an element which is usually called the *cathode* of the tube.   Secondly, there must be an *anode* or plate which is capable of attracting the electrons emitted by the cathode.   The third requirement is the actual envelope (glass or metal) of the tube itself.   The flow of electrons must be protected from the earth's atmosphere or these electrons would collide with the particles of the atmosphere and most of them would fail to reach the anode of the tube.

Since electrons are negatively charged particles, and it is desired to cause them to flow from the cathode to the anode, the anode of the tube must be made positive with respect to the cathode.   The electrons, attracted by the positive charge, thus are drawn toward the anode.   When these electrons reach the anode, they give up their charge, with the result that a definite electrical current flows between the cathode and the positive anode.   The magnitude of this current is a measure of the number of electrons that arrive at the anode per second.

In the amplifier tube used in radio receivers the currents carried by the electron stream may be of the order of milliamperes; in tubes used to level elevators the current may not be much over 0.1 amp; in the largest amplifiers used in transmitting stations (speech and music) the maximum current per tube may be only 6 amp.

Small as these currents may seem to a power engineer, it must be remembered that they involve the mass motion of many billions of electrons, all under perfect control and all speeding on their task of converting energy of one form into another, silently, efficiently, with no moving parts, and with a tube life that in carefully operated apparatus may run as long as several thousands of hours.   These small currents at 10,000 volts or more may represent considerable power.

Tube Classifications.   Electron tubes may be classified in many ways.   First of all, they may be grouped, generally, into (1) tubes whose cathodes give off electrons when *heated* or (2) tubes whose cathodes give off electrons when *irradiated* or *illuminated* with light.   In the first case, the number of electrons that may leave the cathode is determined by the emitting area of the cathode and the temperature to which it is heated.   This type of tube is known as a *thermionic* tube.   In the second case, the area of the cathode and the amount of illumination determine the number of electrons the cathode can emit.   The tube is said to be *photosensitive.*

In each case, the electrons contained in the cathode are in a constant state of motion—thus they have kinetic energy.   When the cathode is heated or when light falls upon it, this electron motion is increased in the same way molecular motion is increased when water is heated.   The increase in kinetic energy supplied to the electrons is just sufficient to allow them to break away from the cathode, in somewhat the way that water molecules break away from the surface of water when it boils.

Vacuum and Gas Tubes.   Both types of electron tubes, thermionic and photosensitive, may be further subdivided according to the nature of the medium that surrounds the elements inside the tube.   In one type, most of the air is evacuated from the tube envelope so that the tube elements are effectively in a vacuum—

thus the term *vacuum tube*. In the other type, the air is evacuated from the tube, but a small amount of some inert gas is then admitted for special purposes. The pressure of the gas in such a tube is still but a fraction of the atmospheric pressure, but these tubes are called *gas tubes*, instead of vacuum tubes. Thus there are vacuum and gaseous, thermionic and photosensitive tubes.

The reasons for introducing gas into the tube envelope will be explained later. The type and quantity of gas admitted is extremely important to the proper operation of the tube, and a great deal of care must be taken to see that no unwanted gas is admitted to either type of tube.

The thermionic tubes in radio receivers are nearly always high vacuum tubes. The pressure in a high-vacuum tube is of the order of 10^{-8} atm.[1] In tubes where inert gases are purposely admitted, the pressure runs from 10^{-6} to 10^{-3} atm.

A small quantity of water vapor will ruin a tube. Other gases, may, in time, be released from the metallic elements within the tube structure. Often the elements may run at red heat making it easy for gas molecules to escape and spoil the emission characteristic.

Tube Characteristics. The two greatest advantages of the electron tube in industrial applications are (1) they require almost no energy from the actuating phenomenon and (2) their action is practically instantaneous. The phototube extracts practically no energy from the light beam which makes it perform its duty. Similarly, the thermionic tube may require so little energy to actuate it that the actuating force is unaware of the tube's presence.

Considerable jargon has grown up among tube people. They call tubes by various names and various systems of names. A tube with two elements, a cathode and an anode, is called a *diode*, but since its fundamental application is that of a rectifier, it is also called a rectifier. A tube, therefore, may have a name which is related to its application or to its structure. But

---

[1] There are several methods of rating vacuums. One standard atmosphere is a pressure of 760 mm of mercury; a micron is a pressure of 0.001 mm of mercury; a bar is one dyne per square centimeter. One bar is the equivalent of 0.00075 mm of mercury or 0.0133×10^{-6} atm. One micron equals 1.333 bars. A high-vacuum tube is one in which the pressure has been reduced to about one bar. Even at this pressure there are about 2.56×10^{13} molecules of gas per cubic centimeter.

whatever the tube and whatever its name, it works because man has found ways of releasing electrons from a metal surface, because these electrons are electrically charged, and because charged bodies may be attracted or repelled by other charged bodies. It is in the electron tube that man has developed his most direct way of utilizing electrons.

THERMIONIC TUBES

Consider a tungsten wire and a metal plate spaced a few millimeters apart and both enclosed in an evacuated glass bulb with wire connections to the two elements brought out through the stem of the glass bulb. If the tungsten wire is heated to a certain temperature by passing an electric current through it, it will emit or "boil off" electrons.

The required temperature depends upon the nature of the cathode surface. At about 2400°K, a pure tungsten cathode will emit about 0.12 amp per sq cm of surface. If the tungsten wire is coated with certain oxides of the rare earths (strontium, barium, cesium, etc.) the temperature at which electrons escape is much lower.

The relation between electron emission and temperature[1] is complicated, but small increases in temperature will cause large increases in emission. A cathode operating at a dull-red heat will have its emission doubled if the temperature is increased by only 100°, and a 1 per cent change in the current through a filamentary cathode may cause a 20 per cent change in emission of electrons.

Electron Speed. After leaving the cathode, electrons are attracted toward the anode with high velocities. The actual velocity depends upon the voltage existing between anode and cathode. In a high-vacuum tube with 100 volts between the two electrodes, electrons will hit the plate with a speed of about 3,700 miles per second. The velocity for different voltages can be computed from

$$v = 5.95 \times 10^7 \sqrt{V}$$

where v is the velocity in centimeters per second and V is the voltage across the tube.

[1] O. W. Richardson, "Emission of Electrons from Hot Bodies," Longmans, Green & Co., Inc., New York, 1921. On electron emission see also Saul Dushman, *Electrical Engineering*, July, 1934, p. 1054.

The Two-element Tube. Figure 1 shows the schematic diagram of a two-element tube connected across a source of a-c voltage E. Actually, this tube has three elements, but it is called a diode, since the only function of the filament is to heat the electron-emitting cathode to a temperature at which it will give off electrons. The heater element consists of a piece of thin resistance wire through which heater current is passed. It heats the cathode by radiation. The two elements which perform useful work are the cathode and the anode.

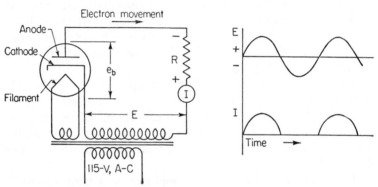

FIG. 1. Simple diode tube, consisting of a cathode and an anode acting as a rectifier, passes current only while the anode is positive with respect to the cathode.

Electrons will move to the anode only when it is positive with respect to the cathode. The a-c voltage source alternately makes the plate positive and negative with respect to the cathode. Thus current will flow only during the half cycles when the proper polarity exists. This is illustrated by the curves shown in Fig. 1. Current flows only half the time, and it flows in only one direction, that is from cathode to anode.

If the tube were not in the circuit, the current resulting from the application of the a-c voltage E across the resistance R would be constantly reversing in accordance with the alternations of the voltage. The tube converts or changes this alternating current into a direct (unidirectional) current, by stopping current flow in one direction. This conversion of alternating current to direct current is known as rectification. It is the most useful function of the two-element tube. The spurts of plate current may be applied directly to charging a battery or any other purpose where such a pulsating unidirectional current is needed.   Or, these pulses may first be applied to a filter which smooths out the current flow, limiting it during the times it does flow, and maintaining it during the time when the tube conducts no current.   By proper filtering, as will be explained in Chap. 4, the current may be smoothed out to any degree, until the a-c voltage across the load (in this case, R) has been converted into a d-c source with an output like that of a battery.

Tube Resistance.   When electrons flow between the elements of a tube, they encounter a certain amount of electrical resistance. As the electrons flow through this resistance, an amount of power is lost or wasted in the tube in the form of heat.   This heat represents power loss and may be calculated by *multiplying* the anode-to-cathode voltage by the current flowing through the tube.   The d-c resistance of the tube may be calculated by *dividing* the anode-to-cathode voltage by the current flowing through the tube.   This resistance is analogous to the internal resistance of a battery or of a power generator.   In a power generator the internal resistance must be exceedingly low or the thousands of amperes flowing through it would cause prohibitive heat loss.   Unfortunately a high vacuum tube has considerable resistance, several thousand ohms, and thus it is not a very efficient device.

The voltage drop across a vacuum tube (e_b) is more or less proportional to the current.   But in a gas tube, this is not exactly true.   Here the voltage drop is practically independent of the current flowing and is very much smaller than in a vacuum tube. For this reason gas tubes are much more efficient as rectifiers because they can handle and control greater power with less loss.

Space Charge.   Since one electron will tend to repel another in its vicinity because of their similar charges, electrons already on their way from cathode to anode make it even more difficult for oncoming electrons to get to the anode.   The preceding electrons act like a negatively charged object in the path of the oncoming electrons.   This condition in the tube is called the *space charge*.   The current to the plate, therefore, is limited by the space charge.

There are other limitations to the number of electrons that will flow to the anode.   The number released from the heated cathode depends upon the temperature of the cathode and the material from which it is made.   If the temperature of a cathode is held constant, thus limiting the number of electrons available, and if the anode voltage is gradually increased from some low value, the number that flows to the anode will increase proportionally until the point where essentially *all* the electrons being emitted by the cathode are being pulled to the plate.   The space charge is no longer the factor which determines the current that flows in the tube.   When this condition exists, the tube is said to be *emission limited*, and only an increase in cathode temperature will effect an appreciable increase in electron flow.   This is illustrated by the curves in Fig. 2.

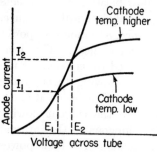

said to be *emission limited*, and only an increase in cathode temperature will effect an appreciable increase in electron flow.   This is illustrated by the curves in Fig. 2.

During the raising of the anode voltage as described in the previous paragraph, it was the space charge within the tube that prevented emission-limited current from flowing as soon as the anode became even slightly positive with respect to the cathode.   The space charge, or its effect, can be mitigated by introducing certain types of gas into the tube, by an increase in anode voltage, or by interposing another element in the space between cathode and anode.   If certain gases are admitted to the tube at the proper pressure, the tube acts very much like a switch—it either conducts current or it does not.   If the voltage across the tube is above a certain critical value, current flows.   If the voltage is less than this value, no current flows.

FIG. 2.   If with a given cathode temperature the anode voltage is raised, the electron current increases up to a point where all the electrons are being taken by the anode.   Now if the cathode temperature is raised, more electrons will be available and the anode current will again increase.

If the space charge is controlled by raising the anode voltage, thus dragging more electrons through the space near the cathode, more current will flow.   However, there are limitations to the extent to which control can be effected in this manner.

The Triode.   The interposition of a third element between cathode and anode modifies the behavior of the tube tremendously and increases the control over the anode current to a very great extent.

It is the introduction of this third element, the *grid*, that makes it possible not only to rectify—virtually the only useful function of a diode—but to amplify both direct and alternating currents and voltages, to generate all sorts of electrical wave forms of power, and to perform the many important jobs upon which the entire electronics industry is now built.

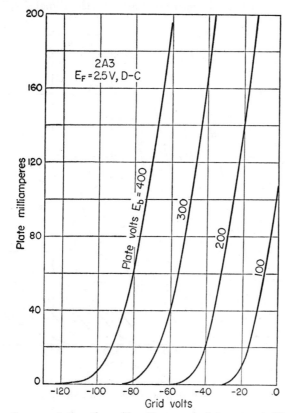

Fig. 3. Curves relating the grid voltage and plate current (E_g-I_p) of a typical triode, the 2A3.

Grid Control. Let us start with a triode, then, and see how the tube acts in response to voltages placed upon its three elements. The triode has the usual source (the cathode) and collector of electrons (the anode, or plate) and a control electrode called the *grid*. The grid is located somewhere between the cathode and the plate and has an open mesh so that electrons can shoot through it on their way toward the plate.   The cathode is operated at a constant temperature so that the number of electrons available per second is constant.

If the grid is positive with respect to the cathode, electrons will be attracted toward the grid, and some may be caught by the grid. But in general very few will actually hit the grid, so wide open is the grid mesh compared to the dimensions of the

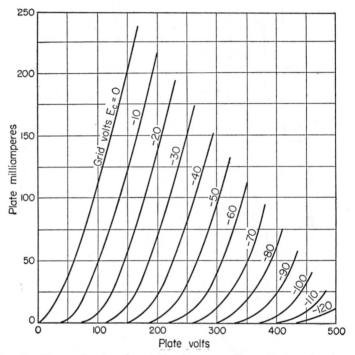

Fig. 4.   Curves showing the relation between plate voltage and plate current $(E_p\text{-}I_p)$ for several values of grid voltage on a 2A3 triode.

electron.   Also the plate is at a still greater positive voltage. The nearer the electrons come to the plate the more they are urged onward.   That is, the attraction between plate and electrons increases as the distance between them diminishes.

If the grid is negative with respect to the cathode, electrons may still get through to the plate, but not as easily.   The grid in this case acts as though it were increasing the space charge. The grid may be looked at as an elegant way to adjust the anode current by remote control.   Since the grid is nearer the source of electrons than is the plate, the grid has greater effect upon the flow of electrons.

Tube Curves. For a certain fixed anode-to-cathode voltage (usually referred to as *plate voltage*), there is a definite plate current for each value of grid voltage for each particular type of tube. Figure 3 shows a set of curves from which the operation of one tube type can be determined graphically. Such a set of curves is known as a "family," and it shows visually how the plate current is related to the grid voltage. For example, let us assume a tube operating with a fixed plate voltage of 200 volts. If the grid voltage is varied up and down between −20 and −40 volts, the plate current will change at an identical rate between 140 and 20 ma. For another plate voltage, but the same grid range, different plate-current limits will be observed.

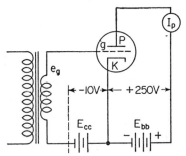

FIG. 5. Triode with a source of alternating voltage in series with steady grid bias. Alternating currents produced in the anode circuit correspond to the alternating grid voltage.

Similarly if the grid voltage is fixed and the plate voltage is varied, a set of values of plate current will result. Such data may be secured from the E_g-I_p (grid voltage versus plate current) curves also. With two families of curves, E_g-I_p and E_p-I_p (plate voltage versus plate current, Fig. 4), one has all the data he needs to design a circuit for use with this tube.

Use of Tube Curves. In Fig. 3 note that for the greater portion of the curves the relation between grid voltage and anode current is essentially linear and that only at the lower end of the curve is there much departure from linearity. Similarly the curves in Fig. 4 showing the relation between E_p and I_p are essentially linear over a large part of the characteristic curve.

In practice the plate supply voltage is fixed at some definite value, say 250 volts, and the average grid voltage is fixed (biased) at some definite value, say −10 volts, both voltages being measured from the cathode, as shown in Fig. 5. Changes in the plate current are effected by variations in the grid-to-cathode voltage.

For example, a 60-cycle voltage from a step-down transformer may be impressed between grid and cathode in series with the 10-volt d-c voltage already in the circuit, as shown in Fig. 5. Now the a-c voltage alternately will add to and subtract from the steady d-c grid voltage so that at some instants the grid is actually more negative than 10 volts with respect to the cathode and at some instants it is less than 10 volts negative. Natur-

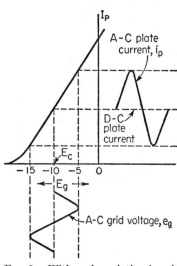

ally, the plate current will vary in accordance with these grid-voltage variations, as shown in Fig. 6.

Note that in all tube discussions the voltages upon the several electrodes are given with reference to the cathode voltage.

Grid Control of Gas Tubes. In a vacuum tube there is instantaneous and continuous control of the anode current by the grid voltage. In a gas tube, however, the situation is altogether different. The gas is in the form of basic molecules and atoms, and the spacing between these elementary enti-ties is very great compared to the size of the electron. Any

Fig. 6. With each variation in grid voltage there is a variation in plate current. Here, capital letters indi-cate steady or d-c values; small letters are the a-c components.

E_g (actual grid voltage) $= E_c + e_g$

electron which may be urged toward a positive electrode will have plenty of space in which to get up high speed and, therefore, to gather to itself considerable kinetic energy. Such a high-speed electron may hit a gas molecule hard enough to knock an electron out of the molecule. Now we have two electrons instead of one and both of them rush onward toward the anode. En route they produce other electrons by collisions with atoms and molecules, and thus the plate current increases.

Each molecule or atom that has lost an electron is now posi-tively charged and will attract electrons from the cathode out to where they come under the influence of the plate. Thus the positively charged remains of these collisions between electrons and atoms serve to neutralize the negative space charge and in so doing enable the other electrons to reach the plate much more easily.

The cumulative effect of these collisions in producing new electrons and in neutralizing the space charge results in a very great increase in plate current.

Each positively charged atom or molecule is called an *ion*, and the process of forming ions by bombardment of gas atoms is called *ionization*. For every gas employed in a tube there is a critical voltage at which ionization will take place. This is the voltage which will impart to the electron sufficient kinetic energy to knock an electron out of a gas atom. For mercury vapor this voltage is of the order of 15 volts.

Once started, the ionization process proceeds quickly (in a matter of microseconds) so that once the tube conducts current (ionizes or "strikes") the plate current rises quickly to its ultimate value. But the process is not instantaneous nor is the reestablishment of the original complex condition inside the tube when the plate voltage is removed and the plate current flow stopped. A few microseconds are required for the atoms to get back their required electrons in order to become electrically neutral or deionized.

Suppose that a grid is placed in such a gas tube and that its voltage with respect to the cathode is such that the velocity of electrons does not reach a value which will cause them to ionize the gas. No current will flow or at least so very little current that it is not useful. Now slowly let us cause the grid to become less negative or slightly positive. The electrons will get up more speed, and soon the point is reached at which ionization occurs, and the flow of plate current becomes very great. But now one can vary the grid voltage over a wide range and the current to the plate does not change at all. The grid has lost control of the plate current. The only way to shut off the plate current is to remove the plate voltage.

For every value of plate voltage there is a critical value of grid voltage that will cause ionization. It is the combination of the two voltages that controls the speed with which the electrons strike the gas atoms and produce positive ions which neutralize the space charge.

The curves which show the characteristics of such a tube (Fig. 7) do not show the relation between *plate voltage* (or grid voltage) and *plate current*—they show the relation between *grid* and *plate voltage* at which the tube begins to conduct current.

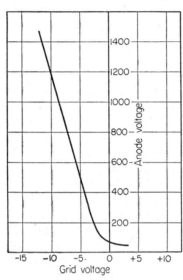

FIG. 7.   Characteristics of a typical gas triode.   For each value of anode voltage, there is a definite grid voltage at which the tube will "fire." If the grid is more negative than this value, no current will flow.

Voltage-regulator Tubes. Since the voltage drop across a gas tube is practically constant, it may be used to regulate voltages. For example, in Fig. 8A is a source of voltage which has an internal resistance R (all devices have such resistance) and a load which requires constant voltage. If the current taken by the load increases, more current will be drawn through the internal resistance of the supply system and a greater voltage drop across this resistance will be produced. There will be less voltage for the load. What is desired is a constant voltage.

In Fig. 8B a gas-filled voltage-regulator tube is shunted across the load and draws a current, along with the load current, through the internal resistance of the supply system. Now if the load requires more current, there will be more load current through the internal resistance but less current will go through the regulator tube. The voltage across resistor R will not change, and the voltage across the load will not change. Circuits for these tubes are discussed in more detail in Chap. 4.

Multielement Tubes. Additional electrodes placed between control grid and anode add to the versatility of the tube. Let us suppose that an oncoming electron gets up enough energy to knock another electron out of the anode upon arrival. This "secondary" electron may tend to go back toward the cathode and to increase the space charge. Such a situation would reduce the effective plate current. To avoid this effect, let us place another grid near the plate and maintain it at a voltage somewhat lower than the plate. Its mesh is rather wide so that it collects

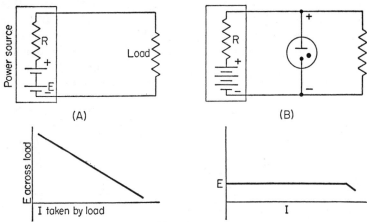

(A)

(B)

FIG. 8. Effect of using a voltage-regulator gas tube. The unregulated power supply furnishes less and less voltage as the current taken increases; if regulated, the output voltage is constant even though the required current increases.

relatively few "primary" electrons. If this grid is somewhat positive or even at zero potential with respect to the cathode, the secondary electron leaving the anode will encounter a fence through which it must jump before it can work backward into the space charge region. Primary electrons coming from the cathode are traveling so fast by the time they reach this low-voltage grid that they are not influenced by its presence. Such a grid is known as a *suppressor grid* since it suppresses secondary emission.

Another grid may be em-

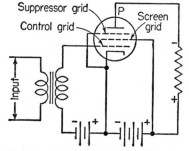

FIG. 9. Multigrid tube. The input is applied between the first grid and the cathode; the output is taken from the plate and the cathode. The screen grid (g_2) is maintained at a positive potential; the suppressor grid (g_3) forces back to the anode any secondary electrons produced.

ployed somewhat closer to the control grid with the following effects. Since any two pieces of metal separated by a dielectric represent an electrical capacitance in which energy can be stored, there exists within the tube an electrical capacitance between the control grid and the anode. In high-frequency circuits this capacitance may couple energy back to the control grid from the anode and cause trouble. If a third grid is placed near the control grid and is maintained at a steady positive d-c voltage it may not only "shield" the plate and control grid but may help urge the electrons on their path from cathode to anode. This is a *screen*

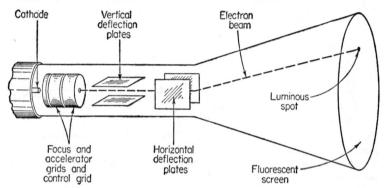

Fig. 10. Electrostatic deflection in a cathode-ray tube. If the vertical deflection plates are alternately positive and negative, the electrons will trace a vertical line on the screen; similar potential variations applied to the horizontal plates will trace a horizontal line on the screen.

grid, so-called because of the screening effect it has between anode and control grid.

In general these multielement tubes have much higher internal resistances than triodes and are much more stable at high frequencies. They are employed where high amplification is desired. A basic pentode amplifier circuit is shown in Fig. 9.

A single envelope may be used to house the structures of several tubes, and in this way space is conserved. Thus the tube user has several double triodes or combinations of diodes and triodes or diodes and pentodes for use where he does not wish to expend the space for two tube envelopes.

Cathode-ray Tubes. The fact that electrons can be attracted toward or repelled from objects by electrostatic and electromagnetic means makes possible the cathode-ray tube—one of the most useful and versatile of modern instruments.

A typical cathode-ray tube configuration is shown in Fig. 10.

Again, electrons are emitted by a cathode. These electrons are concentrated or focused by a focusing electrode which is so charged that it exerts just the proper amount of force to keep the electrons confined in a narrow beam. Positioned along the narrow neck of the tube are two or more anodes which are positively charged so that they will attract electrons. The focusing action, however, directs the electrons through small holes in the anode structures, so that relatively few of them actually stop at the anodes. Instead, the electron beam speeds on toward the flat glass end of the tube, which is coated with certain materials that *fluoresce*, or glow, when bombarded by electrons. Thus wherever an electron hits the screen, as the end of the tube is called, a flash of light may be seen. A steady beam of electrons produces a continuous spot of light.

The control grid of the cathode-ray tube can be charged negative or positive with respect to the cathode. It controls the number of electrons that strike the screen and thereby controls the brilliance of a spot on the screen.

Beam Deflection. Between the electron-accelerating anodes and the screen we may put some device that will alter the path of the electrons before they hit the screen. If two plates are positioned on opposite sides of the beam, by applying proper voltages to the plates the beam can be moved back and forth at will. By positioning another set of plates 90 deg from the first set, as shown in the drawing, we may cause the beam to strike the screen at any desired position by proper combination of voltages. If, for example, the upper plate of the vertical deflecting plates is made positive while the lower plate is negative, the electrons will hit the screen at the top. If the voltages on these two deflecting plates are varied, one becoming alternately positive or negative and the other taking on potentials of the opposite polarity, the beam will trace a vertical line on the screen. The action of the horizontal plates is exactly similar except that the line on the screen will be horizontal.

If the varying voltages placed on the two sets of deflection plates are of correct magnitude and phase, a circle or ellipse or other wave form will be traced out on the screen.

In practice, the voltages whose wave forms are to be examined are placed on the vertical plates, while a "timing" voltage is placed on the horizontal plates to spread out the beam as a function of time. An analogy is a pendulum oscillating over a sheet of paper. If the pendulum carries a pencil, a straight line will be made on the paper. But if the paper is moved at right angles to the line traced out by the pencil, a sine wave will be traced out on the paper. In this case the movement of the paper corresponds to the timing function of the horizontal plates.

The beam may also be deflected by the influence of current-carrying coils instead of the deflection plates. This type is shown in Fig. 11. The charged-plate method is called *electro-*

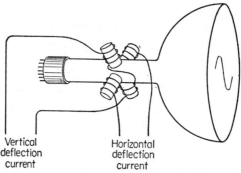

Vertical
deflection
current

Horizontal
deflection
current

FIG. 11. Basic configuration of electromagnetic deflection in a cathode-ray tube.

static deflection, and the current-carrying coil version is known as *electromagnetic deflection.* The latter system is usually employed with larger tubes, since abnormally high voltages are required to deflect the beam over any great distance.

The cathode-ray tube is a laboratory tool of extreme utility, since it not only can measure electrical quantities but also can give the operator a visual picture of the quantities measured. Furthermore, by the use of high voltages, the electrons can be made to effect their transit down the tube in a very short period of time so that events taking place in time of the order of fractions of microseconds can be made visible. The cathode-ray tube is the heart of any modern television system, being employed both at the transmitter to pick up the picture for translation from light variations into electrical variations and at the receiver to perform the reverse function.

The cathode-ray tube is also the heart of any radar instrument. Here two events are made visible—the transmission of a pulse from a transmitter and an echo of this pulse as returned from the target. Since these events may be only microseconds apart, the cathode-ray tube fits into the problem very nicely.

All that is required is to calibrate the face of the tube in the time required for an electron beam to move from left to right. Then any fraction of this distance will require less time, and so the positions of the *pips* caused by the transmitted pulse and its echo are measures of the time required for the radio pulse to go to the target and to return to the sender in the form of an echo. Since the speed of transmission through space, 186,000 miles per second, or 328 yd per microsecond, is known, the radar operator measures target distance in terms of time; and as many a man knows who saw radar in action during the war, he measures it accurately!

Some of the industrial applications of cathode-ray tubes, aside from their conventional laboratory measuring techniques, will be found in later chapters.

The cathode-ray tube is made possible by two important natural phenomena: the fact that electrons can be deflected by electric or magnetic fields, and the fact that the moving electron will produce a point of illumination when it strikes the screen of the tube. This screen is coated with materials called *phosphors* which are fluorescent so that they emit light when hit by an electron.

Numerous phosphors may be employed, some of them glowing for relatively long periods after the collision; these form "long-persistance" screens. Some phosphors produce a green light; others produce other colors. Combinations of certain phosphors will produce a "picture" which is practically white.

LIGHT-SENSITIVE DEVICES

In the tubes discussed so far, electrons are secured from a cathode by heating the cathode until the electrons have imparted to them sufficient energy to escape from the body of the cathode. In another class of electron tubes, however, the electron emission is controlled in another way, that is, by the action of light upon certain photosensitive surfaces.

Phototubes. The phototube consists of a cathode which supplies electrons and an anode which is the electron collector. If the cathode is illuminated by light of the proper wavelength,

electrons will be emitted and can be collected at the anode, which
is kept at a positive potential with respect to the cathode.   In
practice, a voltage of about 90 volts or less is maintained across a
vacuum phototube and the currents are of the order of 20 to
50 μa.

In vacuum phototubes the output current is directly proportional to the intensity of the illumination applied to the cathode,
and thus they may be used for determining light intensity.
These currents are so low that amplification is necessary before

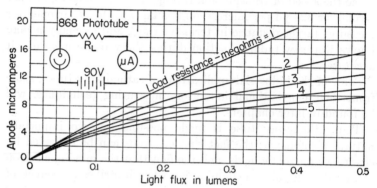

FIG. 12.   Typical phototube characteristics.

the device can be put to much use.   Vacuum phototubes have
come into very wide use in industrial devices and in translating
light variations into electrical and hence into acoustic variations,
as in the sound motion picture industry.   A typical phototube
characteristic and circuit are shown in Fig. 12.

Gas Phototubes.   Through the mechanism of ionization the
currents in a phototube can be increased materially if gas is
admitted to the tube during manufacture.   Thus with a given
input light flux, more output will be secured.

To pay for this increased sensitivity, however, one must put
up with certain disadvantages.   For one thing, the output current is no longer directly proportional to the light intensity.   For
another, care must be taken that the anode voltage is not raised
to the point where complete ionization of the gas takes place,
causing a glow discharge and currents high enough to damage the
tube.

Where linearity of output with light variations is desired, or where the maximum stability is necessary, use of the vacuum phototube is indicated.   Where the maximum response to a given input of light is desired, the gas tube will be preferred.

Multiplier Phototubes.   A fairly recent addition to the tube family is known as a *multiplier tube* because of its peculiar and unique ability to multiply the action of a single phototube many times within a single envelope.   In this tube the fundamental functions are two—the photoelectric effect and secondary emission.   In the second phenomenon electrons striking an anode

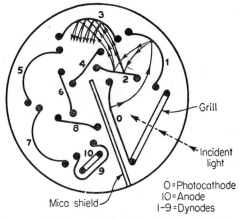

Grill

Incident light

O = Photocathode
IO = Anode
I–9 = Dynodes

Mica shield

FIG. 13.   Schematic of the multiplier phototube with its cathode, nine dynodes, and final anode or collector.

produce additional electrons from the anode surface.   In most tubes this is a disadvantage and means are taken to prevent the effects of these unwanted electrons.   But in the multiplier tube they are put to work.

The action is basically as follows: Electrons are emitted from the illuminated cathode and are formed into a beam by other electrodes so that they fall upon an anode called a *dynode*.   Here they produce more electrons, in the order of three or five per original electron.   These electrons are again focused at another dynode, and here they produce still another multiplication of electrons.   This multiplication is illustrated in Fig. 13, which shows the cross section of a 1P21 multiplier phototube.   With voltages per stage of approximately 100 volts and with 9 stages, gains of over 100,000 can be attained theoretically.

The sensitivity of the multiplier tube is about 2 amp per lumen compared with about 30 μa or somewhat greater for a conventional two-element phototube. This tube is most useful for detecting or measuring extremely low values of light intensity, but it has come into other practical applications. Some of these uses will be described in the chapter on phototubes.

Photoconductive Tubes. If a thin layer of selenium deposited on a gridlike structure is illuminated, the electrical resistance of the selenium changes, becoming lower as the intensity of the light increases. Tubes based on this principle have come into some industrial use but not to the extent to which phototubes

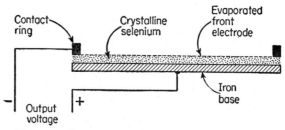

FIG. 14.   Cross section of a Weston Photronic cell.

are employed. These photoconductive cells or tubes pass some current in the dark, which is a disadvantage, and the output current is not linear with respect to the illumination. The power output is, however, quite a bit higher than can be secured from a phototube.

The GE FJ-31 selenium tube will pass a maximum of about 0.5 ma at 125 volts on the anode; its resistance will vary from 0.75 megohm at 100 ft-candles on the selenium element to 6 megohms in the dark if 100 volts is across the tube.

Photovoltaic Tubes. Usually called photocells, these devices function on a different principle. Here electrons cross an interface between two metals, having less difficulty in one direction than in another, so that the tube acts like a rectifier. One such cell is made by evaporating a thin layer of gold, silver, or platinum on a surface of cuprous oxide. Electrons will move from the copper oxide through an external circuit to the front surface of the cell.

The Weston cell, utilized in exposure meters, employs an iron base covered with a thin layer of selenium. Currents obtainable from the photovoltaic cells are of the order of several hundred microamperes or more. By proper choice of external resistance the response in current to changes in illumination may be made fairly linear, or it may become proportional to the logarithm of the light intensity.

A cross section of a Weston Photronic cell is shown in Fig. 14. This type of cell is particularly stable over long periods of time,

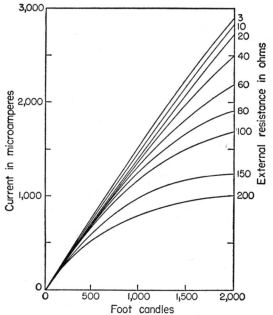

FIG. 15.   Characteristics of a Weston Photronic cell with various values of external resistance.

and for this reason it is found in industrial applications where stability is desirable. No batteries are required for its operation; upon illumination it delivers a current which can be accurately related to the amount of the incident illumination. With proper filters interposed between the cell and the light source, the output of the cell can be made to match the response of the human eye.

Curves in Fig. 15 show typical values of output current for given values of illumination.

REFERENCES

Anderson, E. F. W., Thyratrons and Their Uses, *Electronics*, February, 1938, p. 9.

Bahls, W. E., New Sensitive, and Inexpensive Gas Control Tubes, *Electronics*, September, 1941, p. 33.

Berkley, Carl, and Rudolf Feldt, Cathode-ray Tube Applications in Photography and Optics, *Electronic Engineering*, April, 1949, p. 115.

Bowlus, O. E., and P. T. Nims, Thyratron Frequency Changers, *Electronics*, March, 1948, p. 126.

Cage, J. M., Theory of the Immersion Mercury Arc Ignitor, *General Electric Review*, October, 1935, p. 464.

Coolidge, A. W., Jr., A New Line of Thyratrons, *Electrical Engineering*, May, 1948, p. 435.

Dow, W. G., and W. H. Powers, Firing Time of an Ignitor Type of Tube, *Electrical Engineering*, September, 1935, p. 942.

Dudley, B., Transmitting Tube Chart, *Electronics*, November, 1938, p. 37.

Geiser, K. R., and J. E. Hancock, The Latest in Magnetic Oscillographs, *General Electric Review*, May, 1943, p. 289.

Gillings, D. W., A Note on Grid Control Characteristics of Gas-filled Relays, *Electrical Engineering*, February, 1945, p. 372.

Gould, C. D., Subminiature Electrometer Tube, *Electronics*, March, 1947, p. 106.

Heins, H., Hydrogen Thyratrons, *Electronics*, July, 1946, p. 96.

Hilliard, R. C., Gaseous Discharge Tubes and Applications, *Electronics*, March, 1946, p. 122.

Ignitron, *Electrician*, June, 1934, p. 792.

Improved Welding Timer Expands Spot-welding Use, *Electrical World*, Mar. 24, 1934.

Jaeschke, R. L., Thyratron Braking for Oil Drilling Rigs, *Electronics*, April, 1948, p. 92.

Klemperer, Hans, A New Ignitron Firing Circuit, *Electronics*, December, p. 12.

Knowles, D. D., The Ignitron—A New Controlled Rectifier, *Electronics*, June, 1933, p. 164.

Reiss, J., The Telion; A Versatile Gas Discharge Relay Valve, *Wireless World*, August, 1945, p. 226.

Watrous, W. W., Gaseous Tubes and How to Treat Them, *Electronics*, January, 1942, p. 42.

White, W. C., Trends in Electron Tube Design, *Electrical Engineering*, June, 1948, p. 517.

CHAPTER 3

BASIC TUBE CIRCUITS

In the previous chapter, it was shown that all electronic devices are made up of combinations of tubes and certain basic circuit elements, or combinations of elements. These basic elements, such as resistance, capacitance, and inductance, are organized, or connected, with appropriate power sources to control the movement of electrons and thus to control various industrial processes.

The circuit diagram of a piece of electronic equipment may look like a hopeless maze to the uninitiated, but to the trained technician it represents a map of a system of wires and tubes. By following connections and studying values of components and types of tubes, he can usually tell what the circuit does and how it does it.

The circuit components are readily identified on circuit diagrams by their characteristic symbols, as illustrated in Fig. 1. These symbols have been fairly well standardized, but the symbols used by industrial and electronic engineers may differ, and industrial manufacturers differ among themselves. The symbols used in this book follow the practice of electronic engineers and electronic periodicals.

Tubes are also readily identified by their symbols. Several common types are shown in Fig. 2. The dot within the circle of a tube symbol indicates a gas tube. The way in which the tube is used can only be understood by studying the components employed with it, as will become obvious later.

Practically all electronic devices have some external source of power, since the job of electronics is to *control* power, not to make it. In all circuits containing thermionic tubes a source of heater or filament power must be provided. Most industrial

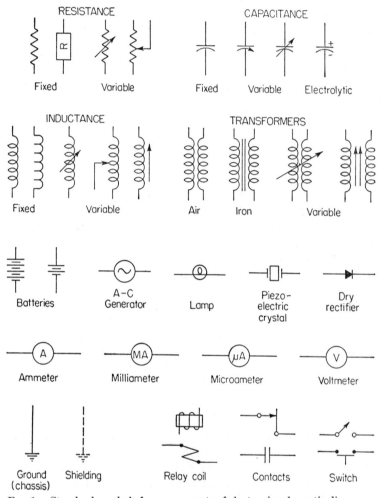

Fig. 1.   Standard symbols for components of electronic schematic diagrams.

circuits use a low-voltage winding on a power transformer for this purpose.   Quite often filament connections are omitted from circuit diagrams to avoid complication, but they are always implied.   The anode-to-cathode voltage for the tubes in a circuit may be either an a-c voltage taken directly from some alternating source, or the anode may be held at some fixed positive potential with respect to its cathode.

Figure 3 shows the fundamental requirements for making a

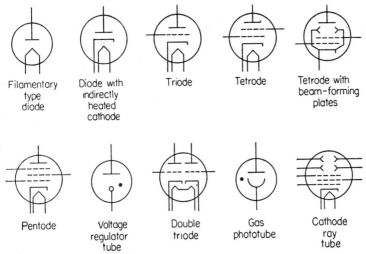

Filamentary type diode   Diode with indirectly heated cathode   Triode   Tetrode   Tetrode with beam-forming plates

Pentode   Voltage regulator tube   Double triode   Gas phototube   Cathode ray tube

FIG. 2. Various tube symbols. Wherever a tube symbol appears in a circuit diagram, it may be considered as a signpost telling the direction of current flow, since electrons can flow only from cathode to plate in a tube.

tube conduct electrons. The step-down transformer furnishes heater current which heats the cathode of the tube and allows it to emit electrons. A source of d-c voltage is connected between the plate and cathode in such a way that the plate is 250 volts positive with respect to the cathode. This voltage may vary over wide limits for different types of tubes, but the anode is almost always positive with respect to the cathode. Thus when electrons are emitted from the cathode, they will be attracted to the positive plate.

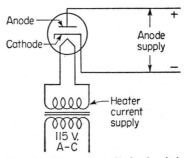

Tubes as Rectifiers. The basic circuit shown in Fig. 3 may be modified to serve as a

FIG. 3. Elementary diode circuit is capable of differentiating only between positive and negative voltages. Electrons will flow from the heated cathode to the plate when the plate is positive with respect to the cathode, but not when the polarity of the applied voltage is reversed.

rectifier, that is, as a device for converting alternating current to direct current. The basic circuit of a rectifier is shown in Fig. 4.

An a-c source has replaced the original d-c source, and a resistance has been placed in series with the tube elements.

Since the anode current flows only when the anode is positive with respect to the cathode, the tube will alternately pass and stop the flow of electrons as the a-c source potential reverses. The plate current will consist of pulses of current that flow every time the anode of the tube is positive with respect to the cathode. The voltage across the series resistor will also consist of pulses which coincide directly with the current pulses and have the polarity indicated in Fig. 4. Also shown are the waveforms for two cycles of alternating current. Rectifiers and their associated circuity are treated in detail in Chap. 4.

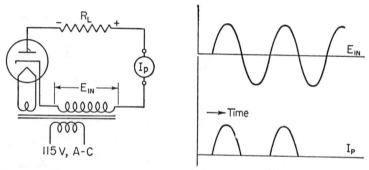

Fig. 4. Elementary rectifier circuit contains a tube, a source of a-c voltage, and a load across which a pulsating d-c voltage appears as the result of unidirectional anode current flow.

The Tube as an Amplifier. Figure 5 shows a triode tube connected as an amplifier. An electronic amplifier may be compared to a box with four terminals. A small varying a-c voltage, or combination of a-c voltages, is impressed on two of the terminals (the input terminals), and an amplified version of that voltage appears at the other two (output) terminals.

We learned in the preceding chapter that the grid of a triode was much closer to the cathode than the anode. And, through the medium of families of curves, we found that greater control over the amount of anode current could be effected by changing the grid voltage than by changing the plate voltage. In Fig. 5 a resistance, R_L, is inserted between the anode and the source that furnishes the plate voltage which causes the electrons from the cathode to stream toward the anode. Whenever any a-c signal is impressed across the input terminals, the voltage of the grid varies accordingly around its bias value E_{cc}. The changes in plate current thus caused produce corresponding changes in voltage across R_L. These output voltage changes are greater than the original grid-voltage changes that caused them, by an amount equal to what is known as the voltage gain of the tube. The output voltage *changes* may be separated from the d-c voltage of the circuit by means of the capacitor C_o, which passes the a-c signal but blocks the d-c voltage. In the same way C_i

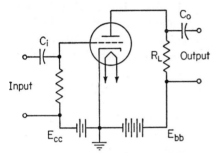

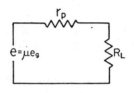

FIG. 5. Basic circuit diagram of a triode amplifier.

FIG. 6. Equivalent circuit of a triode amplifier shows internal (plate) resistance, r_p, and load resistance R_L.

blocks any d-c component present in the signal applied to the input terminals.

In the case of the triode amplifier the voltage gain may be calculated from the simple mathematical formula

$$\frac{e_p}{e_g} = \frac{\mu R_L}{r_p + R_L}$$

where e_p is the output voltage across R_L, e_g is the signal input voltage (the ratio indicating the voltage gain), μ is the *amplification factor* of the tube as given in tube handbooks, and R_L is the total external resistance connected between the plate and its d-c voltage source. The value of r_p, or the internal *plate resistance* of the tube, varies depending on the operating conditions of the tube. However, most tube handbooks give values for r_p for the various types of operation for which the tube is designed, and these values are sufficiently accurate for all but the most specialized tube applications.

Figure 6 shows the equivalent circuit of the basic amplifier circuit of Fig. 5. This type of simplified circuit shows the internal tube resistance, the load resistance, and a voltage source which is equivalent to the signal voltage as reproduced in the tube plate circuit. This equivalent voltage is essentially equal to the grid signal voltage multiplied by the mu or amplification factor of the tube. Sources of direct current are usually omitted from such equivalent circuits. In practice the only value of these "equivalent circuits" is for the study of tubes and their operation under different conditions. In most cases the circuits are only approximately equivalent, and for all but the most simplified types of operations many allowances for discrepancies must be made.

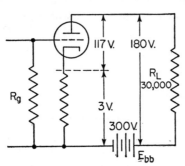

FIG. 7. Complete triode circuit with voltage division between the tube and load for a steady plate current of 6 ma. Here the plate current flowing through a 500-ohm cathode resistor, R_k, produces a 3-volt drop which may be used as grid bias. Of the 300 volts from the plate battery, 180 appears across the load, 117 between the plate and cathode, and 3 volts between the cathode and ground. No current flows through R_g, and there is no voltage drop across it.

In the case of multielement tubes, such as the pentode and tetrode, a different technique must be used for calculating the voltage gain of an amplifier stage. To obtain voltage gain the following formula is used:

$$\frac{e_p}{e_g} = g_m R_L$$

All the symbols have the same meaning as in the triode case, but g_m, the transconductance of the tube, has been substituted for the ratio $\mu/(r_p + R_L)$. Figure 7 shows the distribution of d-c voltage across the load resistance and across the tube on the basis that 6 ma of current is flowing.

These equations require certain modifications in some instances. However, most of the modifications made necessary by deviations from the extremely basic conditions make only slight changes in results. In practice extreme accuracy is unimportant in most cases. It is sufficient to know that a stage provides a gain of about 100 rather than to laboriously calculate the gain to be 95.7. The chances are that the estimate will come as close to the true value as the accurately calculated value, because of inconsistencies in values of component parts and tube parameters.

In practice, therefore, where a definite gain must be provided, it is common practice to construct an amplifier capable of providing more than enough gain and then provide some means for reducing the gain to the desired value.

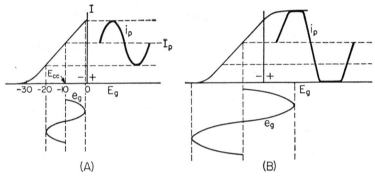

(A)   (B)

Fig. 8. Waveforms show the effects of impressing an alternating voltage between the cathode and grid. In A the waveform of the plate current is like that of the grid voltage, but in B the grid is overdriven so that the plate current is reduced to zero (cut off) at times. In each case, I_p is the plate current with no grid excitation.

Classes of Amplification. In amplifier operation a great deal depends on the *operating point*, or bias voltage, of the grid. To understand this let us examine the typical E_g-I_p curves shown in Fig. 8, where it will be noted that between 0 and about -20 volts on the grid the curve is relatively straight. If the grid voltage is fixed at about the middle of this curve, say -10 volts, and if, then, it is varied as by an additional a-c voltage superimposed upon the steady -10-volt "bias," the plate current will vary in accordance with the varying grid voltage. The form of the plate current will be very similar to that of the grid voltage. This is known as *class A operation*. The grid never becomes positive, never draws current from the input source, and plate current flows all the time.

The tube, however, may be operated under various other conditions. From example:

1. *Considerably increased bias.* Now at some portions of the grid voltage cycle, the grid becomes so negative that no plate current flows. Under these conditions there will be a change in the d-c plate current when the grid voltage is applied.

2. *Greatly increased signal.* No matter what the bias, if the input signal is great enough to drive the grid so negative that plate current cannot flow, then the output waveform will not be like the input. Furthermore, it is also possible to drive the grid so hard that at times it becomes positive with respect to the cathode and will attract electrons and therefore will draw current. The grid structure may get hot and may be damaged. If the grid goes positive enough the plate current may tend to level off so that the output waveform may have a flat top on the upward swings of current as well as a flat bottom (zero) when the plate current decreases (Fig. 7*B*). With a sine wave of input voltage applied, the plate current may assume a trapezoid in form. In other words, there is considerable distortion in the system. This is class C operation.

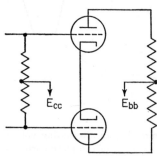

Fig. 9. A push-pull amplifier.

The grid bias employed depends upon the application for which the amplifier is intended. In communication circuits fidelity of waveform may be quite important and class A amplification would be used. The efficiency is low, the fidelity good. If greater efficiency is desired at some sacrifice of waveform fidelity, class AB (greater bias and greater input signal) will be indicated, and if high efficiency is necessary, class C must be used. Now distortion must be tolerated.

By proper adjustment of plate voltage, grid bias, and input signal, the desired compromise between efficiency and fidelity of waveform may be achieved. Two tubes operated in push-pull (Fig. 9) tend to balance out some of the distortion produced in a single tube, especially the distortion produced by even harmonics of the input signal frequency, and are often used where greater power output with less distortion and greater efficiency is desired.

Grid-bias Source. The grid-bias voltage may be furnished in any one of several ways, or by a combination of ways. For example, the bias voltage may come from a battery, from a separate power supply (a source of rectified and filtered alternating current), from the voltage drop along a filament lead if the tube is operated from direct current, or from a voltage drop along a resistor through which the d-c plate current flows. Several of these methods are shown in Fig. 10.

In Fig. 10*B* note that a resistor has been placed between cathode and ground so that the plate current flows through this resistor.

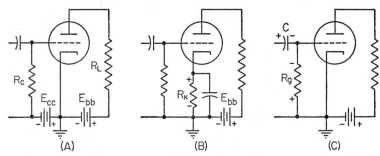

(A)   (B)   (C)

Fig. 10.   Methods of fixing the grid-bias voltage with respect to the cathode. In *A* a battery is employed; in *B* the plate current flowing through a bias resistor, R_k, produces the bias voltage by raising the cathode above ground potential.   In *C* the grid current flows during part of the input voltage cycle. This current charges capacitor *C*.   During the time the grid draws current, the grid-cathode path inside the tube has low resistance so that the time constant of the circuit is short, enabling the capacitor to charge quickly. On the negative half cycle of input voltage the grid does not take current; the grid-cathode path of the tube is high in resistance and since R_g is high, the capacitor cannot discharge quickly.   It retains its charged condition, therefore, and biases the grid negative with respect to ground.   This is known as *grid-leak bias*, R_g being the *grid leak* by which the electrons trapped on the capacitor seek to get to ground.

The voltage drop along the resistor may be employed as grid bias by connecting the grid circuit to the end of the resistor where the voltage polarity is of the proper direction.   In this case, the polarity of the voltage is such that the cathode is positive with respect to ground.   Since the grid is connected to ground, the cathode is also positive with respect to the grid. Looked at from the grid's standpoint, the grid is negative with respect to cathode and this negative voltage becomes the grid bias.

Now if the plate current changes, a change in voltage will be produced along the bias resistor, and the steady grid-bias voltage will also change.   These changes are in such a direction (polarity) that they oppose the input voltages applied to the tube and for this reason the amplification of the circuit is reduced.   This effect is known as *degeneration,* and in many cases it is desirable.

If the degenerative effect is to be eliminated, all that is necessary is to shunt a large condenser across the bias resistor so that the time constant $(C \times R)$ is large compared to the rate at which the plate current changes occur.   Since the condenser voltage cannot change quickly if C is large, the actual voltage across the bias resistor attains some average value which does not vary with plate-current variations.

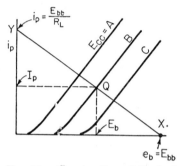

To reduce the degenerative effect to a point where it can be disregarded, the reactance of the capacitor must be only a fraction of the resistance of R_K at the lowest frequency which must be amplified by the tube and circuit.

Fig. 11.   Construction of the *load line* by which all the voltages and currents in a triode amplifier circuit may be obtained. E_{cc} is the fixed grid bias; E_{bb} the fixed plate voltage.

In Fig. 10A a battery supplies the bias; in B the voltage drop along R_K keeps the grid negative with respect to the cathode; and in C grid current which flows when the input voltage forces the grid positive with respect to the cathode produces a voltage drop along R_G of such a polarity that the grid is kept at an essentially constant negative d-c voltage.

In Fig. 10C the time constants for charging and discharging the condenser are different.   When the grid goes positive, the grid-cathode internal resistance of the tube drops to about 1,000 ohms so that RC is small and the condenser charges quickly. On the negative half cycles of the input voltage, however, the grid draws no current and the grid-cathode resistance within the tube is very high, so that the condenser can now discharge only through this high resistance.   The time constant is now high, and thus the condenser tends to maintain its voltage at a constant value, biasing the grid to this voltage.

Load Line.   A very useful device by which the operation of a tube and its circuit may be determined is shown in Fig. 11.

Here the curves relating the plate current (i_p) as a function of plate voltage (e_b) at several values of grid voltage (A, B, and C) are plotted. The straight line drawn across these curves is known as the *load line*. This line represents the load and is independent of the tube. Thus on one graph we have a line representing the tube and a line representing the load. Together they describe the operation of the entire circuit.

The straight load line describes the equation which states that the instantaneous voltage (e_b) between cathode and plate is always equal to the plate battery voltage (E_{bb}) minus the voltage drop across the load resistance. Thus,

$$e_b = E_{bb} - i_p R_L$$

where e_b is the instantaneous voltage between cathode and plate, E_{bb} is the plate battery voltage, i_p is the instantaneous plate current in amperes, R_L is the load resistance in ohms, and $i_p R_L$ is the voltage drop across the resistor.

If no plate current flows, $i_p = 0$ and $i_p R_L = 0$ so that $e_b = E_{bb}$. This locates the bottom of the line shown as point X. If $e_b = 0$, then $i_p = E_{bb}/R_L$, and this locates the top end of the line, or point Y.

At any value of grid voltage, the plate current can be found by determining where the load line crosses the curve representing the tube at this value of grid voltage.

Since the tube is operated with a fixed grid bias ($E_{cc} = B$ volts), the point Q gives the plate current with this bias. This is the steady current that will flow if the grid voltage is not changed. The voltage actually on the plate will be E_b until grid excitation is applied.

Once the load line for the particular circuit has been drawn, much valuable information can be extracted from the diagram. To determine amplification, one need only trace grid-voltage variations along the load line on either side of the Q point and study the resulting plate voltage variations on the plate-volts scale.

Phase Reversal in Vacuum-tube Amplifiers. Referring back to Fig. 5, let us compare the phase of the signal applied to the grid of the tube to that of the amplified waveform appearing at the output terminals. As the grid voltage swings positive, plate current increases, and the voltage drop across the load resistor also increases.   This voltage drop is in such a direction that the top end of the resistance load becomes *more negative* (*less positive*) as the grid voltage becomes more positive.   Likewise, when the grid voltage swings in the negative direction, the plate voltage swings in the positive direction.

Thus the signal, in passing through a single-stage amplifier with the signal applied to the grid and taken from the plate, is changed in phase.   For medium frequencies, this phase shift is almost exactly 180 deg; that is, when the voltage at the grid goes up the voltage at the plate goes down, and vice versa.

Relay Operation.   In many industrial applications a relay operates when a voltage is applied to the grid circuit of an amplifier containing the coil of the relay in its plate circuit.   A relay, as will be explained in detail in Chap. 7, will operate when the current through its coil reaches a certain value.   Let us assume we have a relay that will operate when the current through its coil is increased, say, to 10 ma.   Now if the tube is so biased that it passes less current than this, the relay will not operate unless a voltage is applied to the tube grid large enough in a positive direction to overcome the bias voltage, whereupon the plate current will increase to or above the required 10-ma value.

The circuit may be arranged to release the relay when the grid voltage is increased in a negative direction.   That is, the plate current will drop if the bias is increased, say, from -5 to -10 volts.   This may reduce the plate current from, say, 20 to 5 ma.

Tube Parameters.   To design tube circuits certain facts about the tubes themselves must be known.   Tube manufacturers supply such data.   The next thing is to know how to use this information.   Obviously one must know how much voltage and current to feed the heater which supplies the electrons.   Then one must decide upon a plate voltage and a grid bias.   Typical data of this sort is given by the manufacturer.

The important things one must know about the tube and how it will operate in a circuit are (1) how much the plate current will change with a given grid-voltage change, (2) the effective internal resistance of the tube, and (3) how much the tube will amplify.   These matters are controlled by three tube constants, or parameters.

Transconductance.   The transconductance, g_m, of a tube is the ratio of the change in the *plate current* to the change in *grid* *voltage* which caused the plate current change. In some earlier books, and even occasionally today, this important tube parameter is referred to as *mutual conductance*. Suppose, for example, that the plate current changes 1 ma for a 1-volt change in grid bias. The transconductance is the ratio of these changes. Thus,

$$g_m = \frac{\text{change in plate current}}{\text{change in grid voltage}}$$

and in this case,

$$g_m = \frac{1 \times 10^{-3} \text{ ampere}}{1 \text{ volt}}$$

$$= 10^{-3} \text{ mho} = 1{,}000 \text{ micromhos}$$

This is actually the slope of the E_g-I_p curve as shown in Fig. 12. Values of transconductance run from a few hundred to several thousand micromhos.

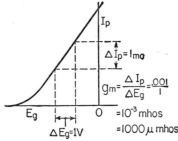

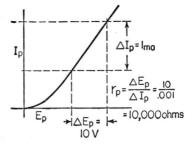

FIG. 12. The important tube parameter, transconductance or mutual conductance, is the slope of the E_g-I_p line; it is the rate at which the plate current varies with the changes in grid voltage.

FIG. 13. Derivation of the tube internal resistance r_p.

Plate Resistance. In any circuit, resistance is the ratio of the voltage to the current. If, therefore, one changes the plate voltage of a tube and notes the change in plate current (with a constant grid voltage), the ratio of these two changes will be a measure of the internal resistance of the tube. Thus,

$$r_p = \frac{\text{change in plate voltage}}{\text{change in plate current}}$$

This is actually the slope of the E_p-I_p curve as shown in Fig. 13. Typical values of r_p run from a few hundred ohms in certain

power tubes to several thousand ohms in many triodes. Tetrodes
and pentodes have internal resistances which run upwards of a
megohm, so that changes in plate voltage produce very slight
changes in plate current.

Amplification Factor. The relative ability of grid and plate
voltage changes to produce given changes in plate current indicates the amplification possibilities of the tube. Thus, if the
plate voltage is changed, say 100 volts, and if this produces a
plate-current change of 10 ma, and if, to bring the current back
to its original value, a change in grid voltage of only 10 volts is
necessary, the grid has ten times as much ability to control
plate current as has the plate voltage. The amplification factor
gives these important data.
Thus

$$\mu = \frac{\text{change in plate voltage}}{\text{change in grid voltage}}$$

to produce a given plate current change.

It is worth noting that the
transconductance, g_m, is the
ratio between the amplification
factor and the plate resistance.
Thus,

$$g_m = \frac{\mu}{r_p}$$

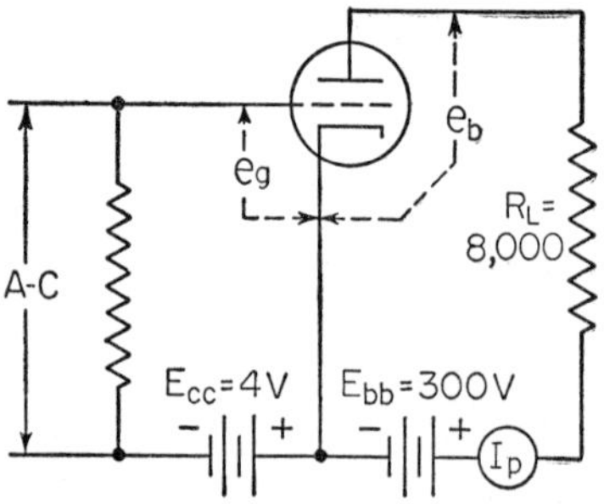

FIG. 14. Typical triode amplifier
problem with voltages indicated.
Small letters indicate instantaneous
voltages and currents.

Typical Amplifier Problem. To show the straightforward way
in which amplifier problems can be tackled and solved, let us
connect a typical triode to a typical load and, with typical values
of voltages, see what happens.

We will use a 6J5 tube with a plate voltage supply (E_{bb}) of
300 volts and with a resistance load (R_L) of 8,000 ohms (Fig. 14).
We will erect the load line upon the plate family of curves as in
Fig. 15. First consider the tube as an open circuit, drawing no
current. The full 300 volts then appears at the plate since there
is no voltage drop along R_L. If, next, the tube is theoretically
shorted, then the full 300 volts of the battery appears across R_L
and the current that will flow is $300/8,000$ or 37.5 ma, the maximum possible current. The plate voltage is zero and the plate
current (if allowed to go through the tube) would be 37.5 ma.

These two sets of values ($E_b = 300$, $I_p = 0$ and $E_b = 0$, $I_p = 37.5$ ma) determine the ends of the load line.

Now suppose we place a battery bias of -4 volts on the grid as in Fig. 14. The intersection of the load line with the

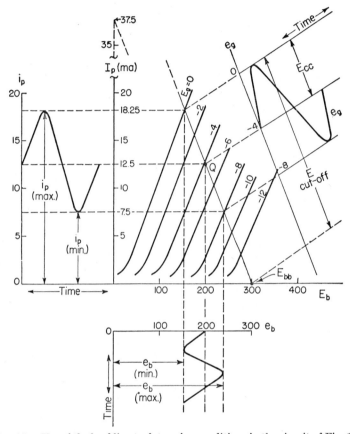

FIG. 15.   Use of the load line to determine conditions in the circuit of Fig. 13.

$E_g = -4$ line shows that 12.5 ma flows (point Q on Fig. 15).[1] Projecting this point to the E_b line shows that the plate voltage is 200 volts.   The voltage across the load must be $300 - 200$, or 100 volts.

Under these quiescent conditions—no a-c input voltage—the

[1] Note that $E_g = E_{cc}$ because there is no drop in d-c voltage in the input circuit.   Otherwise E_g would be less than E_{cc}.

power taken from the battery is $E_{bb} \times I_p = 300 \times 12.5 \times 10^{-3}$, or 3.75 watts, and of this the amount dissipated by the tube will be $200 \times 12.5 \times 10^{-3} = 2.5$ watts, and that dissipated in the load will be $100 \times 12.5 \times 10^{-3}$, or 1.25 watts.

Now let us apply to the grid circuit a sine-wave a-c voltage having a maximum value of 4 volts. This will cause the grid voltage to change, cyclically, from -4 to zero and from -4 to -8 volts. The maximum and minimum values of the plate current, therefore, will be 18.25 and 7.5 ma, and the maximum and minimum values of E_b will be 240 and 154 volts. A grid voltage of 4 volts maximum (8 volts from peak to peak) has caused a total plate-voltage change of $240 - 154$, or 86 volts (peak to peak), which represents a peak a-c plate voltage of 43 volts. The alternating plate current has a peak value of approximately 6 ma. Note, however, that the plate current is not symmetrical, since it increases from the quiescent value more than it decreases from this value.

The maximum and minimum values of voltage across the load resistor are $300 - 154 = 146$ and $300 - 240 = 60$ volts, which represents an a-c voltage with a peak value of 43 volts.

Here the tube and its load are operating under class A conditions; that is, the grid does not draw any current since it is never forced positive with respect to the cathode, and only the straightest part of the E_p-I_p curve is employed. Since the same alternating current flows through the load as through the tube, and since the same peak a-c voltage appears across the load as the tube, the same a-c power is lost in the tube as is developed across the load. The system is operating at 50 per cent efficiency; one-half of the total a-c power is developed in the load where it is useful. The phase relations in such a circuit are shown in Fig. 16.

Impedance Matching. Every generator or source of power contains some internal resistance. If this were not true, a direct short circuit across a small battery would theoretically cause infinite current to flow. When a power source is connected to deliver power to a load, the maximum power will be transferred to the load when the internal resistance of the source is equal to the resistance of the load.

If a load of, say, 12,000 ohms is to be fed power from a tube with an internal resistance more or less than 12,000 ohms, then maximum power will not be transferred to the load if it is connected directly into the plate circuit. A transformer with the proper turns ratio can be used to match the generator to the load, and once more the conditions for maximum power transfer can be attained.

If a resistance load higher in value than the internal resistance of the tube is employed, more voltage will be developed across the load. Where maximum voltage amplification is desired (not maximum power transfer), the load is invariably higher in resistance than the tube.

Power Output. For a triode with resistance load the simplest method of calculating the power output is to construct the load line upon a set of E_p-I_p (Fig. 15) curves and to determine power output from

$$P_o = \frac{(E_{max} - E_{min})(I_{max} - I_{min})}{8}$$

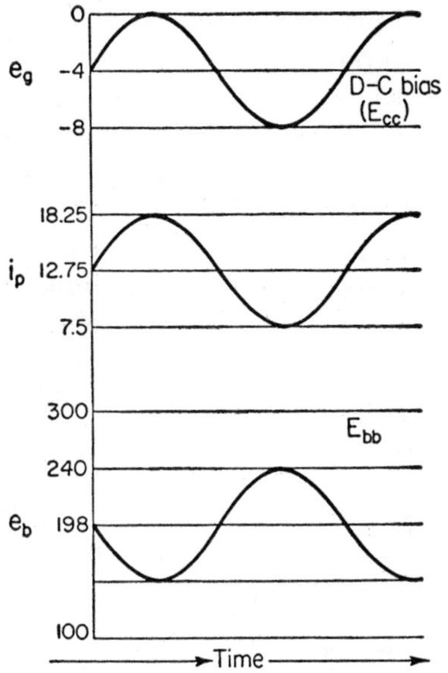

FIG. 16. Phase relations between applied grid voltage and instantaneous plate current and plate voltage. Since the plate voltage goes down as the grid voltage goes up (becomes less negative), there is a 180-deg phase shift across the tube.

With values of grid bias, plate voltage, and exciting grid voltage such that the waveform of the plate current is essentially a sine wave with sine-wave input, and with resistive load, the power delivered to the load is

$$P_o = \frac{(\mu e_g)^2 R_L}{(r_p + R_L)^2}$$

where μ is the amplification factor of the tube and e_g is the rms input voltage.

In designing a power-output tube circuit, the grid bias is calculated (approximately) from

$$E_{cc} = \frac{0.7E_{bb}}{\mu}$$

where E_{cc} is the grid bias, E_{bb} is the plate voltage, and μ is the amplification factor of the tube.

If the steady no-signal plate current exceeds the value which will permit the tube to dissipate the power cited by the manufacturer, more bias must be provided. The rest of the design depends upon the load resistance and is carried out by use of the load line and E_p-I_p curves for the particular tube to be employed.

Cathode Follower. In general tube circuits are high-impedance circuits. That is, the input circuit of the tube represents a very high impedance (thousands or millions of ohms), and the output looks like thousands or tens of thousands of ohms. Where a low-impedance output is desired to work into a low-impedance load (one requiring high current and low voltage), the cathode follower circuit is a useful device.

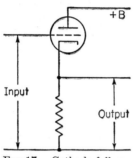

The basic circuit of a cathode follower is shown in Fig. 17 where it is seen that the input is applied between grid and ground and the output is taken across a resistor in the cathode circuit. No load is placed in the plate circuit, the plate voltage being fed directly to the plate. Under these conditions the voltage amplification of the circuit is always less than unity (an actual loss in voltage amplification), but the impedance of the tube as presented to the load becomes very small, actually being equal, approximately, to the normal r_p of the tube divided by the amplification factor, or to the reciprocal of g_m. Thus the output impedance of the tube may be only a few hundred ohms if g_m is large.

FIG. 17. Cathode-follower circuit providing very high input impedance, low output impedance, and a voltage gain less than unity.

MULTISTAGE AMPLIFIERS

Cascade Circuits. If the amplification provided by one tube and its circuit is not sufficient for the job at hand, the output of the circuit may be applied to another tube and circuit and additional amplification secured in this way. In this manner voltage gains up to the millions may be produced. If the individual stages have equal amplification, the total amplification is equal to the stage gain raised to a power equal to the number of stages.

$$\text{Total gain} = (\text{stage gain})^N$$

where N is the number of stages.

Thus if a voltage amplification of 20 per stage is maintained, two stages will have a gain of $(20)^2$ or 400.

Interstage Coupling. There are several ways by which one amplifier may be connected to a succeeding amplifier. The essential idea is to pick off the output voltage of the first stage and to use it to drive the grid of the second stage. The "hot" end of the load of the first tube is the plate end, and this forms the point to which the hot end of the following tube input circuit is connected. Since the plate is at a high positive d-c voltage and since the following grid must be kept at a negative d-c voltage, some means must be provided to prevent the positive plate voltage from appearing between the grid and cathode of the following tube.

Three methods of accomplishing this objective are shown in Fig. 18. In A, separate power supplies are employed so that the two cathodes are not at the same potential. Then the grid of the second tube can be maintained at any desired potential with respect to its own cathode regardless of the d-c voltage of the preceding plate. Such a circuit will amplify both d-c and a-c voltages.

In B a condenser is inserted between the two tubes which draw plate current from a single battery. This condenser will pass a-c voltage variations but will not pass d-c voltages (provided its insulation is good). In either A or B whatever a-c voltage appears across the load of the first tube is applied to the second tube without loss or gain. There is a reversal of phase, however, in the first tube itself, so that a positive-going pulse applied to the grid of the first tube appears as a negative-going pulse on the second tube and as a positive-going pulse in the output of the second tube. Therefore, an odd number of stages reverses the phase; an even number of stages does not.

By using a transformer between stages (Fig. 18C), the d-c voltage of the first plate does not affect the grid of the second tube, and in addition the output voltage of the first tube may

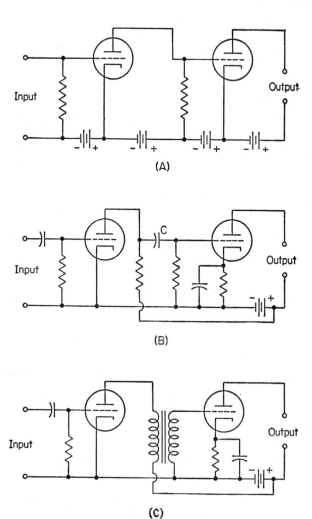

FIG. 18. Three methods of connecting one amplifier to another. In *A*, separate power supplies are used so that the grid of the second tube may be biased negative with respect to its own cathode, although both this grid and the preceding plate are connected to the positive terminal of the B battery. In *B* a capacitor between plate and grid keeps the positive voltage away from the second grid. In *C*, a transformer provides additional voltage step-up and isolates the second grid from the d-c voltage on the first plate.

be increased (step-up transformer) or decreased (step-down transformer).

Figure 18A shows what is known as a *d-c amplifier*, which in general is not very satisfactory. The transformer-coupled amplifier can be designed to amplify a narrow band of a-c frequencies, or a wide band of frequencies, but it will not amplify d-c voltages.

Other more complex interstage-coupling means are used seldom in industrial circuits.

WAVE-CHANGING CIRCUITS

There are numerous situations in industrial electronics where it is necessary, or desirable, to change the wave shape of an input applied signal to obtain some other wave shape in the output. Many electronic counter circuits are preferably controlled by waves of steep wave front, peaked waves for example. One of the jobs of the electronics engineer, therefore, is to produce waves of this shape.

Limiters. In some cases it is desirable to prevent the voltage applied to a circuit from rising above a certain value. Limiter circuits perform this job. There are numerous limiting or "clipping" circuits but only the simplest will be covered here.

Since a simple diode rectifier carries current only when the anode is positive with respect to the cathode, the diode may be used to cut off half of the input applied voltage. In this manner it merely acts as a switch allowing current to flow half the time. In Fig. 19A such a diode is in series with a source of alternating voltage and a load resistor. When the cathode is positive with respect to the anode, no current flows and there is no voltage across R, but when the input waveform reverses and the cathode becomes negative, current is passed by the tube. Thus this circuit will cut off (limit) negative-going pulses. If the other half cycle is to be cut off, the diode connections are reversed.

Diodes may be employed *across* the source instead of in series with it to produce similar limiting action, as shown in Fig. 19B. When the tube conducts, a high voltage drop appears across R and, therefore, the output voltage (from tube anode to ground) is low. When the tube does not conduct, no current flows through R and essentially the entire input voltage appears across the output.

If only a portion of the wave is to be cut off, a battery (or other source of d-c voltage) in series with the tube (Fig. 20) will prevent the tube from passing current until a certain value of input is applied. Then the tube limits, and this portion of the input is

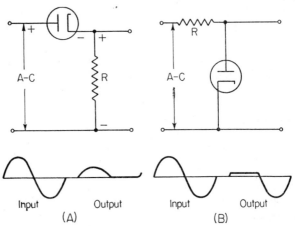

Fig. 19. Simple limiter or clipper circuits. In A the diode is in series with the load. In B the diode is across the load; in this circuit there will be low output when the tube conducts, since most of the voltage will be lost across R.

cut off. Two diodes connected back-to-back across the source will cut off parts of both half cycles so that an applied sine wave becomes trapezoidal in the output.

Limiting can take place in the input circuit of a triode as shown in Fig. 21. Here a resistor is in series with the input. Now when

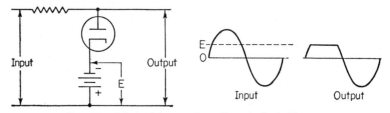

Fig. 20. Method for cutting off part of a half wave.

the grid is driven positive, it draws current. This current produces a voltage drop along R, and the more current the grid takes, the greater will be the drop along R. Since this voltage is of such a polarity that it opposes the applied input voltage, in effect the tube acts as though its input driving voltage had been reduced. Accordingly the output voltage is similarly reduced. During the other half cycle the entire input is applied to the

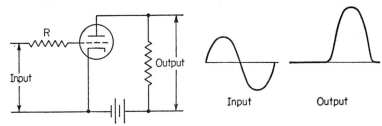

FIG. 21. In the grid circuit of a triode, limiting occurs as the result of a voltage drop across R when the grid draws current.

tube and the output voltage will be similar to the applied signal. Note the usual phase reversal across the tube.

Clampers. Clampers differ from limiters in that they do not chop off all or parts of half cycles. They permit the total variation in input to appear in the output, but they force the waveform to rise and fall from some reference level which is not that of the *average* value of the input. If the reference level is, say, -10 volts, and if the input varies from zero to $+50$, the output will vary from -10 to -60. In this case the output voltage never reaches zero and it may be said that some d-c voltage (-10) exists all the time. For this reason such a circuit is often called a *d-c restorer*.

A simple clamper circuit is shown in Fig. 22 in which R is

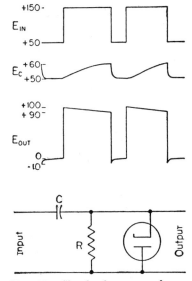

FIG. 22. Simple clamper or d-c restorer circuit in which the major voltage variations occur above the zero axis.

high so that C charges slowly, say to 50 volts, the minimum voltage of an applied square wave. If the condenser has had time to charge, and if the input is suddenly increased to 150 volts, what happens? The difference (100) between the 50 volts and the new voltage must appear across R since the voltage across C cannot change instantly. Thus the output voltage rises to 100 volts. If the new voltage is applied for a comparatively short time, say one-tenth RC, then the condenser will slowly rise in voltage, the output will slowly drop in voltage. This change will amount to about one-tenth of the change in voltage, and therefore the condenser voltage will rise to 60 and the output will drop to 90.

Now if the input is suddenly dropped to its original voltage, 50, the condenser will be left with 60 volts and the difference

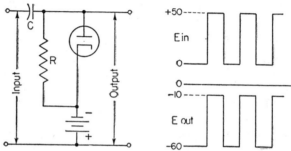

Fig. 23.   Clamper in which the maximum output voltage is maintained at -10 volts.

(-10) will appear across R. Since the applied voltage is in a negative direction, the difference voltage across R will be negative. Thus the output voltage is now -10. The job of the clamper is to prevent this -10 volts from appearing across the output.

The diode connected across R will have a low resistance in the conducting state and when the input suddenly decreases, the cathode becomes negative with respect to the anode, the tube conducts and shorts the circuit so that the output voltage is very low. This removes quickly the condenser charge of 10 volts and permits only a small negative spike of voltage to appear across R.

The output, therefore, rises from 0 to $+100$, drops slowly to $+90$, drops suddenly and briefly to -10, and comes back to 0. The clamp circuit has forced practically all of the voltage variation to be above the zero reference axis, although the input has gone up from $+50$ to $+150$ and back to $+50$.

In Fig. 23 the setup is arranged to clamp the upper extreme

of the output voltage to -10 if time has been sufficient to charge the condenser before the input is applied.

Discriminator. This is a device which produces a d-c voltage which changes as the applied frequency varies. In other words it is a frequency-sensitive circuit. A possible use would be to reverse the direction of a motor if the frequency applied to the input varies up or down from the desired frequency. In this manner a circuit can be kept in tune to the incoming frequency. As this frequency changes or as the local tuning arrangements may vary with temperature, for example, the circuit is automatically kept in resonance.

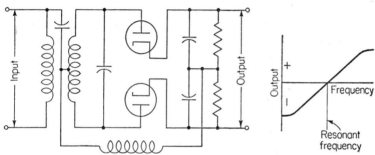

Fig. 24.   Discriminator circuit.   The output is a function of the variation in frequency of the applied input.

The discriminator, whose circuit is shown in Fig. 24, is used in f-m radio receivers to produce an output which varies in amplitude as the incoming signal frequency varies as a result of modulation at the transmitter.   In this circuit each diode gets equal voltages so long as the incoming frequency is equal to the resonant frequency of the transformer, but the diode currents produce equal but opposite voltages across the output.   At other frequencies the diode input voltages are equal but out of phase with the input to the transformer.   The diode output voltages are then unequal and the circuit output voltage is positive or negative depending upon which side of resonance is the incoming signal.

D-C Amplifiers. Although it is possible to arrange amplifier circuits which will operate at exceedingly low frequencies or will amplify direct currents, it is not easy.   The output of a thermocouple or bolometer, for example, is difficult to amplify. Various dodges employed to get around this difficulty will be

discussed in later chapters.   In general, however, it is customary
to convert the slow changes in voltage, or direct current, to
alternating current in some way before amplification.   For
example, the thermocouple voltage may be "chopped," or broken
up, into discrete intervals in some manner.   Then these portions
of the voltage are amplified by conventional a-c amplification
techniques.

Negative Feedback.   As will be seen later, if a portion of the
output of an amplifier is fed back into the input in phase with the
signal applied there, the amplification of the circuit can be
increased up to the point where it becomes a self-excited amplifier, or oscillator.

If, however, the feedback is reversed in phase so that it is out
of phase with the input voltage, then the gain of the amplifier
will be decreased and while this may seem to be a disadvantage,
the process has certain very useful aspects.   Such feedback is
called "negative" or "inverse" feedback.   The over-all effect
is called "degeneration."

Let us suppose that a noise-free signal is admitted to an amplifier so that 100 volts of signal appear in the output.   In the
circuit itself, however, let us suppose that 20 volts of noise or
unwanted signal is produced.   The ratio of desired signal to
noise is $100/20$ or 5.   The signal is five times as strong as the
noise.

Now let us feed back 20 per cent of the output to the input in
such a way that the amplification is reduced by 20 per cent.   To
produce the 100-volt output now, we must increase the input to
the amplifier accordingly; but the internally generated noise
will have been reduced to 80 per cent of its former value or to
16 volts.   The signal to noise ratio now is $100/16$, or 6.6, an
obvious gain over the former situation.

If the amplifier has a nonuniformity in its frequency-gain
characteristic, degeneration will reduce this nonuniformity; and
with sufficient feedback one may exchange tubes with others of
rather widely different characteristics without changing the
amplifier performance very much.   Feedback of this nature is
employed very often to improve the operation of an amplifier,
to increase its stability, or to make it possible to respond to a
wider range of voltage or frequency or other conditions.

The cathode follower circuit (Fig. 17) is the simplest form of

negative feedback.   The literature on this subject is very extensive and the applications are many.

OSCILLATORS

The Tube as an Oscillator.   Let us suppose that a tube is
amplifying whatever voltage is placed upon the grid.   Now in
some manner let some of the amplified plate voltage be impressed
back upon the grid.   If this voltage "fed back" from the output
to the input is in phase with the grid voltage so that it is increasing at the same time the grid voltage is increasing, the net effect
is a greater grid voltage, and, of course, a greater grid voltage
produces a greater plate current.   The same proportion of this
increased plate current is again fed back into the output, and
so on, until the grid voltage has been built up very much beyond
what was originally supplied to the tube from an external source.

The feedback voltage actually acts as though it were reducing
the input losses.   The amplitude of the grid voltage, therefore,
will increase until all the input power losses are overcome, whereupon the applied input grid voltage may be removed.   Now it
will be found that there is still an alternating component of
current in the plate circuit.   The tube is supplying its own grid
excitation.   It is oscillating.

The frequency of the output current or voltage may be as low
as a fraction of a cycle per second, or it may go up into the hundreds of millions of cycles per second depending upon the tube
and circuit constants.   The waveform may be a pure sine wave,
it may be saw-tooth in form, or it may have practically any
shape the designer desires.   The power obtained from such an
oscillator may run into the hundreds of kilowatts or be as low
as a few milliwatts.

The essential conditions for oscillation are two.   (1) There
must be some feedback of voltage from the output circuit to the
input circuit.   (2) The voltage fed back must have the proper
phase with respect to the input voltage.

The tube may feed some of the a-c power generated in its plate
circuit to an external circuit, an antenna, for example, or a piece
of metal that is to be heat-treated.   Under all conditions it is
worth noting that the tube itself manufactures no power.   It
only consumes power.   The anode voltage source is the sole
supplier of power, the tube merely acting as a valve or trigger

which controls the flow of power from the anode power supply
to the load. This is true of all tube circuits whether they are
rectifiers, amplifiers, or oscillators.

There are numerous ways in which the necessary feedback
conditions can be met to make the tube oscillate and generate
alternating currents.

In the simple circuit shown in Fig. 25, the feedback voltage
is produced by coupling a plate-circuit coil to the grid-circuit
inductance. If these two coils are poled correctly, a voltage

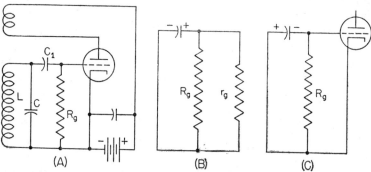

(A)   (B)   (C)

FIG. 25. Simple feedback oscillator in which a voltage is returned to the
input from the output by means of a plate coil coupled to the grid inductance.
In B and C are the effective input circuits for determining grid bias by means
of grid current.

of the proper phase to produce oscillation will be fed to the grid.
When the tube oscillates, its grid is driven positive during portions
of the cycle, and it will draw current charging the condenser C_1.
In this way the tube is biased so that it draws less current than
if the tube were not oscillating. If the plate-circuit coil is
removed from the vicinity of the grid coil, oscillations will cease
and the plate current will rise.

Effect of Time Constant. It is worth noting in this circuit
how the time constant of the input circuit affects the operation.
So far as direct current is concerned the grid condenser is in
series with the grid-cathode path inside the tube (across which
is shunted the grid leak, R_g) and in series with the tuning coil.
This coil has very low d-c resistance and can be neglected.

There are two conditions: (1) when the grid is driven positive
and draws current (Fig. 25B) and (2) when the grid is negative
and does not draw current (Fig. 25C). When the grid draws
current, r_g becomes very low, and the condenser will charge

quickly. When the grid does not draw current, r_g is high, and thus the effective resistance in series with the condenser is high, so it cannot discharge quickly.

Since the condenser discharges at a much lower rate than it charges, it remains charged to a more or less fixed value and of such a polarity that the grid terminal is negative. In this manner the d-c voltage of the grid with respect to the cathode is maintained negative so long as the tube oscillates. If the tube stops oscillating, the condenser soon discharges, and the grid reaches the same potential as the cathode, since there is no current flowing through R_g and, therefore, no voltage drop along it. With the grid at the same potential as the cathode, the plate current will be high. Use is often made of this effect. Under normal conditions the tube is maintained in oscillation with corresponding low plate current. Now if some abnormal condition occurs, the tube stops oscillating, the plate current rises and becomes sufficiently high to operate an alarm or a relay so that the condition which caused the change in plate current can be altered or the system can be made to shut itself down until normal conditions reoccur.

In an elevator control system employing an oscillating tube a metallic vane is interposed between the two coils as the elevator reaches the proper location in the shaft. At this moment the plate current rises and operates a relay which in turn controls the elevator motor.

The frequency of oscillation depends primarily upon L and C in the grid circuit. Anything that will change either L or C will change the frequency. If C is a condenser with two plates fixed in position, then any substance which is interposed between the plates will change the capacitance and hence the frequency. A very sensitive device for determining the thickness of dielectric materials can be made in this way. The dielectric material changes the capacitance of C as a function of the thickness, the moisture content, or some other physical quantity. A frequency meter can be calibrated in terms of moisture or thickness or whatever the quantity is that is to be measured or controlled.

DETECTION, MODULATION

Two functions performed by tube circuits in communication systems are occasionally useful in industrial applications. These are *modulation,* by which a high-frequency voltage is modulated or changed in accordance with a lower frequency voltage, and *detection*, the reverse process, which is carried out in a *detector*, or *demodulator*. Here a modulated wave has the modulation separated from it and made applicable to the required purpose. Both functions take place on some nonlinear characteristic of a tube.

Detector. Consider Fig. 26*A* in which a simple diode is connected in series with a d-c meter and a source of alternating voltages. For a steady value of the alternating current, the d-c

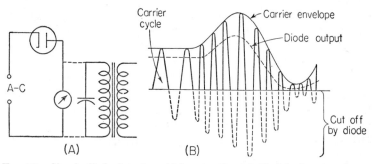

Fig. 26. Simple diode detector which cuts off one-half of the input and produces a change in the average voltage across the transformer as a function of the envelope of the modulation on the carrier.

meter will read a given value of current, somewhere between zero and a peak value corresponding to the peak of the applied a-c voltage. Now if the applied voltage increases, the d-c meter will show an increased current. If the applied voltage varies periodically at a frequency of, say, 1,000 cps, and if the d-c meter could follow a change in current of this frequency (which it cannot), then the meter would show a 1,000-cycle current.

Now if instead of the meter we use a transformer, the *changes* in applied voltage will cause *changes* in the voltage across the primary of the transformer, and these voltages will appear across the secondary where they can be picked up and amplified if necessary. If the changes of the applied voltage correspond to the output of a microphone into which a person speaks, the voltages across the secondary of the transformer will have all the characteristics of the microphone currents.

A by-pass condenser across the primary of the transformer will offer low impedance to the individual cycles of the applied frequency but high impedance to amplitude *changes* of the applied frequency. In such a system the incoming voltage is called a *carrier*, and the changes in its average value the modulation. The by-pass condenser across the transformer gets rid of the carrier but preserves the modulation. Note in Fig. 26B that as the carrier voltage rises, the demodulation voltage rises also and follows the envelope of the input.

Detection or demodulation can occur in the grid circuit of a triode, utilizing the nonlinear grid voltage–grid current curve, whereupon some amplification of the demodulation will occur in the plate circuit. This is accomplished by using a grid condenser and leak resistance of such a time constant that it is long with respect to the carrier frequency but short with respect to the modulation. The voltage across the condenser, therefore, follows the envelope of the carrier but not the individual cycles. This voltage is applied to the grid-cathode circuit of the tube.

If the grid bias is high so that the variations in plate current with changes in applied carrier voltage occur about the lower bend of the E_p-I_p curve, then there will appear in the plate circuit a voltage corresponding to the modulation, and detection will occur.

A grid-leak detector is more sensitive than a plate-circuit demodulator because of the additional amplification secured in the plate circuit; but the grid will draw some current on positive half cycles of the applied wave, and, therefore, it will require some power from the input. The plate-circuit detector is less sensitive but its input impedance is very high since the grid never draws current.

Modulation.   In Fig. 27 is shown an amplifier to whose input is applied a carrier frequency signal of, say, 1 mc. The plate circuit will contain a component corresponding to this frequency. Now if the plate voltage is varied slowly, up and down, the value of the 1-mc current in the plate circuit will also go up or down slowly. In such a process the carrier is said to be modulated. It now carries two kinds of information: the carrier frequency at 1 mc and the modulation, say, at 1,000 cycles. The modulated carrier can be used as a means of transporting the modulation from one place to another over a path which would not transport the modulation alone. The plate current can be modulated at several distinct frequencies, say 1, 5, and 10 kc, and at a remote point, frequency-selective circuits can pick from the incoming carrier the frequency to which they are tuned. In this manner several kinds of information can be sent over the same circuit without interference. In turn the individual modulation frequencies can be modulated, turned on or off, or actually varied at a rate which is slow with respect to the modulation frequency.

Mixers. It is often desirable to mix two frequencies, as in modulating a high frequency with a low frequency, or to produce frequencies which bear some integral relationship (harmonic) to a given frequency, or simply to add two frequencies of the same general order. Circuits for performing these functions are found in radio texts, but a brief survey of them will be given here.

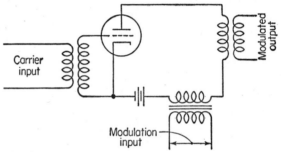

Fig. 27. Modulated amplifier in which both carrier and modulation are impressed, one on the grid circuit and the other on the plate circuit.

A mixer is generally considered as a device for mixing or adding two frequencies not far apart in the frequency scale. For example, in a modern radio receiver operating on the superheterodyne principle, an incoming signal, say at 1,000 kc, is mixed with another frequency generated locally, so that the difference between the two is a lower frequency, say 456 kc. If the 1,000-kc signal is modulated with low frequencies, voice or music for example, the difference frequency will bear this modulation. The difference frequency may be amplified as much as desired and then passed through a detector in which the modulation is recovered to operate a relay or an audio amplifier and loudspeaker.

There are several types of tubes specially designed for this purpose. They have two signal grids, one for the incoming signal and one for the locally generated signal. Since both affect the electron stream within the tube, components of both fre-

quencies exist in the plate circuit.   In addition components equal
to the sum of the two frequencies and their difference also show
up in the plate circuit.   If the output of the tube is tuned to
the difference (or sum) frequency, the other components may be
filtered out.

The sum, or difference, frequency is called a *beat frequency*
since, if the local oscillator is varied in frequency, it can be
brought into tune with the incoming signal so that the difference
frequency may be as small as desired.   When the difference is
within the limits of audibility, the ear will perceive it, and as
the two circuits are brought into synchronism with each other,
the ear will perceive a beat or throb, which will disappear at
zero beat.

If an alternating voltage is applied to any amplifier tube which
is so biased that the operating point is low on the plate-current
curve where there is considerable curvature, then the plate current will contain not only a component of current equal in frequency to that of the applied input signal but also components
of twice, three times, etc., this signal.   The tube is acting as a
harmonic generator.   In practice, where the harmonics are
desired instead of the fundamental component, the tube is
heavily biased and is driven with excess input grid voltage.   In
this manner much distortion is created, which is another way of
stating that the harmonics will be high in amplitude.

In general the output at the second harmonic will be about
half, in voltage, of that of the fundamental.   The output circuit
may be tuned to the second, or other, harmonic, whereupon the
fundamental will not create much voltage across the load.

Where high frequencies are desired, frequency multiplication
is the general practice rather than that of generating the frequency of the desired value directly.   The reasons are (1) it is
easy to make high-stability oscillators which are very constant in
frequency at fairly low frequencies, up to several megacycles, and
(2) amplifiers are much more stable and will give higher gain with
corresponding stability if the input and output are not tuned to
the same frequency.   A frequency multiplier is simply an amplifier that is excited with a high input voltage so that harmonics of
the input appear in the output circuit.   The input, therefore, is
tuned to a low frequency, and the output is tuned to some
harmonic frequency.

In a single tube an input frequency may be tripled without too great decrease in output. Three small tubes used as frequency triplers, therefore, will produce an output at say 27 mc from a 1-mc signal.

On the other hand if a very low frequency is desired, say 10 cycles, then it is possible to produce it by mixing two higher frequencies whose difference is the desired low frequency. Furthermore if one of the oscillators is made variable, then an output frequency continuously variable from zero to some higher frequency may be obtained. Such an instrument is usually called a *heterodyne*, or *beat-frequency* oscillator.

VACUUM-TUBE VOLTMETERS

Since the fundamental action of a diode is to convert alternating to direct current, and since the fundamental action of a grid-controlled tube is to produce a change in plate current with a change in grid voltage, it is natural that engineers have applied both kinds of tubes to standard laboratory measurement problems. In either case a plate current meter may be calibrated in terms of input voltages, and if reasonable care is used, the calibration will be fairly stable. The diode is very useful for measuring peak a-c voltages; the grid-controlled tube may measure both d-c and a-c voltages and currents.

D-C Measurements. The great advantage of the tube for measuring direct currents lies in the fact that it draws so very little current from the source being measured. Therefore it can be employed to measure voltages delivered by high-impedance sources or used where extremely small currents are involved.

A very simple instrument for measuring d-c voltages consists of a triode with the d-c voltage applied to the grid-cathode circuit and with a d-c current meter in the plate circuit. Any change in applied voltage will cause a change in plate current, the magnitude of which is a function of the transconductance of the tube. The plate-current meter may be calibrated to read voltages. If the operating point of the tube is chosen near the center of the E_g-I_p characteristic, voltages above and below this value may be read, and in this manner positive and negative voltages may be measured.

Since all that is desired is to read the *change* in plate current, the steady no-signal value may be bucked out by electrical means, as shown below, or the needle of the instrument may be mechanically turned so that it reads zero when no d-c voltage is applied to the grid-cathode terminals.

In Fig. 28 is shown the circuit of such a voltmeter with an additional battery voltage and resistance shunting the meter so that the steady no-signal plate current can be suppressed or balanced out. This simple circuit will measure potentials of the order of a few volts, from sources which can supply extremely little current.

If the sensitivity is not great enough, the same change in plate current can be produced by lower voltages by preceding the voltmeter tube with one or more stages of d-c amplification. In this way as little as 10 mv will give full scale deflection on a 5-ma meter.

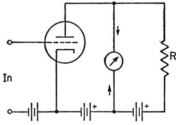

Fig. 28. Simple triode vacuum-tube voltmeter in which any change in the grid voltage produces a change in the plate current. The additional battery and resistor are adjusted so that zero current flows through the meter when no grid signal is applied.

If the open input terminals of the tube are connected with a known resistance, then the voltage across this resistance caused by input current flowing through it may be used to change the plate current. Since the resistance is known, the current through it to cause the change in input voltage can be calculated. In such a manner the tube-meter circuit becomes a microammeter. A multistage amplifier plus the final voltmeter tube will permit measurements of currents as low as 10^{-11} amp. The input impedance presented to the circuit under test may be extremely high, 100 megohms or more.

Stability of the device may be increased at the expense of a loss in sensitivity by placing a resistance in series with the cathode as in Fig. 29. Now an increase in plate current produces a greater grid bias and this causes the loss in sensitivity. On the other hand such a resistor makes the circuit much more immune to change in calibration with changes in supply voltages or tube characteristics. Changing the cathode resistor will change the range of the instrument.

Direct-current instruments of this type are not too well adapted

for measuring voltages or current from low-impedance sources,·
thermocouples for example. The expedient of interrupting the
current or voltage to be measured so that the amplifier-voltmeter
is really measuring a-c values is often employed to get around
this difficulty.

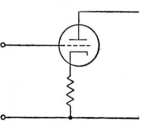

A-C Measurements. If the grid
bias of an amplifier is properly adjusted so that the positive half cycles
of an applied a-c voltage produce a
greater change in plate current than
do the negative half cycles of the
applied voltage, a net change in d-c
plate current will occur. This change
can be employed as a measure of the
applied input voltage. Furthermore
a simple diode changes alternating to
direct current, and such a tube can be

Fig. 29. Use of a cathode
resistor to produce degeneration and consequent greater
stability at the cost of decreased sensitivity.

turned into a useful measuring instrument with the chief disadvantage that it will draw current from the source. That is,
it will have a low impedance. The diode may be preceded by an
amplifier, or a d-c amplifier may follow the diode as means of
increasing the sensitivity.

A very simple circuit is shown in Fig. 30 where the diode is
placed in series with the voltage
source and a d-c meter. The current
read by the meter is proportional to
the average of the positive half cycle,
but if the resistor in Fig. 30 is shunted
with a condenser sufficiently large, the
meter readings will be proportional to
the peak value of the applied alternating voltage. A 6H6 tube with about
5,000 ohms in series with it and the
meter, will deliver a d-c voltage of
approximately 1, 2, and 3 volts for
a-c input voltages of, respectively, 2, 6, and 10 volts.

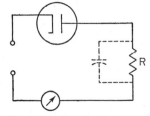

Fig. 30. Simple diode em-
ployed as a voltmeter. The
meter reads current as a
function of the applied a-c
voltage.

Instead of employing a diode, a triode may be used as shown in
Fig. 31. Here the grid draws current on the positive half cycles
of applied input voltage and this current flowing through the
grid-leak resistor changes the grid voltage so that a change in

plate current results.   This device draws current from the source, and, therefore, its impedance presented to the source is not very high.   Again, the steady no-signal plate current can be bucked out so that the meter responds only to changes in plate current.

It is preferable to bias the tube from a battery or other source and to so adjust this bias that the change in plate current for the desired input a-c voltages is greatest.   Thus if a 9-volt peak is to be measured, the bias on the tube can be somewhat more than this.   The tube, therefore, will not draw grid current, and its input impedance will be high. Then the plate voltage can be adjusted to produce the greatest deflection for the 9-volt-peak input, or the plate voltage can be adjusted so that the applied 9 volts will bring the plate current meter to full scale deflection.

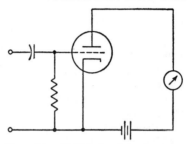

FIG. 31.   Grid-leak detector employed as a voltmeter.   As the input voltage increases, the plate current goes down because of greater bias on the grid as it draws greater current on positive half cycles of the applied input voltage.

Other Voltmeter Types. The literature on this subject is extensive; much work has been done with tubes as measuring tools.   Some circuits are arranged so that the no-signal deflection is maximum.   Then no matter what signal is applied, the current meter reading goes down.   In this manner a sensitive meter in the plate circuit cannot be damaged by applying excessive voltage to the input of the tube.   Some circuits have been arranged in which the tubes are in a bridge circuit so that the meter may read the difference of the two tube currents as a function of the applied input voltage, or in which the effects of variations in supply voltage in one tube are compensated in the other, and so on.

The tube may be used in the following way instead of operating it as a calibrated device.   After the input voltage has been applied and the plate-current reading taken, the unknown applied voltage is removed and another voltage supplied from a potential divider across a known battery voltage is substituted.   When the same plate-current reading is attained, the unknown voltage is equal to the standard volt potential.

In another technique the applied voltage is permitted to create any desired plate current, whereupon the bias is adjusted until the no-signal current is again attained. The change in bias is a measure of the applied voltage.

REFERENCES

Aiken, C. B., D-C Amplifier for Low-level Signals, *Electronics*, October, 1947, p. 124.

Barber, A. W., Diode-triode Peak Voltmeter, *Electronics*, October, 1934, p. 322.

Brumbaugh, J. M., A Feedback D-C Meter, *Electronics*, September, 1938, p. 16.

Cady, W. G., Nature and Use of Piezoelectricity, *Electrical Engineering*, August, 1947, p. 758.

Cathode-follower Design from Tube Characteristics, *Tele-Tech*, April, 1944, p. 44.

Dishington, R. H., Diode Circuit Analysis, *Electrical Engineering*, November, 1948, p. 1043.

Dorr, C. J., and L. N. Galton, Electrical Remote Control, *Electronics*, November, 1942, p. 60, and December, 1942, p. 57.

Dudley, B., Applications of Cathode-ray Tubes, *Electronics*, October, 1942, p. 49.

Fitzgerald, A. S., Feedback in Magnetic Amplifiers, *Journal of the Franklin Institute*, March, 1949, p. 223.

Fitzgerald, A. S., Magnetic Amplifier Characteristics, *Journal of the Franklin Institute*, October, 1947, p. 249, November, 1947, p. 323, and December, 1947, p. 415.

Greene, W. E., Applications of Magnetic Amplifiers, *Electronics*, September, 1947, p. 124.

Greenless, L. E., Simple Pulse-generating Circuits, *Electronics*, January, 1943, p. 118.

Helber, Carl, Designing Saturable-core Reactors for Specific Uses, *Electronic Industries*, December, 1947, p. 4.

Huntoon, R. D., An A-C Operated D-C Amplifier Voltmeter, *Review of Scientific Instruments*, October, 1935.

Ingram, S. B., Electronic Circuit Design, *Electronics*, May, 1944, p. 92.

Jennings, J. E., An Ultra-sensitive Bridge, *Electronics*, September, 1939, p. 38.

Jordan, S. R., The Controlled Transitron Oscillator, *Electronics*, July, 1942, p. 42.

Lewis, H. M., Wave Form Circuits for Cathode Ray Tubes, *Electronics*, July, 1942, p. 44.

Liu, Y. J., Compensated Amplifier Chart, *Electronics*, September, 1939, p. 36.

Mather, N. W., Clipping and Clamping Circuits, *Electronics*, July, 1947, p. 111.

Mayer, H. F., Cathode Ray Oscillograph Applications, *Electronics*, April, 1938, p. 14.

Mayr, Hans, Feedback Amplifier Design, *Wireless Engineer*, September, 1948, p. 297.

Moon, Parry, and W. R. Mills, Jr., An A-C Bolometer, *Review of Scientific Instruments*, January, 1935.

Muller, R. H., R. L. Garman, and M. E. Droz, "Experimental Electronics," Prentice-Hall, Inc., New York, 1942. An excellent review of vacuum-tube voltmeters will be found here.

Murray, Charles, Thermocouple Voltmeter, *Electronics*, June, 1935, p. 190.

Nottingham, W. B., RC Oscillator Analysis, *Electronics*, July, 1942, p. 109.

Osborn, J. A., Magnetostriction Generators, *Electrical Engineering*, August, 1947, p. 758.

Phase Inverter Circuits, *Radio Maintenance*, June, 1949, p. 14.

"RCA Receiving Tube Manual," 1950.

Reyner, J. H., "The Magnetic Amplifier," Stuart & Richards, London, 1950.

Schwarzman, W. A., Power Output of A-C Operated Amplifiers, *Electronics*, August, 1943, p. 94.

Smiley, G., Control Circuits for Industry, *Electronics*, January, 1941, p. 29.

Sturley, K. R., Low Frequency Amplification, *Electrical Engineering*, November, 1944, p. 236, December, 1944, p. 290, January, 1945, p. 335, February, 1945, p. 378, March, 1945, p. 429, April, 1945, p. 470, May, 1945, p. 510.

Thomas, H. A., Electrometer Input Circuits, *Electronics*, December, 1946, p. 130.

Tulauskas, L., Multi-range Vacuum-tube Voltmeter, *Electronics*, July, 1930, p. 170.

Yu, Y. P., Cathode Follower Coupling in D-C Amplifiers, *Electronics*, August, 1946, p. 99.

CHAPTER 4

RECTIFIERS AND POWER SUPPLIES

In preceding chapters it was stated that the job of electronics is to control power, not to produce or manufacture it. In almost all electronic devices a source of power is required—the tubes and other components only transform this power into some useful form for doing a specific job at some desired time.

In most parts of the world power is furnished in the form of an alternating voltage. This type of power, where the voltage and current are actually building up in one direction and then periodically reversing in a sinusoidal fashion, is useful directly in some electronic applications. In most circuits, however, the a-c voltage is converted electronically into a source of d-c voltage.

The circuit that accomplishes this a-c to d-c conversion is known as a rectifier circuit, and the actual elements in the circuit that do the converting are called rectifiers. In some cases the rectifying elements are vacuum or gas-filled electron tubes, and in others dry or metallic type rectifiers are used. In both instances rectification is made possible by virtue of the property of all rectifiers to pass current in only one direction.

As might be expected, d-c power can be converted back to a-c power by electronic means, but this application of electronics finds limited practical use in industrial applications.

Rectifier Circuits. The most basic rectifier circuit is shown in Fig. 1. Here are three circuit elements, all connected in series: the rectifier itself, a source of a-c voltage (shown as the secondary winding of a step-up transformer), and a load (indicated by a resistance) through which it is desired to pass a current in one, and only one, direction. When the source voltage is in the proper direction (Fig. 1A), the rectifier passes current through the load, and a voltage drop appears across the load.

When the source voltage reverses (Fig. 1*B*), which it does once a
cycle, the rectifier refuses to pass current, and all the voltage
appears across the rectifier.   No current flows in the load, and
there can be no voltage drop across it.   Since the source voltage

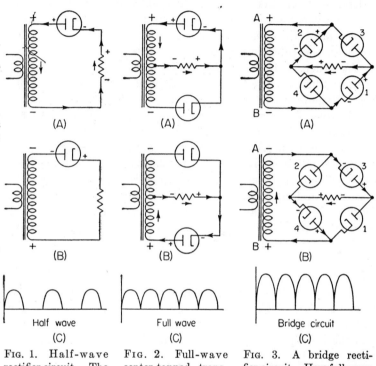

Half wave	Full wave	Bridge circuit
(C)	(C)	(C)

FIG. 1. Half-wave
rectifier circuit. The
arrows indicate the
direction of current
flow. The tube con-
ducts current when,
and only when, its
plate is positive with
respect to its cathode.

FIG. 2. Full-wave
center-tapped trans-
former rectifier circuit.
Two tubes take turns
conducting current,
but the direction of
current through the
load (voltage across
the load) is always
the same.

FIG. 3. A bridge recti-
fier circuit. Here full-wave
rectification is provided
without a center-tapped
transformer. Current
through the load is unidirectional, but pulsating, as
shown in *C*.

is varying sinusoidally, the current that flows is a half sine wave.
It rises from zero to some maximum value, and then returns in a
like manner to zero, where it remains during the nonconducting
halves of the cycle.   This is illustrated by the curves in Fig. 1*C*.
    The rectifier, then, acts like a variable resistance, being very

high during one half cycle and very low during the other half. Ideally, the value of tube resistance should alternate between zero and infinity, but actually this is not the case. There is always a voltage drop across the tube, thus indicating that its resistance never drops to zero. The value of this tube voltage drop in a vacuum rectifier is roughly proportional to the current being drawn through the tube. In the case of the gas tube, however, the tube voltage drop is always some low value, say of the order of 15 volts, regardless of the current. The gas rectifier thus has the advantage of being more efficient, since less voltage is lost in the tube itself.

Full-wave Rectifier. Now consider Fig. 2, which shows the full-wave rectifier complete with transformer windings, rectifiers, and load resistance. Each tube will pass current only when its anode is positive with respect to the cathode. On one half cycle, therefore, the cathode of one tube is positive, the plate is negative, and no current is furnished the load by this tube. During this same half cycle, however, voltage of the proper polarity is applied to the plate of the other tube which passes current to the load. On the next half cycle these conditions are reversed so that the two tubes alternately pass current and refuse to pass current. The end point is a continuous flow of current through the load. The magnitude of this current varies from instant to instant but its direction of flow is always the same. In a full-wave rectifier, then, each tube handles current half the time, but the load has current passing through it all the time.

The full voltage developed across the secondary of the transformer will not appear across the load, because there is some voltage drop in the rectifier, the actual amount depending upon the type of rectifier tube and the current flowing through it. Therefore, in order to supply, say, 300 volts to the load the transformer secondary must produce 300 plus the voltage lost in the tube. If the tube drop is 50 volts, then at least 350 volts must be available to supply 300 to the load.

Another type of full-wave rectifier is shown in Fig. 3. This type, called the *bridge* rectifier, furnishes full-wave rectification without a transformer center tap. It has the disadvantage, however, of requiring four rectifier tubes instead of two. Its action is as follows: When *A* is positive with respect to *B*, electrons flow through tube 1, the load, and tube 2. When the source voltage reverses, electrons flow through tube 3, again through the load in the same direction as before, and thence through tube 4. Again current flows through the load during both halves of the a-c cycle, but the load current is always uni · directional. The voltage at the junction of tubes 2 and 4 is always positive with respect to the voltage at the junction of tubes 1 and 3.

Current Required and Choice of Circuit. The type of rectifier circuit used for a particular application is dependent on a number of factors, the most important of which is the amount of d-c power that must be supplied by the circuit. In general, circuits of low power requirements are single phase; when larger amounts of power are required, three-phase circuits may be used.

Filter Circuits. After the alternating current is rectified, it is usually filtered to supply the load with a constant value of d-c voltage. Filters employ shunt capacitance and series inductance to smooth out the rectifier-circuit current pulses and provide as pure direct current as is desired. In low-level circuits, such as those used in the first stages of amplifiers where considerable amplification follows, the d-c source voltage must be almost completely free from a-c ripple. Otherwise, any ripple introduced in the input of the amplifier stage would experience the same amplification as the signal, and its presence in the output of the amplifier would be objectionable.

Filters have two general forms, depending on whether a capacitance is placed directly across the rectifier output or whether a series inductance is placed between the rectifier and the first filter capacitance. Thus we have the terms condenser input filter and inductance or choke input filter. Examples of both types are shown in Fig. 4.

The condenser input circuit produces a higher d-c output voltage for a given a-c input. It is also more economical than the choke input filter, since it requires one less component, that is, the input choke. However, when a rectifier circuit employing a condenser input filter is first turned on, the uncharged input condenser presents practically a dead short across the rectifier, and extremely large current values may flow until the condenser becomes charged. This effect makes the condenser input filter unusable with gaseous-type rectifiers but satisfactory for vacuum-

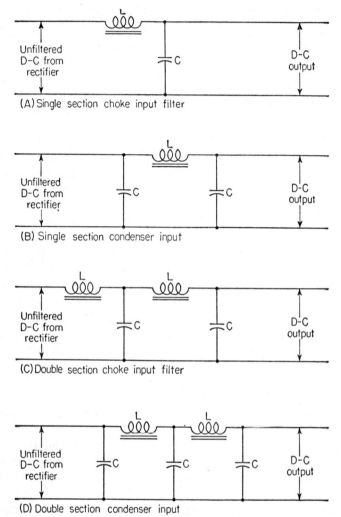

(A) Single section choke input filter

(B) Single section condenser input

(C) Double section choke input filter

(D) Double section condenser input

Fig. 4.   Inductance-capacitance filters smooth out fluctuations in the output of rectifier circuits.

type circuits where current limiting due to space charge within the tube prevents damage to the tube electrodes.

Though the choke input filter provides a slightly lower output voltage, its filtering action and regulation characteristics are superior to those obtainable with a condenser input.   Also, the peak values of current through the tube are much lower, thereby decreasing the peak loads on the rectifier tube and increasing tube life. The choke input filter is most common in industrial circuits.

Bleeder Resistors. In most cases a fixed resistor is placed across the output of a rectifier-filter power supply. It is called the bleeder resistor since it continuously bleeds off a portion of the current supplied by the power supply. This resistor usually has such a value that with the load disconnected it will draw about 10 per cent of the total load current. Its function is to keep some current flowing through the rectifier and filter at all times, thus improving the regulation of the supply. It also acts as a safety measure to discharge the filter capacitors when the load is disconnected and the a-c power to the rectifier is turned off.

Filter-circuit Design. Filter-circuit components are usually selected by compromise after determining the approximate values required for a certain degree of filtering action. It is common practice, and not in most cases too impractical, to provide much more than adequate filtering, just to be sure. At first glance this practice might seem slipshod and careless and a disgrace to accepted engineering principles, but a study of the problem will reveal the merit of such a scheme.

Filter components are usually available in values of inductance and capacitance in whole integral numbers. So, if it is found that a choke of 8 henrys is needed in conjunction with a condenser of 4.5 μf, one might have to settle for 10-henry chokes and perhaps 8-μf condensers.

The percentage of ripple[1] that may be expected from the single-section filter shown in Fig. 4A may be approximated by the equation

$$\text{Percentage ripple} = \frac{100}{LC}$$

where L is the input choke inductance in henrys, and C the capacitance in microfarads. The above equation assumes a full-wave rectifier circuit which has a ripple frequency of 120 cycles per second when operated from a 60-cycle source. If it is desired to calculate filter-component values for other types of

[1] The amount that the d-c voltage varies in percentage of the average value around which it varies.

circuits, suitable adjustment to the L and C values must be made. For instance, if the circuit to be used is a half-wave rectifier, as shown in Fig. 1, the ripple frequency is 60 cps, and twice as much as inductance and capacitance will be required for the same amount of ripple, as calculated by the equation. Similar formula adjustments can be made for other circuits.

It would seem that if a sufficiently large value of capacitance were chosen for a single-section filter, for which the above equation applies, a very small inductance could be used. However, there are limitations that must be applied. The input choke must be large enough to limit to a safe value the peak current that must be passed by the rectifier tubes. An approximation of the smallest choke that can be used in the input of a single-section filter can be made as follows:

$$L_{\min} = \frac{\text{load voltage}}{\text{load current}}$$

where L is in henrys, the load voltage in volts, and the load current in *milliamperes*. It is best to select an input choke with a value of about twice the value calculated above, although a value approximately equal to the calculated value will prevent the filter from acting like a condenser input system.

SELECTION OF POWER-SUPPLY COMPONENTS

In designing a power supply for a given voltage and current rating, many factors must be considered. Cost is usually one of the main items, and among the others are size, weight, flexibility, regulation, amount of ripple that can be tolerated, dependability, chances of short overloads, and so on. Each application presents a new set of requirements.

There are many transformers available on the market, but they cover only typical requirements. It would be impossible for transformer manufacturers to stock units for the infinite number of combinations that might be required. Tubes are also usually selected as a matter of compromise. If a given transformer is on hand that has a 6-volt filament winding for a rectifier, rather than a 5-volt winding, it is common sense to choose a 6-volt rectifier tube rather than to buy a separate filament transformer.

These compromises are best made by a systematic check of the factors involved. It is impossible to set down a rule for designing power supplies. A general idea of components will be presented, however, with the details accompanying individual cases left to the imagination of the reader.

Efficiency is not too often an important factor in power-supply design, since abundant power is usually available. In most factories and plants where industrial electronic equipment is employed, the power required by the electronic control equipment is usually a negligible amount compared to the power required for running the equipment being controlled.

Choosing a Circuit. Of the three general types of single-phase power-supply rectifier circuits, the full-wave rectifier with a center-tapped power transformer is by far the most common. The reasons for this popularity are (1) full-wave rectified current (as opposed to half-wave) is easy to filter into pure direct current, (2) a wide selection of power transformers is available for this type of circuit, (3) moderately high currents can be drawn from such a circuit, since each tube works only half of the time, (4) a wide selection of double-diode rectifier tubes is available for medium power ratings, and (5) the peak values of voltage applied to the rectifier tubes need not be so great as in the case of the half-wave circuit.

The half-wave circuit is popular, however, where (1) current drains are low, (2) not too much filtering is required, (3) where an existing transformer is to be used which has no center tap, and (4) only one rectifying diode is desired.

Bridge rectification may be used where the disadvantage of needing at least three separate filament transformers is not objectionable or where full-wave rectification is desired and an un-center-tapped a-c source must be used.

Reducing Charging Current. The high-surge current caused by charging the input capacitor can be reduced by using a small value of input capacitance, but the filtering action is reduced as a result. Several schemes have been used for limiting the charging-current surges. Two of these are shown in Fig. 5. In each case a second switching action is required each time power is applied to the filter. In Fig. 5A a current-limiting resistor is placed in series with the filter. It limits the charging current. However, once the input capacitor has charged up, the resistance must be shorted out if the full advantage of the voltage increase made possible by the condenser input filter is to be realized. Otherwise, the voltage drop across the limiting resistor would lower the output voltage. The other scheme, that shown in Fig. 5B, shows the condenser switched from one side of the filter choke to the other after it has been charged through the choke. The choke, of course, limits the charging current when power is first applied to the filter, and the charged capacitor is then switched

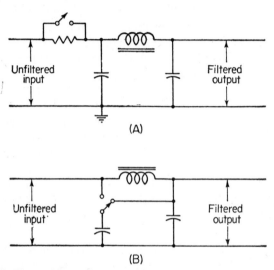

(A)

(B)

Fig. 5. Condenser-input filters provide somewhat higher output voltages, but when these filters are used with mercury-vapor rectifiers, precautions such as those shown must be taken to see that the charging current is not high enough to damage rectifier tubes.

to the input side of the choke where it acts to increase the voltage output in the usual manner.

One disadvantage of the condenser input filter is the fact that the many variables involved make calculation of the output voltage quite involved. Trial-and-error methods are usually required. In many applications this is not a serious disadvantage, since the additional voltage afforded by a condenser-input filter allows some leeway. Any excess voltage can be reduced by a series resistance between the filter output and the load.

If choke input is used, the d-c voltage output will be approximately 90 per cent of the rms value of the voltage across one-half of the secondary (assuming a full-wave rectifier and neglecting any voltage drop due to the internal resistance of the transformer and filter choke). For the capacitor input filter the output voltage will depend to a great extent on the values of filter components and the amount of load current drawn. Curves are available in tube handbooks for calculating the voltage output of a circuit using specific tubes and specified filter components. A pair of typical curves for this purpose are shown in Fig. 6

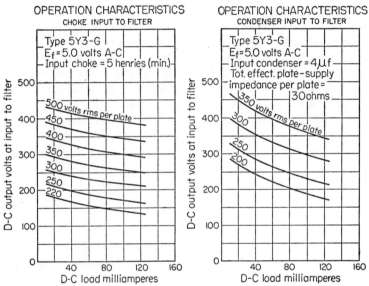

FIG. 6. Typical curves provide all essential information for figuring the performance or rectifier tubes. This example (from the "RCA Receiving Tube Handbook") shows characteristics for the 5Y3G high-vacuum dual-diode rectifier tube.

(from the "RCA Receiving Tube Handbook"). Here are given curves for the popular 5Y3G tube.

As an example, let us suppose we must supply 300 d-c volts at 100 ma. From the curves (Fig. 6) we see that if we use a choke input filter, the rms voltage supplied by the power transformer will have to be 400 volts either side of center tap. But if we use condenser input, only 300 volts are required.

Choosing a Power Transformer. Many factors are involved in the selection of a proper power transformer for a particular supply. Here more than anywhere else in the power-supply circuit compromises are bound to be made. A transformer is chosen that will deliver *at least* the required voltage at the required current. Any excess voltage can be reduced by series resistances or voltage dividers (explained later in detail), and excess current rating is never harmful.

The current rating of a transformer is based on the transformer being used at rated voltage. The important thing is not to exceed the *product* of the voltage and current, which gives the volt-ampere rating. If a circuit is used to produce a d-c voltage equal to twice the rms input voltage (voltage doubling), the current that can be drawn from the transformer is just half the rated value. In multiple-winding transformers where both high voltage and filament windings are included, the volt-ampere rating is the sum of the ratings of each separate winding. As an example, if a transformer is rated at 300 volts rms at 50 ma and it has a filament winding for 5 volts at 2 amp, the total volt-ampere rating is $300 \times 0.050 + 5 \times 2 = 15 + 10$, or 25 watts. If, for some reason, one of the windings is not used, slightly higher power can be drawn from the other winding without damage. Heating is the power-limit-determining factor.

Because the windings of the transformer have finite resistance, a different output voltage will appear for each different value of output current. For example, in the above-mentioned case, the transformer is rated at 300 volts at 50 ma. If twice the rated current were drawn from the transformer (assuming it did not burn up in the meantime because of the increased power loss), the output voltage might drop to 250 volts. From these two sets of data, the actual resistance of the transformer secondary winding may be determined, since the change in current and a corresponding change in voltage are known. The resistance in this case would be 50/0.050, or 1,000 ohms. Now the voltage at 25 ma or any other current can be calculated. (Output voltage at 25 ma is $V_o = 300 - 1,000 \times 0.025 = 300 - 25 = 275$ volts.)

It is important in choosing a transformer to select one, if possible, with proper filament supply windings. Usually transformers have a 5-volt winding for the rectifier filament and a 6.3-volt winding for other tubes.

If a separate filament transformer is used for the rectifier, it must be remembered that the filament of a conventional rectifier tube is usually held at B+ potential and that the insulation from the filament-transformer secondary winding to ground must be sufficient to withstand the B+ voltage.

In some circuits shielding of the transformer is important. Shielding is usually provided by a metallic case that houses the transformer. One of the most vulnerable pieces of equipment to unshielded or poorly shielded power transformers is the cathode-ray tube. Low-level amplifiers are also easily disrupted by unshielded transformers. The theory behind shielding is as follows: A transformer is an electromagnetic device that depends for its operation on the production of strong magnetic fields. Induction between primary and secondary is caused by a field building up and collapsing across the windings of the secondary. In a like manner, currents are induced in any other conductors lying in the transformer field. Shielding tends to localize the field in the vicinity of the transformer by providing a low-reluctance path for the lines of force. But some lines will always escape. There is no perfect shield.

Color Coding. The wire leads from a power transformer are color coded so that the various filament windings and high-voltage windings can be identified. The RMA color code for power transformers is as follows:

Primary leads.................................... Black
High-voltage secondary ends....................... Red
High-voltage secondary center tap................. Red and yellow
Rectifier filament winding......................... Yellow
Rectifier filament winding center tap (if used)........ Yellow and blue
Filament winding No. 1............................ Green
Filament winding No. 1 center tap (if used).......... Green and yellow
Filament winding No. 2............................ Brown
Filament winding No. 2 center tap (if used).......... Brown and yellow

The filament windings are usually readily identifiable because they are much thicker. This is to be expected, since filaments draw currents of the order of amperes, but a few hundred milliamperes is fairly heavy current for a high-voltage winding.

If the leads are not color coded or if the identification of the leads has been lost, the several windings may be tested as follows: Connect a 60-watt lamp in series with the power circuit and the windings, one at a time. The heavy leads indicating low-voltage high-current filament windings will present virtually no impedance to the current, and the lamp will light up strongly. The winding to be connected to the power line will have considerable impedance and will allow the lamp to light up only dimly. The high-voltage windings are still higher in impedance (being made up of many turns of small wire) and may permit so little current to flow to the lamp that it will not light up at all.

Many other factors are often of vital importance in transformer selection. Frequently physical shape and mounting facilities are important. During the war a large number of 400-cps transformers were built, and they will not operate properly on line frequency of 60 cps. If a transformer is designed for operation with the full-wave circuit using two tubes and a center tap, it is possible that the same transformer may not be suitable for operation with a half-wave rectifier circuit. The secondary windings of the full-wave transformer are insulated from the core and shield of the transformer to withstand the peak voltage expected from center tap to either end of the secondary. If this transformer is used with one end of the secondary grounded (connected through the chassis to the shield), the "hot" end of the secondary is actually at a voltage which is twice the design value, and breakdown of the insulation may occur. Many transformers of good design are insulated with a safety factor that will permit their use in such service. However, where dependability is important, the transformers used should be designed for the type of service intended.

Choice of Tubes. The most valuable aid in choosing a tube or tubes for use in a power supply is the wealth of information compiled in the various tube handbooks. Probably the most complete listing of tubes that is readily available in this country is published in the yearly edition of the American Radio Relay League's book "The Radio Amateur's Handbook." This collection has the advantage that it includes tubes of all manufacturers. However, in many cases, sufficient information can be obtained from the various manufacturers' tube manuals. The RCA tube manual is especially complete in this respect. Also, loose-leaf volumes are available (Tung-Sol, RCA and GE) on a subscription basis so that it is easy to make additions as new tubes are developed and as characteristics of others are changed.

With the aid of a tube manual, the selection of a tube for a particular circuit is relatively simple. The manuals provide tube data for various types of circuits and with different types of filters.   All that need be considered, in most cases, is that the tube have ratings equal to or greater than the desired service requires.

The plate-to-plate voltage rating refers to the rms voltage appearing across the entire secondary of the power transformer. Data are also given as to regulation and output voltages for typical filter components.   It goes without saying that the filament ratings, both voltage and current, must be satisfied.

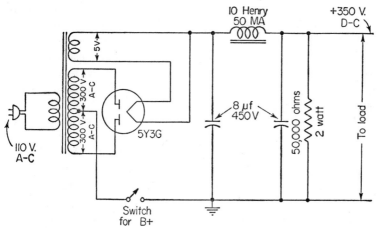

Fig. 7.   Most electronic devices obtain their d-c voltage from a circuit of the type shown, with typical component values.

The peak inverse voltage rating given tubes is an important factor in most cases.   A study of the condenser-input-filter full-wave rectifier circuit of Fig. 7 will show that when one-half of the tube is conducting, the voltage across it is fairly low. However, when the tube current is cut off by the voltage being of the wrong polarity, the full-peak half-secondary voltage and the charge on the input capacitor are in series and impress a voltage across the tube equal to

$$E_{inv} = E_{rms} \times 1.4 \times 2$$

The factor 1.4 converts the rms voltage to peak value.   Actually this value is the maximum voltage that can occur, so the tube must have sufficient insulation in the base and spacing between elements to stand up under that voltage.

Where mercury-vapor tubes are concerned, a peak permissible value of current is given. This is always greater than the maximum-output current rating. It is the current that the tube can stand for short periods of time, such as the current surges that occur when the filter condenser charges when the circuit is first turned on. This peak value is the value used in calculating any series resistance to be used to limit the charging current. The *maximum* current value is the current that can be drawn under normal continuous circumstances.

In the case of mercury-vapor tubes a warm-up period must be allowed before high voltage is applied. This time varies from tube to tube, but most mercury-vapor tubes can safely be operated after a warm-up period (filament current turned on) of a few minutes. Some circuits employ time-delay relays which prevent the application of high voltage until the tubes have had a chance to warm up sufficiently.

Another point to keep in mind is the temperature rating of such tubes as the 866 mercury-vapor rectifiers. Low temperatures increase the voltage that must be applied before the tube conducts current. High temperatures lengthen the filament life somewhat, but when operated at elevated temperatures, the peak inverse rating is reduced. The temperature that is important is the actual temperature of the gas inside the bulb. This can be measured with sufficient accuracy by measuring the temperature of the bulb. For example, a thermocouple can be taped or tied to the bulb when temperature is an important factor and must continuously be measured. Manufacturers' tube data give different sets of operating information for temperatures likely to be encountered in practice.

In designing a power supply, the characteristics of the a-c voltage source must be taken into consideration when sudden voltage surges are likely or possible. A sudden increase in voltage at the terminals of a high-voltage transformer primary may produce many times that voltage increase to the rectifier circuit, and damage to the tubes may result.

Choice of Filter Condensers. The primary factor in filter condenser selection is, of course, the capacitance value of the condenser. The second factor of importance in choosing filter condensers is the voltage rating. This factor is equal in importance to the capacitance rating—if a condenser is rated at too low a voltage, it might break down and render itself and the rest of the circuit useless. Filter condensers are rated in a number of ways. Most common is a working voltage rating, which is usually stamped on the body of the condenser. This rating infers that the condenser will operate in a d-c power supply whose average output voltage is the voltage shown. However, the condenser must be able to withstand considerably more than this value.

Again, in practice, voltage values are a matter of compromise. Most filter condensers are marked in even hundreds of volts, that is, 400, 450, 600, 1,000, 25,000, etc. Any condenser will fit a given application if it has *at least* the calculated capacitance rating and *at least* the proper voltage rating. Where long-term dependability is required, many designers install condensers with voltage ratings many times the anticipated voltage, thus allowing a safety factor. This is common practice in military equipment.

Many of the condensers used in low-power d-c power-supply filters are of the electrolytic type. One important thing to remember in using them is polarity. That is, these condensers must be used in a circuit in which there are direct currents. If the proper operating polarity is not observed, the thin films forming the dieletric may be destroyed. These types of condensers are marked either with plus and/or minus signs, or by a black band that indicates the negative terminal. Often the colors red and black are used to denote positive and negative terminals respectively. In a conventional power supply the negative side of the condenser is connected to the center-tap lead, which is usually grounded to the chassis. So common is the practice of connecting the negative side of filter condensers to the chassis that most metal-can capacitors have the negative electrode connected to the can internally. When the capacitor is mounted on a metal chassis by normal means, the negative side of the capacitor is automatically grounded.

In cases where the negative side of the condenser is not to be connected to ground (as in a negative-voltage power supply such as might be used as a bias supply for the grid of a power tube), care must be taken to see that the negative side is not inadvertantly grounded by connecting the can surrounding the condenser to the grounded chassis. Thus, in certain cases mounting facilities may enter into the selection of capacitors.

Where extremes in temperature and humidity may be encountered, special condensers should always be employed. Several companies make condensers just for such purposes. These units are hermetically sealed so that weather elements cannot damage them. To further enhance reliability, capacitors are available that will actually heal any punctures that occur due to sudden surges of voltage in excess of the voltage rating of the capacitor. These are called metallized capacitors, and they are available at somewhat greater cost.

Selection of Filter Chokes. In selecting filter chokes at least three important factors must be considered. First of all the choke must have sufficient inductance. Next in importance in most cases is the current rating of the choke. The third important factor is the resistance of the choke. These filter chokes are made up of many turns of wire wound on cores made of iron. The long lengths of wire involved have fairly high resistance, and the voltage drop due to the passage of current through the choke causes the output voltage to vary with output current. The chokes with high current ratings will almost always be more expensive than smaller chokes because of the increased weight of wire required. The resistance of the larger chokes, wound with large diameter wire, will be lower than for small chokes, but since the currents involved are larger, the voltage drop across the choke may be no less than that across a low-current high-resistance choke. The inductance contributed by a given choke may vary for different values of current. As more and more current flows through the winding, the core material undergoes a change in electrical characteristics. A core material can carry just so much magnetic energy until it saturates. At this point its magnetic properties are different, and since the inductance of a choke is dependent on the magnetic properties of the core material, the inductance values may change correspondingly.

This property is used to advantage in a special choke designed for use with a choke input filter circuit. Its function is to act as a large value of inductance when a large value is desirable and then to change to a low value of inductance when not so much inductance is required. The inductance thus swings from a high to a low value—thus the term *swinging* choke. When low values of output current are required, the value of inductance of a swinging choke is quite high, but when the current value rises,

the inductance is reduced.   Such chokes are marketed with two
ratings; one for each current value.

Also to be considered in choosing a choke is its insulation.
This is again most important when the choke housing is to be

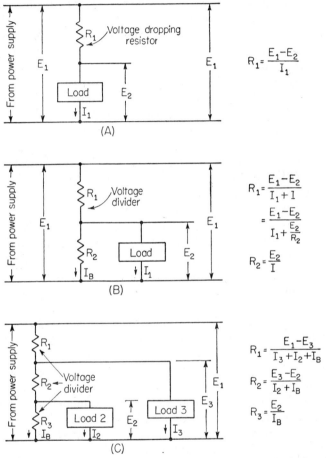

$$R_1 = \frac{E_1 - E_2}{I_1}$$

(A)

$$R_1 = \frac{E_1 - E_2}{I_1 + I}$$

$$= \frac{E_1 - E_2}{I_1 + \frac{E_2}{R_2}}$$

$$R_2 = \frac{E_2}{I}$$

(B)

$$R_1 = \frac{E_1 - E_3}{I_3 + I_2 + I_B}$$

$$R_2 = \frac{E_3 - E_2}{I_2 + I_B}$$

$$R_3 = \frac{E_2}{I_B}$$

(C)

FIG. 8.   When more than one voltage is to be furnished by a single d-c power
supply, voltage-dropping or voltage-dividing resistors may be used.

mounted on a metal chassis to which the negative side of the
power supply has been grounded.   The insulation between the
actual choke winding and the chassis must be sufficient to stand
the same peak-voltage value as the input condenser.

In many cases shielding is an important factor. In circuits where high magnetic fields may be detrimental, good shielding should be used. The reasoning behind this was explained under power-transformer shielding.

Choice of Bleeder Resistors. The method for calculating the required bleeder resistance has already been given. In short, the resistance should be sufficiently low to draw a current equal to one-tenth the total load current. Here again considerable leeway is permissible.

Wire-wound resistors are almost invariably used in this application. The most important rating to be observed is that of power. The resistor dissipates considerable heat, and it should always be located physically as far as possible from any other circuit components where heat may cause damage or malfunctioning.

The minimum power rating for a bleeder resistor may be calculated by Ohm's law.

Voltage Division. Where a single power supply is called upon to furnish several voltages, voltage-*dropping* or voltage-*dividing* resistors are usually incorporated. Examples of each are shown in Fig. 8. In calculating the value of a voltage-dropping resistor, the amount of voltage *to be dropped* is divided by the total current that will be drawn through the dropping resistor. In some applications the simple voltage-dropping resistor has the disadvantage that, when the load stops drawing current, the load voltage immediately rises to the supply-voltage value, unless some preventative measures are taken.

The voltage *divider* system has several advantages, including a degree of regulation of the effect described above. In calculating voltage-divider resistance values, total currents must be used, as shown in Fig. 8*B* and 8*C*. Where numerous voltages are to be taken from a single supply, each resistance must be calculated separately. Also care must be taken to see that resistors of sufficient power rating are used.

ELECTRONIC VOLTAGE REGULATORS

Certain types of electronic equipment require a constant value of d-c voltage to be applied at all times. A simple rectifier circuit is incapable of supplying a steady d-c voltage because of two main factors. First, because of the internal resistance of a rectifier circuit and its filter inductances, any change in external load current will cause a change in the output voltage of the rectifier circuit. Second, if there is a change in the a-c input voltage—and the voltage of most a-c distribution lines is subject to variations—the output voltage of the rectifier system varies accordingly.

Glow-discharge Voltage Regulators. A series of special gas-filled diodes, known as *glow-discharge tubes*, can be used to regulate a d-c voltage across a load, as shown in the circuit of Fig. 9. These tubes contain a gas which ionizes when a sufficiently high voltage is impressed across the tube electrodes. After the gas

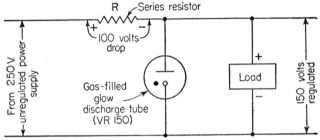

FIG. 9. Glow-discharge voltage-regulator tubes are readily available for holding constant voltages of 75, 90, 105, and 150 volts, where low current requirements exist.

ionizes, the tube conducts current. The amount of current the tube conducts will be just enough to make the voltage drop *across the tube* equal to the rated voltage for that particular tube. And, since the tube and load are connected in parallel, the load will also have that voltage applied to its terminals.

In Fig. 9 the unregulated d-c supply voltage is 250 volts, and a load voltage of 150 volts is desired. Then there must be a drop of 100 volts across R, as shown in the circuit. If the load draws 10 ma of current, then the voltage-regulator tube will draw 10 ma, so that the voltage drop across the series resistance R, which is 5,000 ohms, will be the required 100 volts and the voltage at the load will be 150 volts.

If for some reason the load current should drop to 5 ma, the voltage-regulator-tube current would automatically rise to 15 ma to bring the total current through R back to 20 ma to produce the required voltage drop and load voltage. Without the voltage-regulator tube, if the load current dropped as mentioned above, the voltage drop across R would be less, and the load voltage would rise above the desired 150 volts. If the load should be disconnected entirely (load current zero), the voltage-regulator tube would conduct 20 ma to maintain its 150 volts.

There is, of course, a limit to the amount of current these tubes can draw in order to maintain their constant terminal voltage. For most types currents of the order of 30 to 40 ma can safely be counted on through the voltage-regulator tube. The maximum allowable current for each type can be found in tube handbooks, along with other pertinent informatio pertaining to the tube characteristics.

These glow-discharge tubes are available in several different operating voltage ratings, such as 75, 90, 105, and 150 volts. They may be used in combinations. For instance, two VR 105's may be used in series to regulate a load voltage of 210 volts.

In the tube manuals two voltage ratings for each type are usually given. One is the operating voltage, which is the voltage that will appear across the tube terminals after the gas in the tube is ionized. The other is the starting, or ionizing, voltage, which is the voltage that must be applied to the tube terminals initially to ionize the gas and allow the tube to conduct.

The starting voltage is usually about 20 or 30 per cent higher than the operating voltage, so that actually in a circuit such as Fig. 9 the load voltage will rise to, say, 180 volts when the circuit is first turned on, but when the tube ionizes, the load voltage will return to the desired value.

The main disadvantage of voltage-regulator circuits using glow-discharge tubes as shown, is the fact that the regulated voltages must be some integral sum of the available voltage ratings. As mentioned above, the amount of current the glow-discharge tubes can draw to regulate voltage is limited. Where continuously variable and heavier current ratings are required, more elaborate systems must be incorporated.

Variable-voltage Regulator. A simple voltage-regulator circuit capable of producing regulated voltages over a range of about 100 to 400 volts with fairly good regulating ability is shown in Fig. 10. A similarity between the previous type of circuit and this circuit will be noted in the resistance R, which again is in series with the lead from the unregulated power supply to the load.

The triode shown connected across the load is of the vacuum type, and its internal resistance is determined by the position of the tap on the voltage divider connected across the unregulated supply.   The bias battery shown in the grid lead provides the proper negative grid voltage.   Actually, the grid-to-cathode voltage is the sum of the negative voltage supplied by the battery and the positive voltage appearing between the voltage divider tap and the cathode of the tube.

Assuming the circuit is operating properly and the desired voltage appears at the load (and across the triode), the voltage

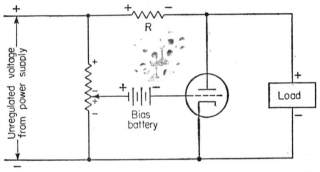

Fig. 10.   Simple variable regulator tube maintains constant load voltage by varying the current through the series resistor R.

drop across R, caused by the flow of tube and load currents, will be equal to the difference between the supply voltage and the load voltage.

If now the value of voltage supplied by the unregulated supply should rise, as it might if the a-c voltage applied to the rectifier increased, the total voltage across the input voltage divider would increase.   A portion of this increase would occur between the grid of the triode and its cathode in such a way that the grid becomes more positive with respect to the cathode.

As the grid goes more positive the tube conducts more current, and the increased current flow through R causes the voltage drop across R to increase.   Therefore, the load voltage is not affected by the change in input voltage.

A somewhat lesser degree of regulation occurs for load current changes.   If the load current drops, the current through R drops, and the voltage at the plate of the triode rises.   This, too, causes more current to flow through the triode, and the increased voltage drop across R as a result of increased regulator-tube current flow brings the load voltage back down.

The circuit of Fig. 11 will be recognized as the same as that of Fig. 10, with the exception of the fact that the bias for the regulating triode, instead of being obtained from a battery, is developed by the flow of tube current through a glow-discharge voltage-regulator tube of the type discussed in the previous section of this chapter.   The results are the same, however.

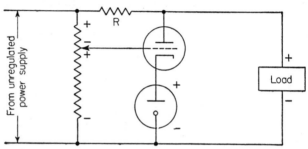

Fig. 11.   Glow-discharge regulator provides fixed reference-voltage bias for the variable-voltage regulator, thus eliminating the bias battery shown in Fig. 10.

Series or Degenerative Voltage Regulators.   The basis of operation of the electronic regulating systems described thus far was, in effect, the connection of a variable-resistance constant-voltage element across the load and varying the current drawn through a fixed series resistor.   Another means by which the output from a rectifier can be regulated is illustrated in Fig. 12A. Here the series resistance used previously has been replaced by a control element which can be adjusted to supply the proper load voltage by changing the amount of series resistance through which the load current must flow.   This form of regulating action may be performed automatically by the circuit shown in Fig. 12B.   The variable resistance element is the plate-cathode resistance of a type 2A3 triode.   Its resistance is varied by the grid voltage, which is in turn determined by the voltage divider connected across the output.   The bias supply voltage is assumed to be constant.   In the actual circuit the battery will be replaced by a glow-discharge tube.

If the load voltage should drop, the voltage between points

A and *B* becomes less, and the grid of the control tube becomes less negative, or more positive, with respect to its cathode.   Thus the voltage drop across the tube decreases, since more tube current can flow, and the output voltage rises to its original value.   This regulating action occurs almost instantaneously.

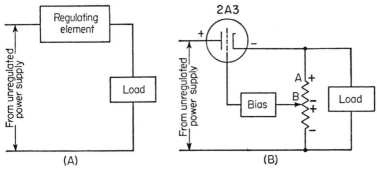

FIG. 12.   Voltage-regulator circuit maintains constant load voltage by varying the resistance of the control tube in series with an unregulated source.

Combination Voltage Regulators.   In the circuit of Fig. 13 the series-control-tube principle is used to regulate the load voltage, and the parallel regulator system is used to supply the regulated bias for the control tube.   This system has the advantage of providing a continuously variable current and, with proper design, as will be described later, the current variations caused by load changes may be of a relatively high order, say several hundred milliamperes.

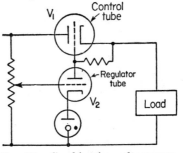

FIG. 13.   Combination voltage regulator provides good regulation over a wide range of voltages.

The series control tube, V_1, acts as a variable series rheostat and the effective resistance it adds to the circuit is determined by the voltage drop between its cathode and grid.   By studying the circuit and figuring the voltage drops and rises between the grid and cathode of the control tube, the operation of this circuit is easily understood.   Triode V_2 is referred to as the regulator tube.   Where good regulation is required, V_2 will be a pentode instead of a triode, since the regulating circuit must have high gain to produce the proper current variations in response to small changes in voltages.

Simple Degenerative Voltage Regulator.   The circuit of an extremely simple but effective voltage-regulated power supply is shown in Fig. 14.   This degenerative circuit compensates changes in output voltage resulting from line-voltage changes and varying load current.

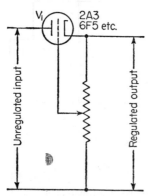 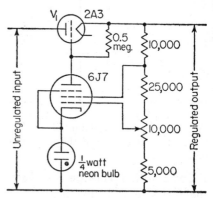

Fig. 14.   Circuit of simple but effective variable-voltage regulator using standard receiving-type tubes as control elements.

Fig. 15.   Practical circuit of a combination voltage regulator with a high degree of regulation.

For instance, an increase in output voltage, as might result from an increase in input voltage or a decrease in load current, increases the current through the cathode resistor across the output terminals.   This causes the bias voltage of V_1 to be increased and the plate current to be decreased.   This action tends to return the output voltage to its original value.

For best regulation, tubes with a high amplification factor are recommended; but this requirement limits the plate current, since tubes with high amplification factors in general have low current ratings.

Where a simple method of manual voltage control is required with not too rigid voltage regulation, tubes such as the 2A3, 6B4, or 6L6 may be used.   The cathode resistor may be replaced by an amplifier having a high amplification factor so that in addition to manual voltage control a high degree of automatic regulation may be obtained.

Triode-pentode Regulator. A type 2A3 triode serves as an automatically adjusted variable series resistor in the positive leg of the full-wave rectifier circuit shown in Fig. 15. The circuit is designed to deliver approximately 180 volts of regulated output for precision electronic circuits.

A type 6J7 sharp-cutoff pentode adjusts the bias on the 2A3 in response to output-voltage variations, and a small neon lamp provides fixed bias for the pentode. For additional protection against line-voltage variations, an automatic voltage regulator can be employed between the power line and the power-transformer primary winding.

Wide-range Voltage Regulator. The voltage regulator shown in Fig. 16 can produce a continuously variable voltage output over a range of from about 3.5 to 300 volts at 300 ma,

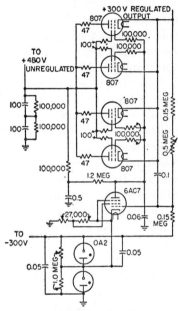

Fig. 16. Wide-range voltage regulator provides constant voltages from a few volts to several hundred volts.

and up to 500 volts with reduced current, as shown by the curve of Fig. 17. An unregulated supply capable of furnishing 480 volts at 300 ma is needed for the regulator-circuit input. The control tube, in this case, consists of four 807 beam-power tubes connected in parallel. A single 6AC7 operated below ground voltage serves as a d-c amplifier that is capable of swinging the grids of the control tubes over the wide range required to maintain constant output voltage.

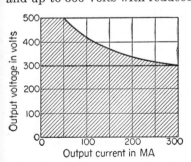

Fig. 17. Output curve for the voltage regulator shown in Fig. 16.

The amount of energy the control tube must dissipate is important in obtaining low-voltage high-current operation. It is calculated by using the highest voltage drop and the largest current through the control tube. In this particular supply the largest voltage across the control tubes is about 470 volts and the greatest current 0.3 amperes. The four 807's must therefore dissipate approximately 140 watts.

Since the highest output voltage occurs when the tube voltage drop is lowest, the internal resistance must be kept low. The double requirements of high heat dissipation and low internal resistance are most economically met by using tubes in parallel rather than using one large tube having sufficiently low internal resistance. The 807 tube will dissipate 35 watts without overheating; thus four 807's in parallel will handle 140 watts and will have only one-fourth the resistance of a single tube.

The low output voltage is obtained by operating the d-c amplifier below ground instead of above ground, as in the circuits previously discussed. When the grid potential of the control tube is highly negative with respect to the cathode, the tube is cut off, limiting the voltage developed between cathode and ground.

To cut off the control tube, the regulating tube acting as a d-c amplifier is operated somewhat below ground. A negative potential for the d-c amplifier is obtained from a power transformer and half-wave rectifier, and regulated with voltage-regulator tubes. Cathode and screen voltages for the 6AC7 are taken from this negative supply, but the plate voltage comes from the unregulated positive supply. The control grid is made variable from -3 to -5 volts with respect to cathode by getting its voltage from a bleeder across the regulated output voltage to the negative supply voltage. The grid potential of the 6AC7 decreases with increasing load on the power supply, thereby cutting off the plate current and raising the plate potential. Since the plate of the 6AC7 and the grids of the 807's are connected together, the 807 grids become more positive and build up the output voltage again. Unloading the power supply has a reverse effect.

The maximum output voltage of this type of supply is the same as the maximum voltage rating of the control tubes, since at low output voltage nearly all of the potential drop in the system is across these tubes. If it is desired to obtain a higher output voltage, a higher unregulated input must be supplied. If it is desired to increase the current rating of the supply, more 807's can be added in parallel, providing the unregulated supply has sufficiently high current rating.

DRY OR METALLIC RECTIFIERS

Much attention has been turned toward dry or metallic rectifiers for converting a-c line power into d-c power for use with electronic circuits. This trend can be traced to several advantages which these types of rectifiers hold over gaseous and high-vacuum rectifiers.

Probably the most obvious advantage is the fact that these rectifiers require no filament power. Hence a great saving can be realized by eliminating filament transformers and their associated complication. Also, having no filament to warm up, these types produce a d-c output almost instantly when the a-c input is applied. In almost every case the metallic equivalent to a tube rectifier represents great savings in space and weight, thereby offering additional advantages for many applications.

Metallic rectifiers are of three basic types: copper oxide, magnesium copper sulfide, and selenium. In each case current flows through the rectifier in one direction only. And in each case the basic unit is a disk of the rectifying material in physical contact with another conductor.

Copper oxide rectifiers are built up from copper disks oxidized on one side with lead washers between or from plates oxidized on both sides. Disks have an output of about 4.5 volts d-c with current ratings of 0.4 amp per sq in.

In the copper sulfide units the basic element is a disk of cupric sulfide in intimate contact with magnesium washers. It will deliver considerable current at low voltages.

Selenium rectifiers are made up of aluminum or steel disks or plates coated with selenium, each disk delivering about 18 volts direct current at current ratings of 0.32 amp per sq in.

Of the several metallic rectifiers available, selenium and copper oxide are by far the most used in commercial applications. These two types have some similar ratings and some very dissimilar ones. In selecting one or the other for some particular application, it is wise to study the characteristics of both.

Disk Construction. Both selenium and copper oxide rectifiers are produced in numerous sizes and shapes; some are rectangular, and some are round or oval. The factor which dictates the area of the disk is the magnitude of the current which it is to carry. The voltage rating depends upon the materials used. For instance, a selenium disk has a voltage rating of around 18 volts, while a copper oxide disk is usually rated in the neighborhood of 8 volts. Where it is desired to operate these units at ratings other than those prescribed for a single element, they may be connected in series or parallel. For instance, selenium units for rectifying 110-volt a-c power consist of several disks (usually

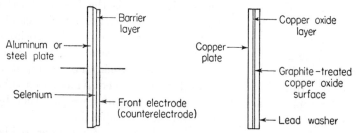

Fɪɢ. 18.   Dry disk rectifiers offer numerous advantages over electron tubes in certain applications.

five) connected in series so that only a portion of the total voltage appears across each.

All copper oxide cells are made with a metal base of copper. Selenium cells, on the other hand, may be made with a base of aluminum, steel, or possibly other metals. The aluminum-base cell weighs about one-fourth as much as steel-base cells of the same ratings. Cross sections of both types of rectifiers are shown in Fig. 18.

Copper oxide cells sometimes consist of a lead washer in contact with a graphite-treated copper oxide surface. With this system the cells are mounted on a bolt, with suitable insulation, to form a "stack," and the proper pressure is applied by tightening a nut on the end of the bolt. The pressure is maintained by means of a tempered spring washer.

Another system makes contact to the oxide surface by plating nickel directly on the surface. The pressure is then maintained by a spring contact washer. Contact to selenium disks is made

:ither by means of a spring washer or by a solid continuous
:ontact.

In either type of stack, cooling is usually provided to increase
,he current-carrying capacity of the unit. Because disk-type

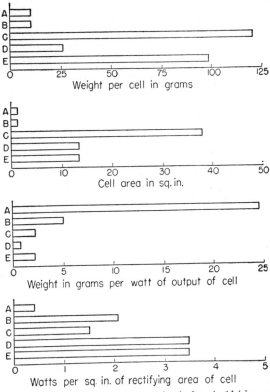

Fig. 19.   Comparative data on a per-cell basis for A, 1½-in. copper oxide
rectifier with no coolling fins; B, same as A but with wide spacing and large
cooling fins; C, copper oxide cell 4⅜ by 5 in., with oxide on both sides,
assembled with normal spacing and operated with cooling fins; D, aluminum-
base selenium cell with natural draft cooling; and, E, same as D except that
E has an iron base instead of an aluminum base.

rectifiers may be affected when exposed to excessive humidity,
corrosive vapors, or fumes, it is customary to treat the assembled
stacks with a varnish or similar protective seal.   For some applications the rectifier units are enclosed in an oil-sealed assembly.

Figure 19 shows some interesting comparative data on a per-disk basis for several different types of selenium and copper oxide rectifiers. Both types are assumed to be connected in a full-wave single-phase bridge circuit and to be operating at normal temperatures. *A* represents a copper oxide disk 1½ in. in diameter used in an assembly with close spacing and no cooling fins. Natural draft cooling is employed. *B* represents a disk

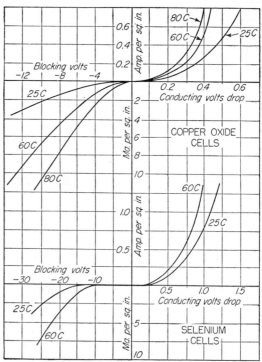

Fıg. 20. Forward and leakage volt-ampere characteristics of copper oxide and selenium cells at different temperatures.

similar to *A* but with wide spacing and large cooling fins. Again, natural draft cooling is employed. *C* is a copper oxide unit 4⅜ by 5 in. with oxide on both sides, assembled with normal spacing and operated with a cooling fan. *D* represents an aluminum-base selenium disk assembled with normal spacing and operated with natural draft cooling. *E* is the same as *D* except that it has an iron base instead of an aluminum base.

Disk Characteristics. To compare the characteristics of these two types of rectifiers, let us examine the curves shown in Fig.

20.   Although the forward resistance of a single copper oxide disk is less than that of the selenium disk, it would be necessary to use two copper oxide units in series to operate at the same voltage as that of one selenium unit.   On that basis, the copper oxide forward resistance may be equal to or greater than that of the selenium disk.

It will be noted that the leakage of both types tends to increase rather rapidly beyond rated voltage.   The leakage also increases

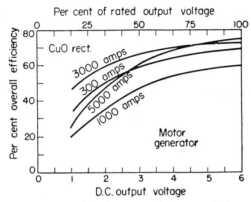

Fɪɢ. 21.   Efficiency curves showing comparison to typical motor-generator set.

rapidly with an increase in temperature.   The importance of staying within these voltage and temperature ratings is apparent.

Rectifier ratings are based on a number of factors, such as the spacing of the individual disks, their size and shape, the size and type of cooling fins, the expected temperature in which they are to be operated, the length of life expected, and the type of application.

The life of a copper oxide rectifier is extremely long—practically limitless.   In fact, the first practical application of a copper oxide rectifier was made in 1924 when such a unit was used to supply direct current to a railroad relay.   That same unit is still in use today.   During the first few months of operation there is some aging, after which the characteristics become stabilized.   Since this aging is partially a function of temperature, it is always desirable to operate the copper oxide rectifier at as low a temperature as possible.   In positioning the stacks on a piece of electronic equipment it is best to choose a place far

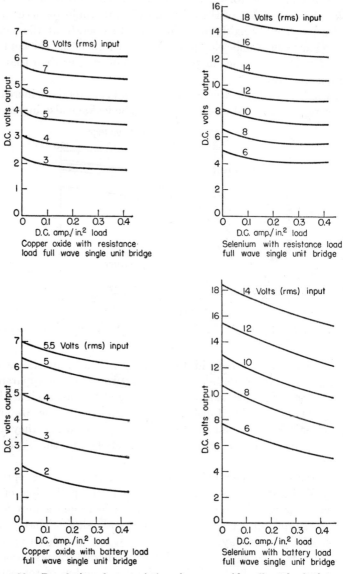

FIG. 22. Regulation characteristics of copper oxide cells and selenium cells on a per-cell basis.

from any heat-producing elements, such as tubes and high-power resistors, and at a place where ventilation will be sufficient.

Efficiency. The efficiency of both copper oxide and selenium stacks does not vary greatly with wide variations in load, particularly from 25 per cent load rating to full load. An interesting comparison between the efficiency of copper oxide electroplating rectifiers and a motor-generator plating setup can be drawn from the efficiency curves given in Fig. 21. This is a low-voltage high-current application, and the curves for the rectifier performance cover the complete unit, including transformer and controls. The values for both setups are somewhat similar from three-fourths to full load, but below three-fourths load it will be noticed that the motor-generator combination falls off rapidly in efficiency, while the rectifier efficiency stays fairly high at reduced loads.

Both selenium and copper oxide stacks are rated on the basis of their stabilized condition. Thus when new, their d-c output voltage may be somewhat higher for a given input voltage than when they have completely aged. Normally where this d-c voltage variation with aging would be undesirable, the transformer used to provide the a-c input voltage to the rectifier should have taps or otherwise be variable to allow adjustment for the desired output.

The regulation characteristics of both types of rectifiers are shown in Fig. 22.

Operation. The operating temperature of selenium rectifiers is largely limited by the melting point of the low-temperature alloy called the *counterelectrode*. This counterelectrode is deposited on the surface of the rectifier to serve as a current-collecting electrode. The melting point of this alloy may be in the neighborhood of 100°C, and to provide a factor of safety, most ratings call for a limit of 75°C.

Copper oxide rectifiers must be operated at much lower temperatures. The temperature rise of a copper oxide unit is usually held to about 12°C. Both copper oxide and selenium rectifiers have temperature ratings based on an ambient temperature of 35°C for full rated output. For higher operating temperatures it is necessary to reduce the rating of both types of rectifiers according to the curves given in Fig. 23. To obtain increased output ratings it is sometimes customary, particularly with the copper oxide types, to employ fan cooling, thus maintaining lower operating temperatures.

Overload Effects. There are many applications for rectifiers in which the power demand is for short intervals of time, followed by long off periods. For this type of operation it is possible to operate metallic rectifiers at higher current densities than would be used for continuous operation. With the higher permissible temperature rise of the selenium rectifier it is possible to operate it for longer increased output intervals than with the copper

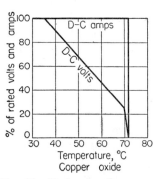 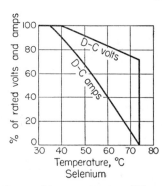

FIG. 23.   Reduced rating curves for unusual temperature conditions.

oxide units. However, with the selenium units it is not permissible to increase the a-c applied voltage above the normal rating, with the result that the higher current densities mean less d-c output voltage.

Copper oxide rectifiers, on the other hand, can be operated at higher than normal continuous-rated a-c voltage, with the result that the d-c voltage can be increased, and in turn the power output can be increased proportionally for intermittent operating conditions.

An example of intermittent operation is the use of a rectifier in circuit-breaker operation, where it may be called upon for only a few seconds duty cycle at a time. Manufacturers' data should always be referred to when selecting a rectifier for intermittent operation.

Stand-by Service. For applications where the rectifier is used only occasionally, between long stand-by periods, the copper oxide rectifier offers advantages. It does not undergo any physical changes, so that rated output voltage can be expected as soon as a-c power is supplied to the circuit, regardless of the length of stand-by time.

The selenium rectifier, on the other hand, undergoes a change when no a-c power is applied. The accompanying decrease in the leakage resistance of the rectifier, or a reduction in the ratio between the forward and the leakage resistance, results in a relatively low-resistance path to the a-c input terminals. Usually no apparent harm is done to the selenium rectifier by allowing it to remain inoperative, but before loading it again at rated voltage, a selenium stack should be fed first a low a-c voltage and then a gradually increasing voltage until full a-c voltage is applied. Reforming takes place quite rapidly with the leakage current rather high at the beginning and falling off rapidly as the voltage reforms the selenium cell.

Typical Circuits. Figure 24 shows the circuit of a selenium stack being used as a half-wave rectifier to provide a d-c voltage from the a-c distribution lines. This type of circuit is frequently found in small radios and pieces of electronic equipment where only 100 or so volts is required. It differs from the conventional thermionic rectifier tube circuit mainly in the absence of a rectifier filament connection and in the addition of a series protective resistance R_1.

The stack terminal marked "K" (for cathode) or $+$ should be connected to the positive side of the electrolytic filter capacitors and to the B$+$ line. This terminal, if not marked, can be identified by the crystalline appearance of the alloy. Series resistance R_1, a minimum of 5 to 22 ohms, is placed in the circuit to protect the stack and capacitors against the effects of current surges during operation and to limit the value of rms rectifier current to not more than 2.5 times the rated d-c output current. The minimum value of R_1 depends on the load current rating of the stack, being 22 ohms for 100 ma and below, 15 ohms for 100 to 200 ma ratings, and 5 ohms for above 250 ma.

In this half-wave circuit the physical condition of the selenium rectifier and that of the input filter capacitor are somewhat interdependent. For instance, if the input filter capacitor is leaky, the excessive current through the capacitor may cause the stack to overheat. If the rectifier is not sufficiently formed, the electrolytic capacitor may in turn overheat and possibly decrease in capacitance because of internal changes.

Typical values for the filter capacitors are 40 to 100 μf, but very large input capacitors should not be used without increased values of limiting resistance, since the charging current would be very high and would tend to overheat the selenium rectifier, accelerating aging or possibly causing failure.

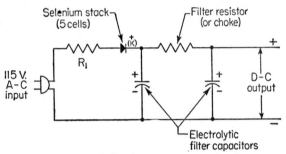

FIG. 24. Basic selenium-rectifier power-supply circuit provides approximately 100 volts d-c output. Series resistor R_1 limits the initial current.

The selenium rectifier circuits shown in Fig. 25 are voltage-doubler circuits. Here again the series protective resistor is important and should have a value of from 25 to 50 ohms depending on the input-capacitor value and the load conditions.

Most commercially available selenium stacks are rated for service in circuits such as these. They are rated to withstand a

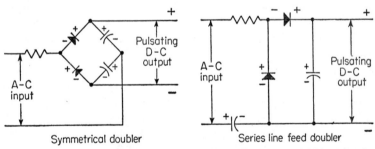

FIG. 25. Selenium rectifiers may be used in the voltage-doubler circuits shown to produce approximately twice the voltage of the line.

maximum of 380 volts peak inverse voltage and 900 volts across the insulation between each terminal and the mounting fixtures. In all cases the applied a-c voltage should not exceed 130 volts rms.

The copper oxide rectifier usually consists of four units connected in bridge form for full-wave rectification. A typical circuit is shown in Fig. 26 along with a drawing showing a simple physical layout for such a rectifier. The value of current available from copper oxide circuits is practically limitless. Units have been designed for currents as low as a few microamperes and up to tens of thousands of amperes for plating applications. However, the fundamental circuit usually remains the same with the size and number of disks or plates changing to meet the current and voltage requirements.

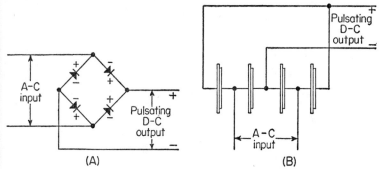

(A)   (B)

Fig. 26.   Bridge circuits are frequently used in conjunction with dry disk rectifiers.

General Comparisons.[1]   The copper sulfide rectifier is lowest in first cost, life, and efficiency, and best in regulation. The selenium rectifier has the smallest size and weight for a given rating and better efficiency and longer life than the copper sulfide. The copper oxide rectifier has the longest life, is equal in efficiency to selenium, is best for instrument use and for intermittent load, and does not unform during idle periods.

HIGH-VOLTAGE POWER SUPPLIES

The need for very high voltages at comparatively low current values is often found in industry. Some typical applications are dust precipitation, electronic spraying, nuclear instrumentation, and cathode-ray oscillography. Cases may be found where voltages as high as 50,000 might be required, but the current need be no more than 1 ma or so.

There are several general types of high-voltage supplies, all

[1] "Radio Engineering Handbook," 4th ed., McGraw-Hill Book Company, Inc., New York, 1950.

performing a similar function, that is, converting readily available power into the desired high-voltage low-current d-c power.

60-cycle Power Supply. The 60-cycle power supply is relatively simple and straightforward. As shown in Fig. 27, it consists of a transformer with a high voltage secondary, a winding for the filament of the rectifier, and, of course, the rectifier tube itself. The tube is connected in a half-wave circuit, and the filter components indicated in the diagram are usually adequate for most applications.

The main disadvantage of the 60-cycle system is its weight, since iron-core transformers are almost always used at 60 cycles. Also, because of the high ripple content of the output of the

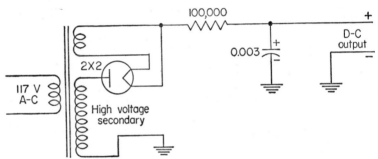

Fig. 27. The simplest form of high-voltage supply is the 60-cycle version with appropriate high-voltage step-up transformer, rectifier, and filter.

rectifier and the relatively low frequency of the ripple, large filter components must be used. And where a power line supply is not available, the supply is useless unless some kind of inverter is used in conjunction with a battery supply.

R-F High-voltage Supplies. Another type of high-voltage low-current d-c power source is the radio frequency, or r-f, supply. In this case an r-f oscillator feeds the primary of a special transformer which steps up the oscillator output to the desired voltage value for the rectifier.

A typical high-voltage r-f power supply circuit is shown in Fig. 28. This circuit uses a small beam-power tube (6V6) as an oscillator, the output of which is coupled to the primary of an air-core step-up transformer. This primary winding is the inductance of the tuned circuit of the oscillator.

A well-insulated two- to four-turn loop is usually included on the step-up transformer for the purpose of providing current for the high voltage rectifier (V_2) filament. The tube usually used in this type of circuit, the 1B3GT, requires only ¼ watt of filament power.

Such power supplies may be built to supply voltages as high as 50,000 volts, with good regulation. Since they operate in the range of 50 to 500 kc, the filter capacitors used need only be a few thousandths of a microfarad, with appropriate voltage

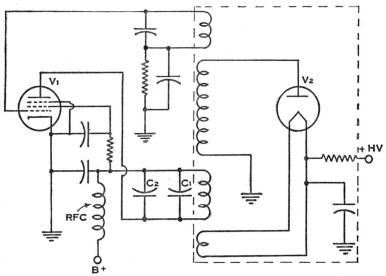

Fig. 28. The r-f high-voltage power supply has the advantage of light weight and light filter requirements, but it requires shielding and fairly critical adjustment and design.

ratings. A series resistance is used instead of the filter choke incorporated in heavier current filters, since, with the low current involved, the d-c voltage drop across the filter resistance is quite low.

The main disadvantage of this type of supply is the fact that it must be carefully shielded or the strong r-f field set up around the step-up transformer will be radiated and might cause interference to television and other electronic equipment in the vicinity. Also, as may be seen from a comparison of the circuit diagrams of typical r-f and 60-cycle systems, there are more components in the r-f supply that might fail.

Radio-frequency supplies are exceptionally light in weight, and they effect a saving in space required for filter capacitors. They can be operated from any power source capable of supplying the required voltages to the r-f oscillator. The efficiency of a typical power supply with a well-designed step-up transformer is fairly good.

Pulse-type High-voltage Supplies. The pulse-type high-voltage supply is not found so often in industrial applications as the two previously mentioned sources. Its most common use is in television receivers, where high-current pulses in the sweep circuits may be transformed into high-voltage pulses. A typical circuit of a pulse-type supply would include a blocking oscillator so arranged that its pulse output is fed to the primary of a step-up transformer. This is very similar to the r-f supply, but the frequency of operation is usually lower, being determined by the blocking-oscillator transformer and oscillator voltages. Extremely sharp pulses exist in the plate circuit of a blocking oscillator. Thus extremely high secondary voltages can be expected from the output of the step-up transformer. These pulses may be rectified and filtered, but attention must be given to the fact that the high voltage is derived from very steep pulses, and accordingly adequate filtering is a bit more difficult.

Charged Capacitor Supplies. If we apply a d-c voltage across the two plates of a capacitor and then remove the voltage source, a charge will remain fixed on the two plates and will diminish only slowly, the rate depending on the leakage resistance of the capacitor and the leakage of any external connections.

One high-voltage power supply system takes advantage of this effect. Let us assume that 1,000 volts d-c is desired, and a source of, say, 200 volts d-c is readily available. If we charge five capacitors in parallel with the low voltage, as shown in Fig. 29, then each one will have a charge of approximately 200 volts. Now, if we remove the charging voltage and connect the capacitors in series, the voltage across the series combination will be equal to the sum of the voltages across each capacitor, or in this case, 1,000 volts. Of course, when a load is applied to the series combination, the voltage drops very quickly, but when only low current values are needed, this system is useful. The capacitors are usually arranged with a switching system so that they are periodically charged in parallel and discharged in series. Then, with suitable filtering, the output of the system becomes a d-c voltage with a ripple content depending on the size and type of filter employed.

Each capacitor chosen for this type of service should have a voltage rating somewhat higher than the low voltage to which it is to be subjected during charging. The capacitance should be as large as possible, because better regulation will be obtained, since a larger capacitor loses its charge more slowly than a small one.

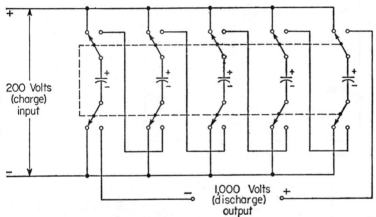

FIG. 29. High voltage may be derived by charging a series of capacitors in parallel and discharging them in series so that their charges add.

900 Volts—0 to 4 Microamperes. Figure 30 shows the circuit of an extremely simple high-voltage power supply useful in portable applications where approximately 900 volts are required, with load currents in the neighborhood of a few microamperes. The circuit consists of a pulse-type oscillator coupled to a miniature rectifier.

The frequency of operation is determined (1) by the time constant of the RC combination in the neon-tube supply circuit, (2) by the particular characteristics of the plate circuit choke, and (3) to a lesser extent by the supply voltage. This supply voltage may be furnished by two 67½-volt batteries.

The choke used in the original circuit[1] is a UTC 0-5 hearing-

[1] Alexander Thomas, High Voltage Supplies for G-M Counters, *Electronics*, December, 1948, p. 100.

aid transformer with the primary and secondary connected in series. The NE-2 neon bulb may be replaced by a NE-51, which is a based type of identical characteristics. In operation the neon bulb glows sufficiently to be used as a pilot light to indicate that the supply is operating.

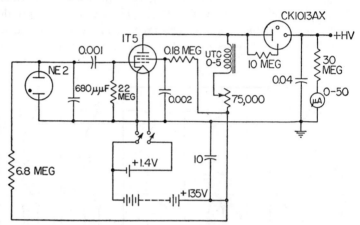

FIG. 30. Simple pulse-type high-voltage power supply for portable equipment.

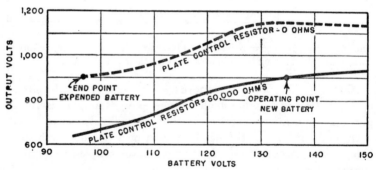

FIG. 31. Output curves for the supply shown in Fig. 30 show the effects of an aging battery.

A 0.04-μf capacitor, selected for the smoothing filter capacitor, is low in cost and convenient in size. With the circuit delivering 900 volts the ripple voltage using the filter shown will be of the order of 0.3 volt. A circuit similar to the one shown but using a miniature type 1U4 tube and higher plate and screen voltages is capable of delivering 1,900 volts.

A set of curves showing how the output voltage varies as the batteries age is shown in Fig. 31.

Adjustable Output 60-cycle Supply.   The high-voltage supply shown in Fig. 32 has an output adjustable from 0 to 30,000 volts, and currents as high as 0.5 ma can be drawn with approximately 5 per cent ripple at full load.   The high voltage output is available in either polarity with respect to ground simply by changing a few connections.

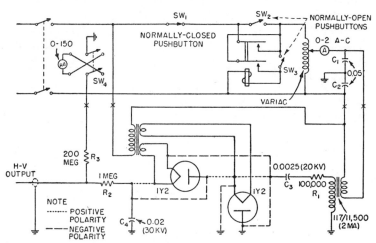

FIG. 32.   Reversible 60-cycle high-voltage supply with a continuously variable output.

Continuous voltage control is effected by use of a filament transformer that energizes the rectifier filaments continuously and a Variac by means of which the input voltage to the high-voltage transformer can be varied smoothly from zero to maximum.

A voltage-doubler circuit is used.   The peak voltages generated by or developed across the various components are indicated in the diagram.   This particular voltage doubler permits certain reductions in component ratings.[1]

In the original model[2] special open-core transformers were used

[1] Waidelich and Gleason, *Proceedings of the Institute of Radio Engineers*, December, 1942,

[2] Victor Wouk, Portable High-voltage Power Supply, *Electronics*, July, 1949, p. 108.

but any transformers with the required ratings can be employed instead.

As shown in the diagram, the supply can be divided into two parts, a console for remote operation and the supply itself. For this arrangement the meter, switching, and adjustment facilities are mounted on the remote console.

To avoid corona, sharp points at high voltage are avoided. Where they cannot be avoided, these regions should be surrounded by anticorona shields. This is particularly important around the filaments of the rectifier tubes.

Converting Direct Current into Alternating Current Using a Thyratron. The circuit of an electronic converter that supplies

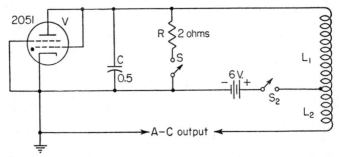

Fig. 33.   Simple inverter circuit converts 6-volt d-c power to 110-volt a-c for portable use.

alternating current for powering a-c equipment from a d-c source is shown in Fig. 33. It operates from a 6-volt battery and contains no moving parts. It incorporates a type 2051 thyratron and a small output transformer, only the secondary of which is used. L_1 is the 0- to 8-ohm tap, while L_2 is the 8- to 500-ohm tap. Of course the output of the transformer may be rectified and filtered to provide a high d-c voltage from a low d-c voltage. The unit described has been used to run a regular radio receiver with a 6V6 output tube, and there is no noise or hum present in the output.

With the switch S_2 closed and S depressed momentarily, current will flow from the battery through L_1 and R. The current is limited in value by R and the resistance of the inductive winding. When S is opened and left in that position, an induced voltage appears across V and C. This voltage will be in series with the battery voltage on each alternate cycle.

When both of these voltages are in a positive direction with respect to the anode of the tube, the gas will ionize and the tube will conduct current in that one direction. The gas-filled tube can be considered as a switch of zero resistance in this direction. Therefore both the induced current and the current from the battery will flow in the circuit.

When the induced voltage plus the battery voltage falls to about 12 volts, the tube will extinguish and effectively open the circuit. With the circuit open, the field in L_1 will collapse, the induced voltage will ionize the tube, and the cycle will repeat until S_2 is opened. The entire circuit is analogous to that of an ordinary automobile ignition circuit, with the exception that the breaker points are replaced by the gas-filled tube.

D-C Power for Portable Equipment. Batteries may be used when d-c power is needed at a location remote from a-c power. High operating voltages can be obtained through the use of batteries in series, but this method is expensive, and the batteries are heavy and bulky and must be replaced very often. However, these disadvantages are often overlooked in the interest of portability, since a dry battery can be operated in any position and its operation is quite dependable.

Storage batteries are capable of furnishing considerably more power than dry batteries. In addition, they can be recharged. However, rechargeable batteries usually give relatively low voltages, and in order to use them with electronic equipment requiring relatively high plate voltages, means must be provided for stepping up the battery voltage. A transformer cannot be used directly to step up a d-c voltage, because a transformer depends on a changing voltage and a changing current for its operation. However, through the use of a vibrating switch, the d-c current from a battery can be caused to flow through a transformer primary, first in one direction and then in the other direction. The voltage appearing at the secondary terminals is not sinusoidal, but it is suitable for conversion into direct-current by rectification to obtain a d-c voltage. There are two general types of vibrator circuits. Both are illustrated in Fig. 34. The voltage appearing at the secondary of the transformer must be rectified to be presented as d-c to the filter circuit. In Fig. 34A rectification is accomplished by a dual-diode rectifier tube. In B, however, advantage is taken of the fact that the secondary voltage varies in time synchronism with the vibrator reed that reverses the direction of current in the primary.   An additional pair of contacts on this reed serve to rectify the secondary voltage by making the current flow through the load in only one direction.   The "synchronous" vibrator is somewhat more complex than the nonsynchronous type and requires fairly critical adjustment.   The nonsynchronous vibrator requires a tube or some other form of rectifying element.

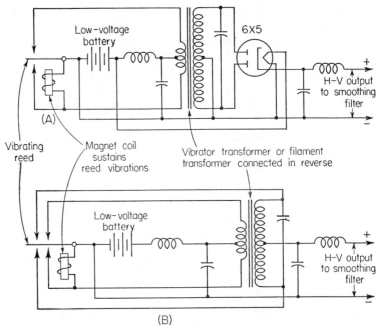

FIG. 34.   Vibrator circuits of the type shown are usually used for powering mobile communications equipment.

The chokes and condensers used in the vibrator circuit help to reduce the external radio interference caused by the constant making and breaking of the high current involved.   The value of the condensers is best determined by experiment, and can be found by starting with something in the neighborhood of 0.005 μf and increasing the size until the least interference is noticed.   The optimum filter condenser can be determined even more accurately by the use of an oscilloscope to check for irregularities in output waveform.

If vibrator power supplies are to be used in conjunction with radio receiving equipment, care must be taken to see that all power supply wiring is shielded and that r-f chokes are placed in series with output leads which can not be shielded.   The voltage surges create large amounts of noise throughout a large part of the radio spectrum, and will cause interference on almost any signal.   The degree of filtering and shielding required to eliminate this racket is best determined by experiment under actual operating conditions.

Voltage-multiplier Circuits.   Figure 35 shows a series of circuits capable of producing d-c output voltages greater than the peak values of the impressed a-c input voltages.   In each case a capacitor is first charged and then allowed to discharge through the load in series with another voltage, the total effect being additive.

In Fig. 35A let us assume that the first half of the impressed a-c cycle makes terminal A positive with respect to B. C_1 charges through V_1, but V_2 is cut off, because its cathode is positive with respect to its anode.   When the input voltage reverses, V_1 is cut off.   But the output voltage is equal to the instantaneous input voltage plus the voltage across C_1, since both voltages are in series.   Thus electrons flow through the load in the direction indicated, under the compulsion of twice the peak voltage of the a-c input voltage.   This current flow occurs during only half the cycle, but C_2 stores up a charge during that half cycle and delivers it to the load during the other half. A suitable filter will iron out any fluctuations.

The circuit shown in Fig. 35B is another voltage doubler, which provides full-wave rectification, instead of half-wave as in the case of Fig. 35A.   The main disadvantage of this type of circuit is the fact that neither side of the d-c circuit may be connected to the a-c line.   This is a handicap when the input a-c voltage is supplied directly from the a-c distribution lines, because, if the chassis of the power supply and its equipment is connected to B—, as is the usual practice, the chassis will be "hot" with respect to any external grounds such as water pipes and the like.   An isolation transformer placed between the line and the doubler circuit will remove this hazard.

Another doubler circuit is shown in Fig. 35C.   This circuit is recommended where the a-c input is in the form of sharp pulses

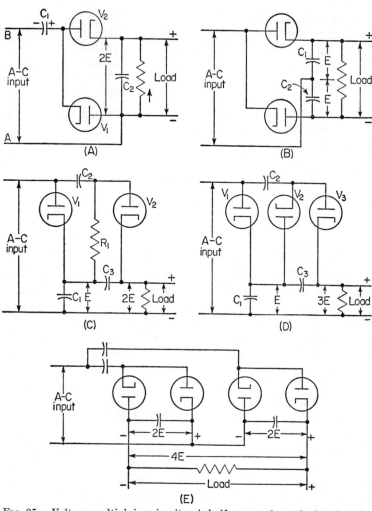

FIG. 35. Voltage-multiplying circuits: A, half-wave voltage doubler has the advantage of permitting grounding of the input line and the output negative terminal. B, full-wave voltage doubler. C, alternate voltage doubler. D, voltage tripler. E, voltage quadrupler.

rather than sinusoidal waves, a situation that is becoming more and more common, since pulse-type power supplies are used in almost all modern television sets, and voltage-doubler circuits are usually employed where voltages of the order of 10,000 volts or more are required. In this circuit (Fig. 35C) the pulse input appears across V_1 and C_1 charging C_1 nearly to the peak-to-peak pulse voltage. Condenser C_2 is charged through R_1 to the same value as C_1. Its charge adds in series with the applied voltage and the sum is rectified by V_2, thereby charging C_3. Nearly twice the pulse input voltage appears at the cathode of V_2.

Figure 35D illustrates a typical tripler circuit which is more suitable for a-c voltages of the more symmetrical type, that is, the sinusoidal or semisinusoidal voltages produced in 60-cycle supplies or r-f supplies. In operation, as the plate of V_1 swings positive, V_1 conducts, charging C_1. On the negative swing V_1 is nonconducting and C_2 is charged through V_2 by the amount of charge on C_1 plus the negative peak voltage. On the next positive swing V_3 conducts, charging C_3 by the amount of the charge on C_2 plus the peak positive voltage swing, while at the same time C_1 is again charged to its original value.

If the rectifier voltage between the cathode of V_1 and ground were E volts, then a voltage three times E would appear across the output terminals, resulting from E across C_1 in series with $2E$ from C_3. It should be observed that C_2 and C_3 must be rated to stand twice the peak voltage of the rectifier, while the rating of C_1 need only be equal to that of the peak a-c voltage.

A voltage quadrupler is shown in Fig. 35E. It consists essentially of two half-wave doublers in series. The idea of connecting doublers in series is not limited to quadrupling. Higher multiplications may be made in applications where the inherent poor regulation can be tolerated.

The doubler condensers shown should be of relatively high capacitance, at least 16 μf and preferably more. Voltage ratings in terms of input voltage E are indicated on the diagrams.

Voltage-multiplier circuits have certain limitations which prevent their use in many applications. Most important is the poor regulation and inability to supply large amounts of current. To get full output voltage from a type of supply that depends on charging condensers in a chainlike fashion, the condensers must store quite large quantities of energy. Also, where the B− side of the rectifier cannot be connected to chassis ground, a definite hazard exists, and in many cases where equipment may not always be handled by experienced personnel, this factor may present an extremely serious danger.

REFERENCES

Beranek, L. L., Applications of Copper Oxide Rectifiers, *Electronics*, July, 1939, p. 15.

Bousquet, A. G., Improving Regulator Performances, *Electronics*, July, 1938, p. 26.

Chin, P. T., Gaseous Rectifier Circuits, *Electronics*, April, 1945, p. 138.

The Copper Oxide Rectifier, *Electrical Engineering*, November, 1948, p. 1051.

DeBlieux, E. V., High-voltage Rectifier Circuits, *General Electric Review*, February, 1948, p. 22.

Falls, Warren H., Rectifiers: Selenium and Copper Oxide, *General Electric Review*, February, 1947, p. 34.

Harris, L. D., Electronic Voltage Regulator, *Electronics*, January, 1946, p. 150.

Howells, P. W., A Special-purpose Power Supply, *General Electric Review*, June, 1947, p. 34.

Klemperer, Hans, Dielectric Igniters for Mercury Pool Cathode Tubes, *Electronics*, November, 1941, p. 28.

Koonts, Paul, and Earle Dilatush, Voltage-regulated Power Supplies, *Electronics*, July, 1947, p. 119.

Lee, Reuben, Solving a Rectifier Problem, *Electronics*, April, 1938, p. 39.

Mautner, L., Voltage Regulated Power Supplies, *Electrical Engineering*, September, 1947, p. 894.

Mentzer, J. R., Multi-voltage Regulated Power Supplies, *Electronics*, September, 1946, p. 132.

Panofsky, W. K. H., Graphical Solution of Rectifier Circuits, *Electronics*, April, 1941, p. 42.

Reed, F. L., Metallic Rectifiers for Motor Power Supply, *Electrical Engineering*, August, 1947, p. 763.

Schmidt, A., Jr., Operating D-C Motors from Controlled Rectifiers, *Electrical Engineering*, June, 1948, p. 516.

Scott, H. J., Rectifier Filter Design, *Electronics*, June, 1938, p. 28.

Strong, W. F., Power Supplies for Electrostatic Precipitation, *Electrical Engineering*, March, 1949, p. 229.

Stout, M. B., Behavior of Half-wave Rectifiers, *Electronics*, September, 1939, p. 32.

Taylor, S. G., Ballast Tubes as Automatic Voltage Regulators, *Electronics*, January, 1942, p. 26.

Waidelich, D. L., Analysis of Full-wave Rectifier and Capacitor Input Filter, *Electronics*, September, 1947, p. 120.

Waidelich, D. L., Voltage Multiplier Circuits, *Electronics*, May, 1941, p. 28.

Wallis, C. M., Half-wave Gas Rectifier Circuits, *Electronics*, October, 1938, p. 12.

CHAPTER 5

LIGHT-SENSITIVE TUBES

Thermionic electron tubes have heat as their immediate source of energy—a cathode is heated by an electric current, and when the proper temperature is attained, electrons are emitted. In another large class of electron tubes a cathode is radiated with a beam of light. The cathode thus illuminated emits electrons. Here again the electrons, after escaping from the cathode, are directed toward a positively charged plate and upon arrival there give up a quantity of electricity. The summation of the arrival of these carriers per unit of time constitutes an electric current measurable in amperes or fractions of an ampere.

There are several classifications of light-sensitive tubes, as indicated below. The terminology used in dealing with this group of tubes is exceedingly loose. In popular language the light-sensitive tube is an electric eye, but it is far from that. It will be seen later that the photocell seldom sees as the human eye sees.

For years the three widely used types of light-sensitive tubes were called indiscriminately *photocells*, *photoelectric cells*, or *phototubes*. Recently, however, the word phototube has become associated with tubes of the photoemissive type, and when reference is made to either of the other two types, they are specifically described and listed under the general heading of photocells.

Value of Light-sensitive Tubes. From a practical viewpoint the light-sensitive tube provides the industrial engineer with another element or medium of control. Other electron tubes secure their impulse largely from variable electrical quantities; the phototube enables an engineer to use a beam of light and places at his disposal the vast science of optics. Thus the phototube adds one more fundamental property of nature, that of light, to the repertoire of the control engineer. The microphone and amplifier make it possible to use sound for purposes other than communication; the phototube makes it possible to employ light for purposes other than illumination. The beam of light now controlling many processes, many of them complex, requires no space and when not in use may be simply put out of the way by turning off the light source; it is instantaneous in its action, having no inertia; it is inexpensive to maintain, and has two degrees of control—magnitude and wavelength.

Types of Light-sensitive Tubes. The general types of electron tubes utilizing a beam of light to control electrical energy are as follows:

1. *Photoemissive,* in which a beam of light causes a surface to emit electrons. An analogy is the thermionic tube in which a heated cathode emits electrons. In the latter case heat energy is converted into electrical energy (at very low efficiency); in the former case light energy is converted into electrical energy (also at very low efficiency). These electrons are attracted toward a plate maintained at a positive potential by an external source of voltage; this electron-carried electric current is amplified (usually) by means of thermionic tubes which, in turn, control relays or perform other useful functions involving power.

2. *Photoconductive,* in which the resistance of a material to the flow of current is materially altered when it is illuminated by a beam of light. Selenium is an example of this type of light-sensitive material. An analogy is a conductor whose electrical resistance varies with temperature.

3. *Photovoltaic,* in which a passage of electrons from one material to another is accelerated by illuminating the surface with light. Like phototubes, these devices act as rectifiers, the electrons passing more readily from one plate or surface to the other than they do in the opposite direction. The voltage developed by these surfaces is independent of the area illuminated; but the power output varies as the area. The analog is a wet or dry cell or chemical battery in which current flows from one electrode to another and in which the terminal voltage is independent of the area of the active material. The Weston Photronic cell, widely used in light intensity meters, and the General Electric copper oxide cell, similarly employed, are typical (see Chap. 2 for typical data).

Photoelectricity. The light-sensitive cell is about 65 years old. The fact that certain surfaces emitted electrons when illuminated with ultraviolet light has been known since the time of Hertz, 1887, but most of the rapid development of the photo-tube into a rugged, uniform, long-lived product has taken place within the last 15 years.

The phototube is not by itself able to do much. The currents taken from it are so feeble (millionths of an ampere) that usually they must be amplified before being put to use. Although photo-tubes have increased in sensitivity so that they are ten times better than those of 15 years ago, the maximum current is only a matter of about 60 μa when a tube receives about 1 lumen of light, about what an average tube gets from a 50-watt lamp at a distance of 6 in.

The meagerness of the photocurrents is due to the small amount of energy that is absorbed by the light-sensitive surface from the beam of light. A cathode of a thermionic tube may be heated by several watts of energy, much more than is absorbed by the phototube cathode. Thus the former emits electrons to the extent of milliamperes or even amperes while the latter emits only microamperes. Even if the currents obtainable from a phototube are so small, the tube is of tremendous importance. It is a light valve of incredible speed and remarkable accuracy. By means of intermediate apparatus it will control vast quantities of power, although the actual energy derived from the beam of light directed on it may be infinitely small.

The laws of photoelectricity emission were derived by Einstein in 1905 and have proved to be of vast importance to physicists in setting up modern atomic and quantum theories. These laws state simply that (1) the number of electrons emitted from a cathode surface depends exactly and linearly upon the intensity of light falling on that cathode and (2) the velocity of the electrons thus emitted depends only upon the surface of the cathode and the wavelength of the light but not upon its intensity or any other factor. This phenomenon can be explained only by the quantum theory; in fact the photoelectric effect forms one of the foundations of this theory.

Fundamentals of the Phototube. A phototube consists essentially of two elements in an exhausted container in which there may or may not be an inert gas at a low pressure. The cathode has the property of emitting electrons under the action of light. The most common materials used for this purpose are the alkali metals.

A potential of 15 or 20 volts on the anode is sufficient to attract all the electrons that are emitted; an increase of anode voltage above this value will cause little or no increase in current in the high-vacuum tube. When a low pressure of an inert gas is present, however, the original current is increased by the ionization of the gas by as much as ten times. The amount of ionization increases rapidly as the anode voltage is increased until a point is reached at which the tube breaks into a glow discharge. Since this glow discharge will destroy the tube, it is always necessary to limit the anode voltage to well below this value and to use a resistance in series with the cathode for an additional protection.

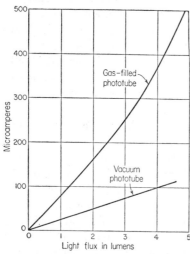

FIG. 1. These curves show the principal differences between gas and vacuum phototubes. Gas tubes produce greater current differentials for a given illumination change, but vacuum-tube changes are more linear.

Phototubes, therefore, are classified as vacuum or gas-filled. In general, the vacuum types are the most stable in their characteristics and give an output directly proportional to the light flux incident on the cathode. The gas-filled tubes have the advantage of greater output per unit light flux due to the ionization of the gas.

Gas versus Vacuum Tubes. The vacuum tube has a linear relation between current and light intensity; the gaseous tube does not have this linear relation. This is illustrated in the curves of Fig. 1. For general control uses, the gaseous type is frequently applied because of its greater sensitivity; for the purposes of measuring light intensities vacuum tubes are used because of linearity and ease of calibration.

The gaseous tubes usually use argon. The gas must be inert so that it does not react with the sensitive surface, and it must not *clean up*. In the latter process positive ions acquire sufficient speed under the action of the electric field in the tube to be permanently driven into the walls of the tube, and thus the gas pressure is decreased by a decrease in the number of gas molecules. Neon and helium are used in some tubes.

The amplification due to ionization may be considerable; in practice a ratio of 10 (the "gas-amplification" ratio) is about as high as is consistent with stability.

Phototube Ratings. *Maximum anode current* is the maximum instantaneous value of current that should be allowed to pass through the tube.

Maximum anode voltage is the maximum instantaneous value of voltage that should be impressed on the tube.

Gas amplification ratio is the ratio of the current that flows when ionization exists to the current due to primary electrons only.

Sensitivity is expressed as the current in microamperes per lumen of light flux. It is usually measured at a light intensity of 0.1 to 0.5 lumen.

Table 1 gives characteristics of several of the commercial phototubes in use at the present time, the figures in the column "cathode surface" representing a classification drawn up by the Radio Manufacturers Association and the National Electrical Manufacturers Association and defining the spectral response of the several cathode surfaces. An approximate sensitivity curve for each of these surfaces is given in Fig. 2.

Phototube Characteristics. In the upper left-hand corner of Fig. 2 a curve showing the spectral response of the human eye is presented for comparison. The eye can "see" light wavelengths approximately within the range of 4,000 to 7,000 angstroms. The eye is most sensitive to light at 5,550 angstroms (green) and its sensitivity falls off on either side of this maximum. (As the wavelength of the light decreases through blue and ultraviolet, it passes out of the visible range, as it does when the wavelength increases through red to infrared.)

So it is with phototubes. Each particular type of surface has its own spectral response curves and its own wavelength of peak sensitivity, as shown by the RMA curves. It will be noted that

TABLE 1

Type	Cathode surface	Cathode area, sq in.	Sensitivity, μa/lumen (2870°K source)	Max avg current density, μa	Max voltage	Interelectrode capacitance,[1] $\mu\mu f$
Vacuum phototubes						
917 919	S-1	1	20	10	500	2
922	S-1	0.4	20	5	500	0.5
925	S-1	0.4	15	5	250	1.5
PJ22	S-1		20		500	
926	S-3	0.4	6.5	5	500	0.5
929 IP39	S-4	0.5	45	5	250	2.6
934	S-4	0.3	30	4	250	1.5
IP42	S-4	0.03	25	0.4	150	1.7
935	S-5	0.8	20	8	250	0.6
FJ405	S-6	0.8	12	8	200	5.0
Gas-filled phototubes						
IP29	S-3	0.78	40	5	100	9
IP37	S-4	0.78	120	5	100	5.5
868	S-1	0.78	90	5	90	8
918	S-1	0.78	150	5	90	10.5
IP40 930	S-1	0.5	135	3	90	10
5581	S-4	0.5	135	3	100	5.5
921	S-1	0.44	135	3	90	10
5582	S-4	0.44	120	2	100	5.5
927	S-1	0.3	125	2	90	10
5583	S-4	0.3	135	2	100	5.5
IP41	S-1	0.25	83	1.5	90	8.5
928	S-1	0.5	65	3	90	10
920	S-1	2 × 0.3	100	2	90	9
5584	S-4	2 × 0.3	120	2	100	5.5

[1] Maximum gas amplification factor for gas-filled types.

the S-5 curve and the S-6 curve indicate sensitivities in the ultraviolet range. They can, in fact, see light to which the human eye is insensitive.

The cathode area column of Table 1 is useful in converting amounts of light into intensity units, or vice versa. The sensitivities of the phototubes are given in microamperes per lumen, based on a light source made up of an incandescent tungsten filament at a color temperature of 2870°K. This value was

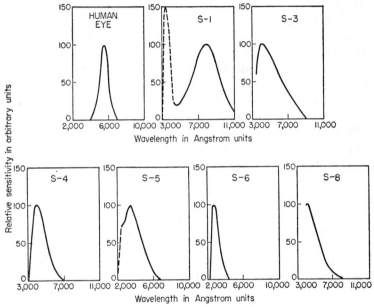

FIG. 2.   Curves of the sensitivities of several phototube cathodes at different wavelengths of light.

adopted simply as a basis for comparison of the various types. Actually this column is of little value for the S-5 and S-6 phototubes, for they are almost invariably used in the ultraviolet region at or around their sensitivity peaks.

The remaining columns show maximum average current densities (microamperes per square inch of cathode surface) and the maximum voltages that should be used across the phototube. In practice these voltages are seldom used. In fact in most cases voltages of the order of 10 or 20 volts are used, because higher voltages may produce certain physical changes within the tube that gradually change the response characteristics of the cathode surface.

The interelectrode capacitance of the phototubes is of importance only when the phototube is considered as a circuit element and the effect of the capacitance between the cathode and anode of the phototube might affect the operation of the circuit in which the tube is used. For the gas-type tubes the maximum gas amplification factor is listed in the last column instead of interelectrode capacitance, because in the application of these tubes, with their relatively nonlinear characteristic curves, their interelectrode capacitance is seldom of importance. These capacitances must be taken into account only when the illumination changes at the cathode surface occur at a high rate, in the higher audio-frequency region, or with a steep wave front and where accurate current variations corresponding to these illumination changes are required.

Phototube Circuit Design. To specify the circuit constants for phototube operation, one must know the luminous intensity of the light source to be employed. This may be determined by measurement, or by comparison with a standard lamp by means of a phototube, or by comparison with a Mazda C lamp by means of a phototube. Mazda C lamps of 50 to 100 watts are rated at approximately 1.0 candle power per watt at normal voltage. This is accurate to within 10 to 20 per cent.

When the candle power of a point source is known, the light flux in lumens on a given area is found from

$$L = \frac{\text{candle power} \times \text{area}}{\text{(distance)}}$$

where the distance and area use the same basic units, and area is measured perpendicular to the direction of light flux.

Phototube Circuits. The fundamental operation of the phototube is to produce a flow of electrons through the tube and the voltage source when the cathode is illuminated. Therefore, the simplest phototube circuit consists only of a tube, a battery, and a sensitive current meter. If the tube is a vacuum type, the current through the meter will be directly proportional to the amount of light falling on the cathode. Since the average phototube produces current of the order of a few microamperes only, the indicating instrument in such an illumination meter must be of the proper sensitivity, say 100 μa full scale. Figure 3 shows such a simple circuit.

This simple arrangement will measure light quantities from 0 up to about 5 lumens.[1]

Phototube-relay Circuits. The current changes brought about by varying amounts of light falling on the light-sensitive cathode of a phototube are very seldom of sufficient magnitude to do much work. In general, current changes of the order of 5 or 10 μa might be expected. Currents of this low order are incapable of operating most relays and/or solenoids. Even the most sensitive relays require currents of 50 to 100 μa for reliable operation.

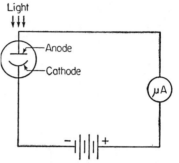

FIG. 3. Basic phototube circuit. The battery provides current, and the microammeter measures changes brought about by different light intensities on the phototube cathode.

The need for one or more stages of vacuum-tube amplification is apparent. A simple circuit capable of amplifying the light-sensitive effect of a phototube is shown in Fig. 4. As the amount of light falling on the cathode increases, more electrons are emitted, and the current flowing around the circuit composed of the phototube, battery B, and resistor R will increase.

The vacuum-tube bias may be adjusted so that little or no

[1] The several important light units are as follows:

Luminous flux is the rate of flow of light energy. The unit is the flux on a surface of unit area all points of which are at equal distances from a point source of one candle.

Luminous intensity is the amount of light on a given surface divided by the solid angle subtended by the surface. It is light *density*. The common unit is the candle; and candle power is luminous intensity expressed in candles.

Illumination is the density of light flux on a surface, that is, the amount of light divided by the area of the surface. When the foot is the unit of length, the unit of illumination is the foot-candle. It is the amount of illumination on a surface all points of which are one foot from a point source of one candle. It is also the illumination on a surface one square foot in area on which the uniformly distributed flux is one lumen.

Other units are used, depending upon the basic units of length employed, but those given here are customarily employed in this country.

current flows in the plate circuit when the phototube is not
illuminated.   Then, when light falls on the phototube, plate
current flows in the amplifier circuit, and the relay closes.   This
type of circuit is capable of initiating simple control functions
where certain action is to be effected when the light rises above
a certain level.   For example, this circuit could be used to ring

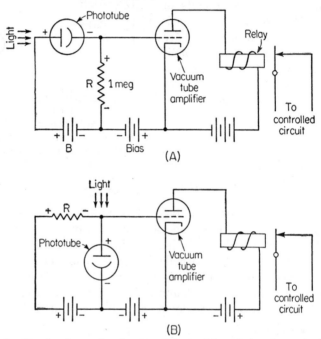

Fig. 4.   Simple phototube circuits.   The position of the phototube in the
circuit depends on the type of operation desired.   In *A*, the relay closes with
increased illumination.   In *B*, the relay opens with increased illumination,
or it closes when illumination is decreased, depending on the initial setting.

an alarm when a door into a darkroom is opened, or to turn off
street lights when daylight returns in the morning.

   To reverse the action, that is, to give an alarm when illumination fails, the phototube and resistor are interchanged as in Fig.
4*B*.   This circuit will actuate the relay when illumination falls
below some predetermined value.   With a normal amount of
light falling on the cathode, a certain amount of current flows,
and the voltage drop across the phototube is equal to the voltage
of the battery minus the drop across resistor *R*.   If the illumina-

tion on the phototube cathode decreases, less current flows in the battery circuit, the voltage drop across the phototube increases, as does the positive voltage of the vacuum-tube grid with respect to its cathode.   Thus the vacuum-tube plate current decreases.   If the vacuum-tube grid bias is adjusted so that the relay is closed under the first condition of illumination, the relay contacts will open as a result of decreased illumination.

This is the type of circuit required for opening doors when a light beam is broken.   The switch which would normally actuate

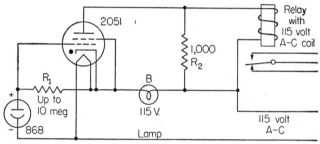

Fig. 5.   Simple gas-tube relay circuit.   A lamp in series with the cathode can be used as the light source for the interrupter system.

the door-opening mechanism is replaced by the relay contacts of the amplifier circuit.   When the beam is broken, the amount of light on the phototube decreases, the current in the phototube decreases, the voltage drop across the phototube increases, thereby decreasing the negative bias of the vacuum tube.   This causes more amplifier plate current to flow and the relay in its plate circuit to operate.

Simple Thyratron Circuit for Phototubes.   Since a thyratron will pass more current than a high-vacuum amplifier tube, it is sometimes useful to employ a combination of phototube and thyratron as in Fig. 5, which shows the simplicity of a most useful circuit.[1]   The entire unit may be enclosed in a small case. If a mirror is employed with such a setup to reflect the light to the phototube, the light source, a 60-watt lamp, may be in the same enclosure with the phototube and thyratron.   The lamp itself should be of the movie projector type since the illumination is concentrated in a small space.

[1] Gilbert Smiley, Control Circuits for Industry, *Electronics*, January, 1941, p. 29.

Note that the lamp and the tube heater are in series across the 115-volt line. The lamp reduces the line voltage to the proper value for the tube heater. The phototube in series with R_1 is placed across the tube heater. As the illumination changes, the voltage drop along this resistance is applied to the grid of the thyratron. Resistor R_2 serves to absorb the inductive kick of the relay coil during the nonconducting half cycle of the applied line voltage. In this example both phototube and thyratron

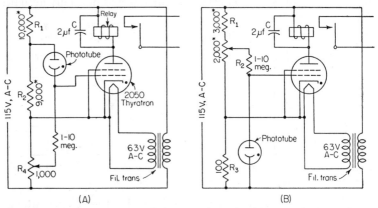

(A)   (B)

* If a vacuum type phototube is used R_1 is omitted (shorted) and its value of resistance is added to R_2.

Fig. 6. Refined phototube circuits include adjustments for setting initial conditions.

operate from alternating current without benefit of a transformer or rectifier.

Somewhat more refined phototube-thyratron circuits are shown in Fig. 6. In Fig. 6A a relay closes when the illumination exceeds a certain amount, as determined by the phototube sensitivity and the value of R_4. In Fig. 6B the relay closes when the illumination falls below an amount determined by the setting of R_2. In this circuit R_1 is necessary only if a gas tube is employed; its value should be approximately 3,000 ohms. Its function is to limit the current through the tubes to their safe operating values. Negative bias for the thyratron is furnished by R_3. Capacitor C prevents relay chatter during the negative half cycles when the thyratron does not conduct current. The circuits of Fig. 6 will operate relays with closing current ratings as high as 25 ma.

Phototube-amplifier-thyratron Circuit. If the voltage changes brought about by the illumination changes are not sufficient to operate the thyratron properly, they can be amplified before being impressed upon the thyratron as shown in Fig. 7. Lower illumination level changes will now produce more positive relay action than can be attained by the simpler circuits of Fig. 6. In this circuit one-half of the 6F8G tube rectifies the alternating current. The rectified current is filtered by the *RC* combination and is applied to the phototube as smooth direct current. Changes in amplifier plate current produce voltage changes along

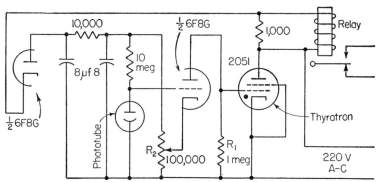

FIG. 7. This improved circuit for detecting smaller light variations employs an additional stage of amplification. Half of the 6F8G rectifies alternating current for the phototube power source.

R_1 and thus affect the thyratron. By adjusting the bias on the amplifier by the potentiometer R_2, the firing point of the thyratron can be made to coincide with the desired illumination change.

Other Simple Phototube Circuits. An a-c operated vacuum-tube relay circuit is shown in Fig. 8. This circuit has the disadvantage of requiring a special transformer. This drawback is eliminated by the circuit of Fig. 9, where a vacuum-tube amplifier is operated directly from the a-c line. The only transformer necessary supplies tube heater current, and it could also supply power to the light source. This circuit is often used as a safety device to protect an operator whose hands may get into dangerous zones. So long as the illumination on the danger area is not eclipsed by the operator's hands, the machine will work.

An exceptionally fast-acting and simple rectified a-c operated

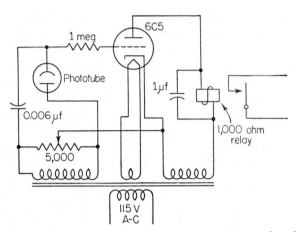

Fig. 8. This a-c operated phototube circuit provides good action with extreme simplicity.   The only special requirement is the transformer.

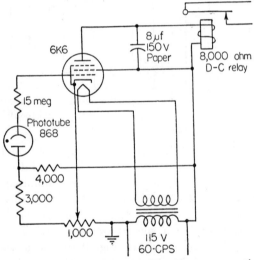

Fig. 9.   This a-c operated phototube circuit employs a conventional filament transformer and a relatively inexpensive relay.

phototube circuit, which can easily be applied to a wide variety of applications, is shown in Fig. 10.   This particular circuit is taken from "Phototubes," an RCA book containing much information for the designer of phototube and control equipment.

The circuit incorporates standard receiver-type tubes whose filaments are connected in series across the line with a series

voltage-dropping resistor of 200 ohms.   The 25Z6 operates as a
voltage doubler and provides about 300 volts across R_3.   Either
position of the phototube may be used, depending on whether
an increase or decrease in illumination is to be detected.   The
circuit can be used to operate a relay or to provide an indication
on a d-c milliammeter.

Circuit adjustments are as follows: Set R_3 and R_6 at their
maximum positive extremities and adjust R_7 until the maximum

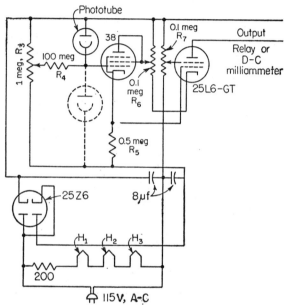

FIG. 10.   Simple phototube circuit using conventional receiving-type tubes
to obtain good sensitivity and stability.

desired plate current (load current) is being passed by the
25L6-GT.   This value depends on the rating of the relay coil
used or on the meter used as an indicator.   Next the tap on
R_6 is moved toward the negative end until the plate current of
the 25L6 begins to decrease.   Then with the phototube fully
illuminated R_3 is adjusted until the 25L6 plate current is affected.

If meter indication is used, it can be employed in adjusting the
circuit initially as described above.   For the alternate position
of the phototube appropriate changes in initial adjustment must,
of course, be made.

Remote Coupling to Phototube. If the amplifier and indicating device used with a phototube are to be located at some distance from the phototube itself, as is often the case, interesting problems arise. Such applications require special attention, since just connecting long wires between the phototube and its amplifier would introduce certain difficulties.

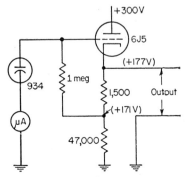

A simple means for matching a phototube to a long line is shown in Fig. 11. The phototube is a type 934, and its output is transformed to low impedance by a triode acting as a cathode follower. For the component values given, Fig. 12 shows that the output varies

Fig. 11. The cathode-follower circuit is useful where the phototube is located some distance from the amplifying circuit.

almost linearly from 0 to about 10 volts while the phototube current increases from 0 to 1 μa as a result of increasing illumination.[1]

This type of circuit can be used where space limitations prevent the amplifying equipment from being integral with the phototube. Further amplification of the phototube signal, if required, may be accomplished by any d-c amplifier with sufficient stability and gain. The microammeter is only for adjustment purposes and need not be included after the device is set up.

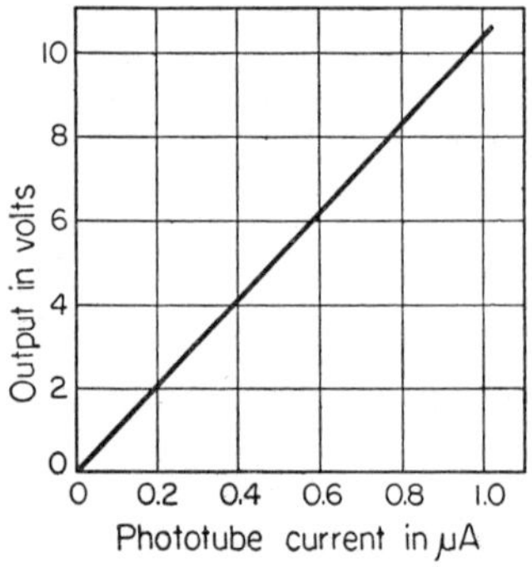

MULTIPLIER PHOTOTUBES

We have seen how the addition of gas within the envelope of a phototube will increase its sensitivity by the process of ionization.

Fig. 12. Curve showing linearity of output obtained from the cathode-follower circuit of Fig. 11.

Another scheme by which the phototube output current can be increased, this time by a very great extent, is to use secondary

[1] Norman Alpert, Phototube Amplifier with Low Output Impedance, *Electronics*, October, 1949, p. 108.

emission. The photomultiplier tube gets its tremendous sensitivity by application of this phenomenon in which additional electrons are produced when "primary" electrons strike a target, in this case the anode of a phototube.

In the multiplier phototube a conventional cathode emits electrons when illuminated, and these electrons are collected by an anode. But in the process additional secondary electrons are produced, perhaps several times as many as the primaries which strike the anode. The secondary electrons are directed

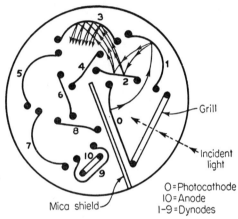

FIG. 13. View looking down from the top of a multiplier phototube. Light strikes the cathode, and the electrons emitted as a result strike the first dynode. This in turn causes secondary electrons to be emitted, and these strike the next dynode, and so on. The result is a multiplication of the number of electrons originally freed by the light hitting the cathode.

so that they do not impede the oncoming primaries and actually strike a second anode where they produce a still greater number of secondaries. This process continues until the electrons have gone through eight stages of amplification and are collected at the final anode.

Between the two elements of any one stage is maintained about 75 to 100 volts so that the total voltage from the cathode to final anode is of the order of 700 to 1,000 volts. In practice the individual anodes are called *dynodes* to distinguish them from the final anode from which the output is taken.

Table 2 gives data on four such tubes which are physically similar with cathode areas of 0.3 sq in. and an output capacitance of 4 $\mu\mu$f. The voltages given in the table are maximum values and are seldom if ever employed. Note in the table the column marked "dark current." All phototubes emit some electrons even without measurable illumination. In the conventional diode tubes this dark current is of no importance. With the photomultiplier, however, the dark current must be taken into account when the tubes are required to indicate or measure the existence of light of very low levels and where the output current may be of the same order as the dark current. In such cases the dark current must be balanced out before any readings are made.

TABLE 2

		Sensitivity and gain				Max anode current, ma	Max voltage		Dark current max, μa	Max temperature, °C
Type	Surface	75 volts per stage		100 volts per stage			Total	Last stage		
		Sens., amp/ lumen	Gain × 10⁶	Sens., amp/ lumen	Gain × 10⁶					
931-A	S-4	1.5	0.15	10	1.0	1.0	1,250	250	0.25	75
1P21	S-4	6	0.3	40	2.0	0.1	1,250	250	0.1	75
1P22	S-8	0.09	0.03	0.6	0.2	1.0	1,250	250	0.25	50
1P28	S-5	0.45	0.03	3	0.2	0.5	1,250	250		75

Multiplier Phototube Circuits. Circuits for the multiplier type phototube have special requirements. For the progressive secondary emission amplification to take place, each stage of the nine in a typical tube must be progressively higher in voltage than the preceding one. Therefore some source of high voltage is required. Figure 14 shows two basic circuits.

For greater accuracy, voltage regulation must be employed. The circuit of Fig. 15 is of the self-compensating type. The voltage-regulator tubes form a voltage-dividing network so that voltage variations caused by line-voltage fluctuations are larger at the seventh dynode than the changes felt by the others. This different voltage is sufficient to counterbalance the original voltage change. This circuit will serve satisfactorily where extreme accuracy is not essential, and the anode current may be measured by a microammeter without further amplification. The over-all voltage required is 900 volts; 75 volts appear between the elements of each stage.

It will be noticed that the positive side of the power supply is grounded. The 20,000-ohm resistor serves to filter the full-wave

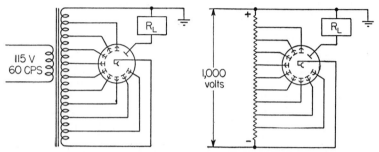

Fɪɢ. 14. Typical methods for furnishing stepped voltages for multiplier-phototube operation.

rectified current output from the rectifier. It should be kept in mind that when measuring the voltage at any point in this circuit the positive side of the voltmeter should be grounded, because the polarity is reversed compared to usual practice.

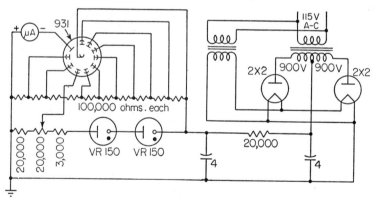

Fɪɢ. 15. Circuit for providing stable operation of a multiplier phototube by regulating part of the voltage applied to the dynodes.

The output of this circuit can be increased by about ten times by increasing the voltage steps to about 120 volts. With about 100 volts between stages, however, a similar degree of output current augmentation can be derived by using a 931A multiplier phototube instead of its predecessor, the 931, for which the circuit was developed.

Stabilized Control. Where a great deal of measurement of low-intensity illumination is anticipated, the circuit shown in Fig. 16 may prove helpful. It incorporates controlled and stabilized voltages for the dynodes of the photomultiplier, a balancing circuit for dark-current adjustment, and a stable amplifier for still further increasing the sensitivity of the multiplier tube. The circuit is designed so that line-voltage fluctua-

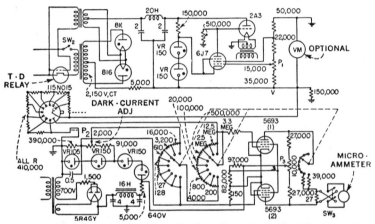

FIG. 16. Complete circuit of a multiplier-phototube unit with attenuators and a stable amplifier.

tions produce negligible effect on the reading of the meter. Two power supplies are used, one full-wave and one half-wave.

Two VR150 tubes are used as a reference voltage source for the 6J7 control tube in the multiplier-phototube high-voltage supply. The total voltage and thus the sensitivity of the dynodes can be varied by potentiometer P_1. The time-delay relay delays application of high a-c voltage to the 816 rectifiers until their filaments have come up to safe operating temperature.

The low-voltage power supply voltages are stabilized by voltage-regulator tubes, as shown. This supply furnishes operating voltages for the 5693 tubes and the anode voltage for the multiplier phototube. Notice that the ninth dynode is grounded so that it is connected to the positive extremity of the high-voltage power supply. The anode, however, is kept at a still higher voltage than the ninth dynode because it gets its voltage from the separate power supply which is positive with respect to ground. The dark-current adjustment P_2 is across a portion of the voltage-regulator-tube voltage divider. The polarity of the voltage it selects is such that the effect of the IR-drop in the anode circuit of the multiplier phototube can be balanced out.

The multiposition switch enables different degrees of sensitivity to be selected. A multiplying factor of 5 for each step gives a total sensitivity range of 500,000,000 to the instrument.

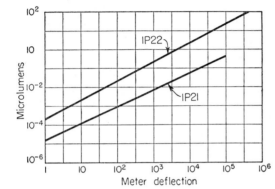

FIG. 17. Curves showing differences between 1P22 and 1P21 phototubes used in the circuit of Fig. 16.

The multiplier tube is coupled directly to the first 5693 amplifier stage. Potentiometer P_3 is used to balance the bridge-type amplifier with the sensitivity switch set for maximum sensitivity.

The useful range of this instrument can best be appreciated by studying the curves presented in Fig. 17 for two typical tube types which may be used in this circuit. Before making measurements the instrument should be allowed to warm up for 15 to 30 minutes. After that only small changes in calibration will occur from tube fatigue or other circuit instabilities. This slight drift effect can be compensated for by occasional readjustment of P_2, with no light falling on the phototube cathode, and with P_1 and some small light source of predetermined brightness.[1]

AVOIDING D-C AMPLIFICATION

One of the most difficult problems in phototube work is the stabilization of the information derived from the phototube

[1] Plymale and Hansen, Stabilized Circuits for Photo-multipliers, *Electronics*, February, 1950, p. 102.

currents which are inherently unstable and quite small. For this current-change information to be of value, it must be amplified, and in many applications the amplification of such phenomena as a gradual rise in current or a change in current from one steady value to another is difficult.

In other words light is inherently a d-c phenomenon. That is, as far as electronic circuitry is concerned, two different values of light flux represent two different currents flowing through some circuit. Whenever an amplifier is designed to amplify a single change like that, certain precautions must be taken. Direct-coupled amplifiers, or some suitable substitute, must be employed.

Direct-coupled amplifiers are naturally unstable devices. To maintain the plates of tubes positive with respect to other elements in the same tube and yet connect the grid of the tube directly to the plate of the preceding tube, wide ranges of voltages are required. These are not readily available, and they are difficult to control and regulate, especially when appreciable current must be drawn from them.

Light-chopper Systems. Many ingenious methods for eliminating the necessity for d-c amplifiers with their difficulties have been devised. Probably the most simple and economical is the use of a chopper in the light beam which falls on the phototube. Schematics of several typical systems are shown in Fig. 18. In A the light passes through a motor-driven toothed wheel, which periodically interrupts the light beam as it rotates. Thus the phototube alternately *sees* light and dark. Since the phototube reacts practically instantaneously, the phototube current resulting from the on-and-off light beam is in effect an on-and-off current, or alternating current (actually the current may be said to be a pulsating direct current, but if this type of current is passed through a capacitor or transformer, the d-c component is removed, and an a-c voltage results). This fluctuating voltage may be amplified by conventional band-pass amplifiers without direct coupling.

The magnitude of the alternating current produced by the chopped light beam will depend on two things: First, the low-current swing will depend on the incidental light that falls on the phototube cathode when a tooth of the chopper wheel is between the light source and the phototube. Second, the high-current period will depend on the brightness of the source it views when there is nothing between it and the source. If the chopper wheel is so positioned that no external light hits the phototube when a tooth passes the phototube window, the low-current swing will always be some low, fixed value. The magnitude of the difference between low- and high-current values and

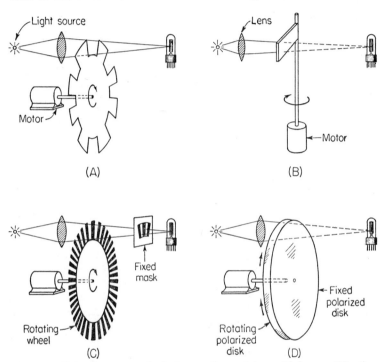

Fig. 18. Light-chopper methods frequently used to avoid d-c amplification in phototube work.

thus the magnitude of the fluctuating current will depend almost entirely on the illumination produced by the source.

The pulsating current thus produced has the form of a square wave, but its waveform may be made sinusoidal by suitable filters, or by passing it through a transformer or some other similar type of circuit. This alternating voltage may be amplified by conventional capacitor or transformer-coupled circuits.

The other chopper systems shown in Fig. 18 operate on substantially the same principle. In B, the light is chopped by a

vane connected to a rotating shaft, whereas in C it is interrupted
periodically by a rotating wheel and mask arrangement. The
slots in the mask are identical in width to those of the rotating
wheel. Thus when the slots of the wheel and the mask are
aligned, light passes through. When the wheel moves so the
wheel slots are aligned with the opaqued portions of the mask,

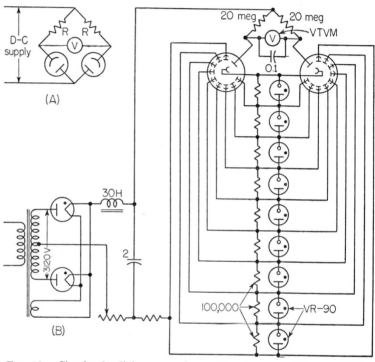

FIG. 19. Circuits for light comparison. B makes use of two multiplier
phototubes with regulated voltage steps.

the light is cut off. Figure 18D shows the use of polarized glass.
As the rotating disk changes its angular relationship with the
fixed disk, the light is alternately cut off and allowed to pass.
With this scheme two pulses of light will be transmitted for each
rotation of the disk.

Light Comparison. If it is only necessary to *compare* the
intensity of illumination of one source to that of another, d-c
amplification can be avoided. By the use of a suitable set of
standards or some calibrated and variable source of illumination,

measurements can be made with extreme accuracy by the comparison method.

A circuit in which a pair of phototubes comprise two of the legs of a d-c bridge is shown in Fig. 19A. As long as the illumination falling on the cathodes of the two phototubes is identical, the bridge will be balanced, and no voltage will be read by the voltmeter.

Higher sensitivity can be obtained by substituting multiplier-type phototubes in the circuit, as shown in Fig. 19B. The 100,000-ohm potentiometer in series with the d-c power supply can be set so that different degrees of light unbalance will cause different vacuum-tube voltmeter deflections. This adjustment is especially helpful in calibrating the meter for different purposes.

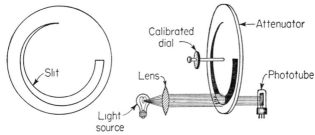

FIG. 20. Variable-slit attenuator for adjusting the illumination from a standard light source for comparison measurements.

The voltages for the multiplier phototube dynodes are stabilized by VR90 tubes. In some applications the high degree of stability thus afforded might not be necessary, since the bridge system relies on the comparison of two values and not on the measurement of a single value.

In using the bridge system, some standard of illumination is exposed to one phototube, and the unknown is applied to the other. To get a quantitative measurement of the unknown, the light emitted by the standard must be changed to correspond to that emitted by the unknown, as indicated by bridge balance. If the standard is a lamp, its light output might be recorded in terms of the current flowing through its filament, but more often, some kind of calibrated attenuator is used in conjunction with the standard. A typical shape for the attenuator is shown in Fig. 20. It is connected to a dial of some sort, which is calibrated in light units. As the narrow part of the attenuator is moved between the standard light source and the standard phototube, only a portion of the light emitted by the source is seen by the phototube. For this system an excess of light is required; that is, to measure intermediate values of illumination in a photobridge, the standard must be somewhat brighter so that attenuation can be introduced for making the actual measurement.

To save the expense of using two phototubes in a bridge for comparison of illumination, the system shown in Fig. 21 has been devised. It is used primarily for comparing the light-transmission characteristics of materials, but by slight rearrangement it could be used to compare reflectivity, or to compare light sources.

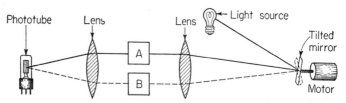

FIG. 21. The tilted mirror attached to the motor shaft shifts light back and forth between the calibrated attenuator or sample and the unknown for comparison measurement.

A motor-driven reciprocating mirror shifts the light back and forth periodically between the two substances whose light-transmission characteristics are being compared. After the light passes through the substances, it emerges and is combined into a single beam again by a lens. The beam that reaches the lens will be a steady value only if the light-transmission characteristics of the two substances are equal. If one substance allows more light to pass than the other, more light will hit the phototube during the time the light passes through that substance, and the phototube current will be a pulsating direct current with a frequency equal to the frequency at which the light beam is shifted. This pulsating direct current can be converted into an a-c voltage and amplified by conventional amplifiers.

A much simpler circuit for use in comparing two values of illumination is shown in Fig. 22. Here two identical vacuum-type phototubes are connected in series across a 200-volt d-c power supply, which must be well-regulated for stable operation of the circuit. If the amount of light falling on the cathodes of these tubes is equal, the voltage drop across the tubes will also be equal. If, however, the light falling on tube 1 becomes greater than that falling on tube 2, an additional current will tend to flow through tube 1. The voltage across tube 1 decreases. The net result is a rather large change in voltage which is brought about by a very small change in current.

The circuit contains a vacuum-tube voltmeter for measuring the voltage across one of the tubes. The use of a standard voltmeter would, of course, load the phototube circuit prohibitively. For very stable operation the vacuum-tube voltmeter tube must

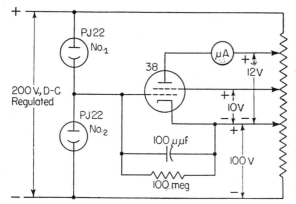

Fig. 22. Simplified system for light comparison where extreme sensitivity of the multiplier-phototube circuit is not necessary.

be shielded from light, since it will show slight photoelectric tendencies at high illumination levels.

This circuit has been operated[1] for hours without deviating from balance position by a tenth of a microampere, as read in the vacuum-tube voltmeter plate circuit.

Unusual Phototube Applications. Many applications of phototubes are quite obvious, such as devices used to measure the optical characteristics of materials. Setups for determining transparency, translucence, gloss, reflectivity, density, and fluorescence should be fairly easy to imagine. Also, devices for determining light output from various sources under varying conditions are straightforward applications.

By the use of suitable filters, it is possible to check the spectrum of light transmitted, and by a variation of this scheme using the comparison method, it is possible to evaluate paints and dyes

[1] D. G. Fink, Precise Light Measurement, *Electronics*, June, 1934, p. 190.

and to match them. This application is of extreme importance to industries such as printing, cloth making, decorating, paints, advertising, etc. For example, certain manufacturers of commercial products insist that their packages be of a specific color and that all of their advertising be printed showing the product in exactly its natural color. Color comparators are required in such cases to determine the mixture of the primary colors involved in making the desired color.

Frequency Measurement. The speed of rotation of a machine can conveniently be measured by photoelectric techniques. Electric impulses can be generated for each revolution by allowing a phototube to pick up light reflected from a rotating machine. The phototube signal is then applied to an amplifier and subsequently to a counting mechanism, such as an electronic counter, or a cathode-ray tube.

Much research is now being carried out to determine relationships between solar disturbances and anomalies of radio transmission. Years ago expeditions set out to photograph the sun's corona from remote parts of the earth where total eclipses were expected. The moon served to block out the light of the sun and permitted the photographing of the sun's corona. Modern means employ a scanning system that allows a phototube to look at small portions of the sun's atmosphere in some definite pattern that can be reconstructed and subsequently studied. The amount of information available by these means is much greater, and the expense is but a fraction of that involved in the old system.

A form of photoelectric device provides the basis for modern television. A scene is scanned, and light energy is transformed into electrical energy to form a television signal.

Simplified Television. The diagram of Fig. 23 illustrates the use of a phototube in a simplified television system. Here a line pattern (raster) is formed on the face of a regular cathode-ray tube—the brighter the better. Then, this raster, consisting of uniform-intensity lines, is used to illuminate a subject. For example, imagine that a negative is placed before the raster. Where the photographic negative is transparent (where it would print black in photographic processing) the light may pass through easily. However, where the negative is black, the light is interrupted. Thus a phototube looking at the light passing through the negative would see the dot of light as it scanned transparent areas, but the light would be cut off when the dot passed black areas.

If the cathode-ray tube is scanned in some regular manner in an exactly timed fashion, the phototube signal will bear a relationship to both time and to the negative used. By providing another cathode-ray tube with the same scanning signals as the first, but causing the beam of the second tube to vary in intensity with the phototube signal, the raster of the second tube will show

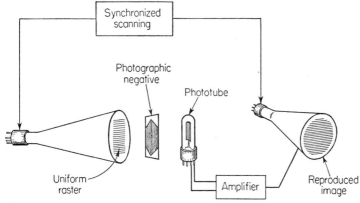

FIG. 23. This simplified television system uses a phototube to pick up variations in light from a cathode-ray-tube flying-spot scanner.

a reproduction of the negative applied to the first. This system is actually used in a simplified form of television transmission for certain industrial applications. Some amateur radio operators are employing this system for the transmission of television picture signals.

The idea of scanning, that is, using a dot that covers an area in some accurately timed fashion, is not limited to television. One bank uses this system to send reproductions of signatures from teller to file clerk for verification. Facsimile equipment operates on the same principle and allows news services to transmit photographs over great distances, simply by scanning and picking up an electrical signal that corresponds to the information presented in the picture.

Waveform Generators. Phototubes may be used to generate almost an unlimited variety of voltage or current waveforms.

Figure 24A shows a disk with a number of slots cut in it. When the disk is rotated, the slots alternately illuminate and shade the phototube. The phototube output signal will in this case be a square wave. The frequency of the square wave will, of course, depend on the speed of rotation of the disk. By shaping the holes in the disk, different waveforms can be generated.

Another version of the same principle involves a window through which the light passes on its way through the wheel slits to the phototube. This system is illustrated in Fig. 24B. As

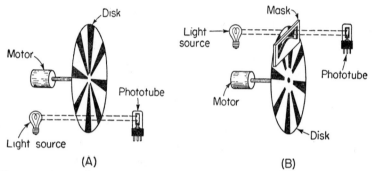

(A)   (B)

FIG. 24.   Methods for producing a-c waveforms by means of a phototube.

the slit crosses the window, the amount of light reaching the phototube depends on how much of the window is covered by a mask. Here again a wide variety of waveforms may be obtained by using different shaped masks.

A highly refined version of the latter principle is illustrated in simplified form in Fig. 25.[1] This instrument is known as the *Photoformer*. It employs considerable electronic ingenuity; a complete circuit explanation is presented in the reference.

The path traced by a cathode-ray tube beam, as we have already learned, depends on the voltages applied to the vertical and horizontal deflection plates. To explain briefly the operation of the Photoformer, let us assume that a voltage is applied to the horizontal deflection plates that makes the dot travel from left to right on the face of the tube at some regular rate and then back again. In other words a triangular wave is applied to the horizontal plates.

[1] D. E. Sunstein, Photoelectric Waveform Generator, *Electronics*, February, 1949, p. 100.

Now, let us place a mask in front of the cathode-ray tube face and a phototube in front of that. Then, let us take the phototube signal and feed it through an amplifier into the vertical deflection plates of the oscilloscope in such a way that the beam moves up when the dot is hidden from the phototube and down when the phototube sees the dot. Thus the voltage applied to the vertical deflection plates will vary in accordance with the mask shape and keep the dot always right on the line. If a sine-wave mask is used, the voltage applied to the vertical plates will be sinusoidal,

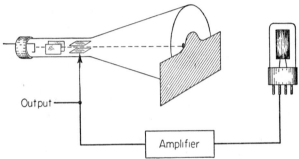

Output

Amplifier

FIG. 25. A phototube and a cathode-ray tube provide a wide variety of available waveforms. The spot on the tube screen follows the contour of the opaque mask.

and so on. This voltage may, of course, be used for any purpose, and by substituting different shapes of masks, a wide variety of waveforms may be obtained.

Sound Reproduction. Moving pictures make use of a system similar in principle. Sound is nothing more than a combination of waveforms applied to a transducer capable of setting the air in motion. The sound track on modern movies is simply a moving mask that determines the amount of light that can pass between a source and a phototube. The phototube signal is amplified and applied to loudspeakers.

The applications of phototubes are numerous. They have found practical places in almost every branch of science and industry today.

REFERENCES

Antes, L. L., Accurate Sorting of Colored Objects, *Electronics*, June, 1944, p. 114.

Asset, Gabrielle, A Phototube Galvanometer Amplifier, *Electronics*, February, 1945, p. 126.

Baker, A. K., Photoelectric Effects on Neon Tubes, *Electronics*, September, 1939, p. 52.

Barnett, G. F., Photoelectric Dust Meter, *Electronics*, December, 1946, p. 116.

Cockrell, E. D., Phototube Control of Packaging Machines, *Electronics*, October, 1943, p. 94.

Edelman, A., Photocell Experience in the Factory, *Electronics*, March, 1938, p. 15.

Ewald, Philip, Photoelectric Cooling Control, *Electronics*, November, 1941, p. 55.

Gucker, F. T., Jr., Sensitive Photoelectric Photometer, *Electronics*, July, 1947, p. 106.

Hagues, H. J., Photoelectric Industrial Controls, *Electronics*, April, 1944, p. 114.

Hanson, V. F., A Phototube Absorption Analyzer, *Electronics*, January, 1941, p. 40.

Hewlett, C. W., High-sensitivity Photoconductive Cell, *General Electric Review*, April, 1947, p. 22.

Kramer, Andrew W., Photovoltaic Cells, *Instruments*, June, 1944, p. 340.

Lang, D. F., Photoelectric Potentiometer Recorder, *General Electric Review*, November, 1943, p. 623.

Rajchman, J. A., An Electrically-focused Multiplier Phototube, *Electronics*, December, 1940, p. 20.

Roberts, W. O., Photoelectric Sight for Solar Telescope, *Electronics*, June, 1946, p. 100.

Side Shifts of Paper Corrected in Roll-winding Machine, *Electronics*, April, 1943, p. 144.

Sweet, M. H., Logarithmic Photometer, *Electronics*, November, 1946, p. 105.

Walker, D. S., Phototube-controlled Flame Cutter, *Electronics*, July, 1945, p. 100.

Wilson, E. D., Initial Drift in Photocells, *Electronics*, January, 1939, p. 15.

Wrobel, H. T., and H. H. Chamberlain, Photometric Equipment For Blocking-layer Light-sensitive Cells, *General Electric Review*, April, 1946, p. 25.

CHAPTER 6

THYRATRON TUBE CIRCUITS

The basic differences between high-vacuum amplifier tubes (pliotrons) and gaseous triodes and tetrodes (thyratrons) are as follows: Amplifier tubes are, in general, high-voltage low-current tubes; thyratrons are high-current low-voltage tubes, although the voltage can be quite as high as those employed in high-vacuum tubes circuits. The voltage drop across an amplifier

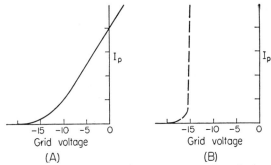

Fig. 1. Typical characteristics of vacuum tubes (A) and gas tubes (B).

tube is high compared to that across the thyratron, and therefore, the power wasted in the amplifier is much greater than that lost in the gas tube. In an amplifier tube the grid has complete and continuous control over the plate current—it can modulate the plate current to any degree. In the thyratron the grid can only control the starting of the anode current; it cannot stop it. High-vacuum triodes are essentially amplifiers of voltage, current, or power. The gas tubes are essentially relays, acting much as a mechanical contactor but without moving parts and without contacts to pit and wear out. Thyratrons may also be considered as grid-controlled rectifiers.

The reason for the vastly greater power-controlling ability of the thyratron lies in the fact that the space charge of the electrons does not exist once conduction through the tube has started. The electron density (current) between cathode and anode in a thyratron may be as high as 10^{12} or 10^{13} electrons per cubic centimeter compared to 10^2 in a highly evacuated tube.[1]

The largest triode amplifier tubes in general use may have a plate current as high as 6 amp and a plate voltage of 15,000. This represents about 100 kw of power. On the other hand a thyratron may have a rated current of 600 amp maximum and an average current of 100 amp at 1,500 volts. A mercury-arc type of tube has been built which has 12 anodes, each of which will handle 4,000 amp at a d-c voltage of 1,500.

Thyratron Characteristics. In Fig. 2 is represented a typical thyratron tube characteristic. The curve shows the relation between anode and grid voltages necessary for conduction to start. That is, if the anode is 1,000 volts positive with respect to the cathode, no current will flow until the grid voltage has been decreased (made more positive) from some high negative value to about -5 volts or less. If the grid voltage is fixed, then raising the positive anode voltage above the critical value will cause the tube to conduct. Control can be exercised in two ways: either by lowering the negative grid voltage, or by raising the positive anode voltage.

In practice the grid is biased not at the critical point, but at a point somewhat more negative than this value, so that slight changes in the applied voltages, transients, changes in characteristic due to age or other factors cannot fire the tube when it is undesirable.

When current flows, it is actually limited only by the ability of the cathode to supply electrons and by the resistance in the external circuit of the tube. Once conduction has begun, there is only one way to stop it—that is to remove the anode voltage. After a time interval which varies from tube to tube, but which is of the order of 10 to 1,000 microseconds, the grid regains control and prevents flow of current. This time interval is required for the gas ions to recombine with electrons and to lose their charge, and for the electrons to lose their freedom. Similarly, a

[1] A. W. Hull, Fundamental Processes in Gaseous Tube Rectifiers, *Electrical Engineering*, August, 1950, p. 695.

brief time is required for ionization to occur, but in industrial circuits where the power is the conventional 60-cycle type, these periods of lack of control are usually of little consequence.

Comparison of Vapor and Gas-filled Tubes. Several gases have been used in grid-controlled rectifiers, or thyratrons. For tubes to be operated on low voltages, neon or other inert gas is

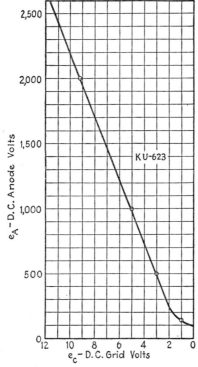

Fig. 2. Typical thyratron characteristic shows the relationship between grid and plate voltages necessary for firing.

used, whereas for higher voltages, mercury vapor is generally employed. The neon or gas-filled tubes have the advantage that they are unaffected by temperature, whereas the mercury-vapor tubes are critical to temperature changes. Neon tubes have a considerably higher voltage drop than mercury tubes. Argon-filled tubes, however, have a drop of only 1 or 2 volts more than mercury-vapor tubes. The FG-81 is a good example of an argon tube. Because of their tendency to flash-back, or conduct current during the part of the cycle when the anode is negative, neon or other gas-filled tubes are restricted to the lower voltages.

The power lost in thyratrons is very small and proper choice of tube and circuit will produce efficiencies as high as 99 per cent. The sum of the cathode power and voltage-drop loss for a mercury-vapor tube with a thermionic cathode is about 7 watts per amp under favorable conditions. With a mercury-pool cathode the loss is about 20 watts per amp.

Temperature Effect. Since the ionization voltage of mercury vapor depends upon temperature, it is natural that tubes employ-

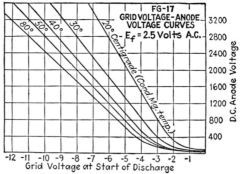

FIG. 3.   Curve shows the effect of temperature on thyratron characteristics.

ing mercury vapor as the source of ions have variations in characteristics depending upon the ambient temperature. A typical set of curves for such a tube is shown in Fig. 3.

Tube Types.   Owing to the fact that there are negative-control and positive-control tubes, as well as three-element and four-element tubes, the number of combinations of characteristics possible at any given current or voltage rating may be large.

Since the bias voltage on a thyratron is always somewhat greater than that required to prevent the tube's firing, and since design experience teaches that the firing of a thyratron must be positive, it is usual practice to drive the grid well beyond the critical point when firing. This practice creates the need for a finite amount of grid power, and any circuitry devoted to feeding the grid must be capable of delivering this power. The grid current after discharge is many times the value before discharge. This is not generally detrimental, since the tube has already been conducting before grid-current flow. Under certain conditions grid current may upset a weak grid circuit, causing incorrect firing of associated tubes, or it may result in saturation of the grid transformer which may occur after the tube has ceased firing and the grid is again trying to exercise its control function, thus distorting the grid input voltage. The grid current before discharge, however, is a real limitation upon the tube when used with very high impedance grid circuits such as are frequently encountered in photoelectric or other control arrangements. This grid current invariably produces a loading effect on these circuits that tends to reduce the actual grid voltage. In very high impedance circuits this effect tends to make the operation of the tube independent of the intended actuating voltage. In addition this loading effect may vary; for example, as the tube warms up, its characteristics change.

Shield-grid Thyratrons. To overcome some of these difficulties, four-element or shield-grid tubes are available. Under the same conditions the shield-grid tube will pass much less grid current than the three-element tube. The shield grid protects the control grid from cathode material sputtered or evaporated from the cathode. The discharge is protected against extraneous charges which may accumulate on the walls of the tube envelope, which may sometimes be troublesome. The shield closes all possible paths between anode and cathode except the opening in the grid baffles adjacent to which the control grid is situated. The control grid can be made smaller physically, which results in less grid current both before and after discharge. Thus the power required by the grid circuit to control the starting of the discharge is reduced.

There is another advantage of the four-element grid-controlled rectifier. The starting characteristic can be varied by varying the potential at which the shield grid is held, making it possible to have a tube whose starting characteristic can be made either positive or negative. By impressing a fluctuating potential on the shield grid, the tube can be made to have a negative control characteristic over some portion of the cycle and a positive control characteristic over the remainder of the cycle. By varying the phase relation between the two grid voltages, interesting and valuable control effects can be worked out.

Furthermore, the shield-grid construction tends to prevent transient conditions in the plate circuit from affecting the grid

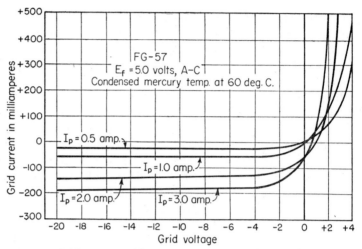

FIG. 4.   Grid-voltage–grid-current curves for various anode currents.

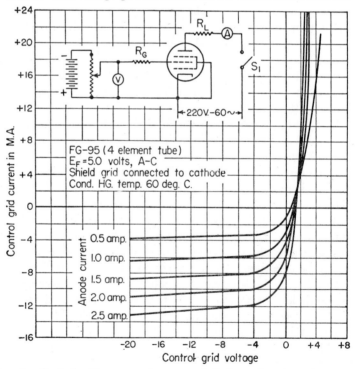

FIG. 5.   Control-grid current after start of discharge in a four-element gas tube.

circuit and the operating conditions of the circuit. The grid is protected from heat from the anode, cathode, or ion stream, and therefore there is less tendency toward secondary emission of electrons by parts of the tube other than the cathode.

The sole disadvantage of the more complicated tube is simply its greater complexity (one more terminal).

Methods of Rating Three-element Gas Tubes. Like all electrical and mechanical machines, gas and vacuum tubes have definite ratings which differ among tubes of different types. The

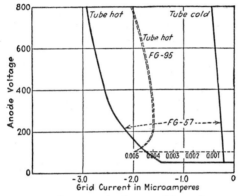

Fig. 6.   Curves show grid currents in three- and four-element tubes, hot and cold, at start of discharge.

following ratings and terms relating to grid-controlled rectifiers, or thyratrons, are in general use.

The *maximum peak inverse voltage* is a rating common to both rectifiers and controlled rectifiers. It is the highest instantaneous voltage that the tube will safely stand in the direction opposite to that in which it is designed to pass current. In other words it is the safe arc-back limit with the tube operating within the specified temperature range. The relations between the peak inverse voltage, the direct voltage and the rms value of alternating voltage depend largely upon the individual characteristics of the circuit and its power supply. The presence of line or keying surges, or any other transient or waveform distortion, may raise the actual peak voltage to a value which is higher than that indicated by normal design formulas. The maximum rating of a tube, therefore, refers to the actual inverse voltage and not to the calculated values.   A cathode-ray oscillograph or a calibrated spark gap across the tube may be used to determine these actual peak values.   In single-phase circuits the peak inverse voltage on a rectifier tube for sine-wave conditions is approximately 1.4 times the rms value of the anode voltage applied to the tube. In polyphase circuits the peak inverse voltage must be determined vectorially.   This rating is often abbreviated *mpiv*.

The *maximum peak forward voltage* applies only to controlled-rectifier types.   It is the maximum instantaneous voltage that can be held back by the action of a suitable grid voltage.

The *maximum instantaneous anode current* is the highest instantaneous current that a tube will stand under normal operating conditions in the direction of normal current flow.   This applies to both rectifying tubes and grid-controlled rectifiers.   The length of time which a given tube will stand this instantaneous current or the frequency with which it will stand an instantaneous current surge of a given duration depends upon tube heating.

The *maximum surge current* rating is a measure of the ability of a tube to stand extremely high transient currents.   This rating is intended to form a basis for set design in limiting the abnormal currents that occur during short-circuit conditions.   It does not mean that the tube can be subjected to repeated short circuits without the probability of a corresponding reduction in life and the possibility of failure.

The *maximum average anode current* is a rating based on tube heating.   It is the anode current as measured on a d-c meter, and it represents the highest average current which can be carried continuously through the tube.   In cases where current surges are not of sufficient frequency to operate a conventional meter, it is necessary to calculate the average current over a period not to exceed a definite interval of time which is specified for each design of tube.   For example, a tube with a maximum instantaneous anode current of 15 amp, a maximum average anode current of 2.5 amp, and an integration period of 15 seconds could carry 15 amp for 2.5 seconds out of each 15 seconds, or 7.5 amp for 5 seconds out of every 15 seconds.

The grid-current ratings are given in terms of the *maximum instantaneous grid current* and the *maximum average grid current*, and the integration period is the same as for the plate current.

Cathode Protection. When a vapor tube of the hot-cathode type is placed in operation by accident or inadvertence before the cathode has reached operating temperature, damage may be done to both the tube and the circuit in which it operates. To prevent this damage,[1] cathodes must have ample heating time to ensure operating emission current before the tube is placed in service. Accordingly, gas tubes are given two ratings: an initial preheating period and a reheating period after power interruptions.

It is obvious that short interruptions require less time for reheating, owing to the heat storage in the cathode. Protective relay devices should, therefore, be judged by their ability to protect under all operating conditions and by whether they conserve all operating time compatible with safety by appropriate reheating characteristics and by responding to voltage changes.

The time delay for heating or reheating must be accomplished by keeping the tube nonconducting either by grid control or by holding the anode circuit open until maximum emission current is available. The former is accomplished by a bias arrangement or a phase-shift scheme, whereas the latter uses anode contactors operated by a time-delay relay. Time-delay relays used with the preceding methods of control may be classified in the order of increasing desirability as follows:

1. Thermal timers
2. Mechanical timers
3. Thermionic timers

The thermionic time delay is very effective, since it is possible to use a cathode-anode space characteristic similar in heating and cooling to the tube that is to be protected. Figure 7 shows a diode heater shunted across the vapor-tube heater and a relay which closes the power to the anode of the vapor tube when the diode cathode has reached proper emission value. A series of diodes has been developed for this type of protective service.

Controlling Anode Current. In a two-element rectifier, anode current flows whenever the anode is positive with respect to the cathode. In the gas triode, another variable controlling factor enters; the voltage of the grid. Of course, current to the anode

[1] L. D. Miles and M. M. Morack, Thermionic Delay Relays for Cathode Protection, *Electronics*, April, 1935.

can flow only when that anode is positive, but unless the grid has the proper voltage, no current will flow, even if the anode is positive.

There are two general methods of controlling the flow of current in such tubes, an *amplitude* method and a *phase* method. In the amplitude method the voltage amplitude applied to the grid is varied until conduction starts, or, with a fixed grid voltage, the anode voltage is increased until current flows. The phase method implies the application of alternating current to anode and grid. When the phase between these a-c voltages is such that the grid of the tube is given the proper critical voltage at some portion of the half cycle during which the anode is positive, current will flow during the remainder of that cycle.

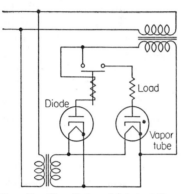

Fɪɢ. 7.   Circuit for obtaining time delay before applying high voltage to a vapor diode.

If sinusoidal alternating voltage is applied to the circuit in Fig. 8, and if the grid voltage is adjusted so that current flows during the entire positive alternation, the tube merely acts as a half-wave rectifier. Since the grid voltage is fixed, it is not possible to cut the flow of current to less than a quarter of an a-c cycle. If the discharge is not initiated during the first half of the positive alternation, it will not begin at all. Therefore the possible anode current values are three: (1) no current, caused by the adjustment of the grid voltage too low to start the anode current at the peak value of anode voltage, or (2) current flowing

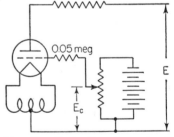

Fɪɢ. 8.   Basic thyratron circuit illustrates grid control of plate current.

during the entire half cycle when the anode is positive with respect to the cathode, and (3) current flowing for some period between the complete half cycle and the quarter cycle.

The above method of controlling the flow of current may be termed an amplitude method of control. The point in the first half of the positive alternation at which current begins to flow is governed by the adjustment of the grid-voltage slider on the potentiometer so that this voltage bears the required relation to the anode voltage.

The same effect may be secured by using alternating current on both anode and grid but where the frequency of the grid voltage is lower than that of the anode. This method of control is still an amplitude method—if the grid potential is always so low that it does not attain the critical voltage, current will never flow. As soon as the grid voltage is so adjusted that it reaches this critical voltage, the current starts and will continue until the end of the positive half cycle of anode voltage when the grid will regain control through the deionization of the gas. Here again it is impossible to limit the current to a value less than one-quarter cycle.

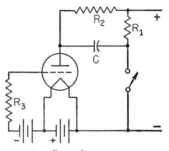

FIG. 9. Capacitor serves as a voltage-storage device in a d-c thyratron circuit.

By increasing the frequency of the grid voltage, the average current may be made to approach a continuous current to any desired degree. The method is essentially one of permitting the current to flow during any desired number of cycles and, depending upon the starting characteristic of the tube, controlling the point in the cycle at which conduction starts.

Control by Direct Current. Because of the distinct, though small, time required for the ions to diffuse after the discharge has been cut off by shutting off the plate voltage, when the tube is controlled by direct current, the plate voltage must not only be reduced to zero, but it must be maintained there for a small fraction of a second. This may be accomplished in several ways. One is by the capacitor shown in Fig. 9. When the tube carries current, the drop across it will be of the order of 15 volts. The rest of the line voltage, say 250 volts in this case, is impressed across the resistance R_2. Thus at the terminal of the capacitor attached to the anode the voltage is $+15$, while the other terminal of the capacitor is at $+250$ volts, being charged from the line through the resistance R_1. Now if the switch is closed, the 250-volt terminal of the capacitor will become zero, and the other terminal will suffer an instantaneous drop in voltage equivalent to $15 - 250$ volts or to the value of -235 volts.

It is worth noting carefully what happens in this circuit, since the action is characteristic of all RC circuits. Before the switch is closed, the terminal of the capacitor connected to the tube is $+15$ with respect to ground but -235 with respect to the other terminal—which is maintained at $+250$ from the line. When the switch is closed this difference of potential still exists across the capacitor, since there has not been time for the charge to leak off. Thus the one terminal goes to zero, and the other must still be negative with respect to this terminal. In other words it must go -235 volts. Because the tube anode is connected to this terminal, it too must go negative by 235 volts with respect to ground or cathode potential.

Thus the plate becomes negative, the anode current ceases, and the grid has regained control. If the time of deionization is less than the time required to recharge the capacitor through R_2, the grid has regained control and the anode current will not restart.

A Self-stopping D-C Circuit.[1] The circuit of Fig. 9 can be made to start and stop automatically by putting a glow tube across or in place of the switch. Then as soon as the capacitor potential equals the breakdown potential of the glow tube, the latter begins conducting, and the potential across its terminals drops. The potential of the anode with respect to the filament is therefore suddenly lowered by an amount approximately equal to the difference between the breakdown and extinction potentials of the glow tube. The capacitor discharges until the potential across its terminals equals the extinction voltage of the glow tube, which then goes out allowing the capacitor to recharge. If the discharge is slow enough to give the rectifier time to deionize before the anode again becomes 15 volts positive, then the anode current can be cut off by making the grid sufficiently negative. Just as long as the grid is more positive than the critical control value, the only effect of the glow discharge is to cause a periodic interruption of tube current.

[1] H. J. Reich, Self-stopping D-C Thyratron Circuit, *Electronics*, December, 1931, p. 240.

Since the condenser does not discharge completely, it is necessary to use higher capacity than when a switch is used. The glow tube should have a breakdown voltage which is slightly lower than the load voltage and the extinction potential should be as low as possible. No ballast resistance should be used in series with it. A 10-μf condenser in conjunction with a UX-874 voltage-regulator tube will cut off a 1-amp current through an FG-67 tube. Greater care in the choice of the glow tube would without doubt make possible the reduction of condenser size.

The average time interval between the setting of the grid voltage and the extinction of the arc is controlled by changing the value of the resistance which may well be the plate resistance of a vacuum tube. If the rectifier grid is made positive for only an instant, it will pass current for a short interval of time the average length of which may be adjusted by changing the value of the resistance.

Vacuum-tube Control of Gas Tube. In many control circuits the action of a variable resistance is desired but the usual types of rheostats, involving sliding contacts and mechanical movement, are not applicable. The ideal type of control device is represented by the vacuum tube in which the plate current may be controlled by the magnitude of the voltage applied to the grid and in which only a negligible amount of power is required to exercise this control. Unfortunately high-vacuum tubes are not available which will furnish the amounts of power (at convenient voltages) frequently required in connection with regulating problems encountered in power engineering. The gas type of tube, on the other hand, has the disadvantage that the anode current cannot be controlled continuously by the magnitude of the grid voltage. Circuits involving combinations of these two types of tubes will furnish the required amounts of power (at convenient voltages). All that is necessary is that variations in a control voltage be made to cause a phase shift of the voltage in one part of an electric circuit with respect to that in another part.

Tube-controlled Circuit. A second thyratron may also be used instead of the switch of Fig. 9 to force the anode negative. The circuit is in Fig. 10 where the plates are connected to each other by a condenser. To limit the current to the tube, a resistance is in series with each anode and the line. Suppose one of the tubes to be conducting and the other idle. The voltage of the anode of the conducting tube is 15 while that of the other tube is 250.   Now if the nonconducting tube grid is raised to the point at which current flows, its anode voltage drops from 250 to 15 volts, a drop of 235 volts.   The anode voltage of the first tube must fall an equal amount since they are connected together by a condenser which cannot discharge instantaneously.   Thus the first anode is reduced from 15 to −220 and the flow of current ceases.

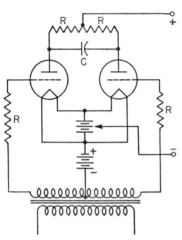

FIG. 10.   Circuit showing the use of a second thyratron instead of the switch in Fig. 9 to force anode negative.

If the time constant of the condenser circuit is high enough to prevent the voltage across the condenser from rising to the value at which the first anode will be positive until the ions lose their charge, the grid of the first tube has control and current will not flow.   In this process the discharge shifts from the first to the second tube.   The grid voltage may be impressed by a transformer as shown in the figure, or in any other desirable way.   A most important application is derived from this circuit by using one winding of a transformer instead of the plate resistances to limit the rate of charge of the anode condenser.   Across the secondary of this transformer will be alternating voltages because of the shift of discharge from one tube to the other and of course this alternating current can be used for any desired purpose.

This is the function of *inversion*, the conversion of direct current into alternating current.

Phase Control of Anode Current.   A more elegant method of controlling the average current consists in varying the phase between the grid and anode voltages.   This method determines how much current is permitted to flow in each cycle.   The method of control is shown in Fig. 11.   Here E_p is the anode potential, assumed to be a sine wave, and E_g the grid voltage, positive above and negative below the line, that will just allow the tube to fire at the corresponding value of E_p. Voltage V_g is a sine wave applied to the grid (V_g need not be a sine wave or of the same frequency as E_p). Consider that this wave be moved along the horizontal axis so that it may be moved into or out of phase with E_p. The tube will fire at the earliest point in the cycle at which V_g crosses E_g (in the figure, point P). When the grid and anode voltages are out of phase, no current flows. If the grid voltage is advanced, current flows during part of the cycle, and by advancing the grid voltage until it is in phase with the anode voltage, the current can be made to flow during the entire half cycle.

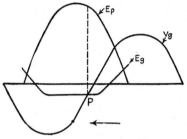

FIG. 11. Basic circuit illustrates phase control of anode firing.

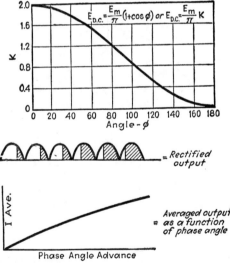

FIG. 12. Handy reference chart for determining average current for the circuit of Fig. 11.

The average current flowing may be found from the expression

$$I_{avg} = I_{max} \left(\frac{1 + \cos \phi}{\pi} \right)$$

where ϕ is the angle at which the tube starts to conduct current. Figure 12 gives the value of $(1 + \cos \phi)$ as a function of ϕ.

Circuits for Obtaining Phase Control. There are many ways of obtaining phase shift between anode and grid voltages. The

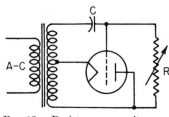

combinations of resistance and capacitance, or of resistance and inductance, are legion. For example, in Fig. 13 a combination of R and C is used. The cathode, grid, and anode voltages are all obtained from a transformer. The grid connection being at the opposite end of the transformer winding from the anode has an

Fig. 13. Resistance-capacitance phase-shift circuit.

opposite polarity with respect to the cathode. Thus when the anode is positive, the grid is negative. This need not be the case, of course. The grid can be maintained positive with respect to the cathode if desired.

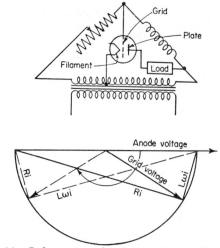

Fig. 14. Inductance and resistance phase-shift circuit.

The voltages across C and R are 90 deg apart. Combining them vectorially gives the total voltage appearing across the transformer winding. By making R very large the phase difference between the grid and the anode is great with consequent decrease in the time per cycle the tube conducts; by making R

equal to zero the grid and anode become in phase and the tube
will conduct current throughout the positive half cycle.

A circuit in which an inductor and a variable resistor are used
and the corresponding relations between the grid and anode
voltages are shown in Fig. 14.   In
both Fig. 13 and Fig. 14 the varying
degrees of control are secured by
changing a resistance.   Of course,
this change can be accomplished
manually as by turning a dial on
a resistor (as in illumination control) or automatically by any varying process, function, or moving
part, or it may be effected by the
varying resistance of a light-sensi-
tive tube under different intensities of illumination.

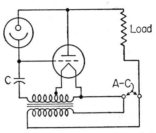

Fig. 15.   Plate current is varied
by changing phototube current.

For example, in Fig. 15 is a phototube between grid and plate.
Here the varying control is made possible by the varying rate at
which the capacitor is charged through the phototube.   The

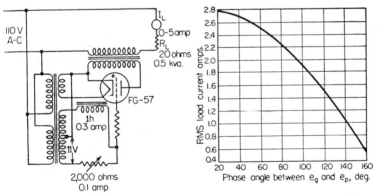

Fig. 16.   Use of transformers in an a-c circuit extends the versatility of
control.

current through the phototube varies continuously and uniformly
as the illumination varies.

Current Control by Transformer and Phase Shift.   The circuit
and curve in Fig. 16 show an example of the ability of the controlled rectifier to pass more or less average current to a load by

means of a phase-shift circuit (resistance and inductance), by changing the impedance of a transformer in series with the load.

Bridge Circuit Phase Control.   The phase relation between grid and plate may be controlled by a bridge incorporating resistances, or resistance and reactance.   If the resistance or the reactance is varied, the grid phase will shift and control will be obtained.   One such system of control uses for the reactance a small solenoid with a movable core.   When the free-hanging solenoid is raised or lowered, the grid phase is shifted and the tube output is varied accordingly.   In another type a resistance is varied by making one side of the bridge a resistance thermometer, thereby providing heat regulation.   Another form uses

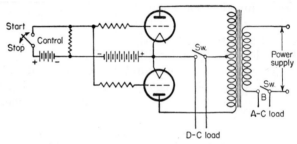

Fig. 17.   Typical arrangement for obtaining switch-type control through the use of thyratrons.

a stack of carbon disks under variable pressure.   A movement of 1/100,000 in. serves to actuate the system.

Thyratrons as Switches.   The simplest and one of the most important functions of a thyratron is that of a simple switch, turning current off or on.   Compared to an ordinary switch or contactor the tube has greater sensitivity; that is, it will control a given amount of power with a small expenditure of power. It has greater speed and may have a life of 10,000 hours or more.   It is quiet in operation, and there is no spark hazard as from a switch.

A typical circuit is given in Fig. 17, in which the controlling element may be a manually operated switch, a clock, thermostat, or a phototube.   The load may be for either direct or alternating current.   The control voltage is shown as direct voltage, but usually it is an alternating voltage.   The bias voltage is usually from rectified alternating current obtained from a copper oxide rectifier.

Such a circuit may be used to control motors, magnets, contactors, or to saturate the core of a reactor as in illumination or welding control. Applications such as turning lights on at dusk and off again at sunrise by a phototube, cutting hot steel bars to desired lengths, opening doors at the approach of a person, wrapping packages, dispatching products to predetermined stations, sorting objects, counting—all of these applications and many others are in daily use.

When the load is in the a-c output, for example in welding, and when the tubes are not conducting, the transformer has a

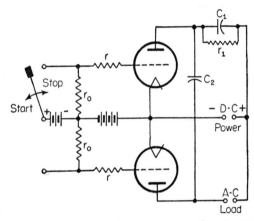

Fig. 18.   Industrial circuit using two thyratrons.

high impedance, and little current will flow in the a-c load. When the tubes take current, this impedance decreases so that full power will flow into the load.

Figure 18 shows a d-c circuit using two thyratrons, one to energize the circuit and the other to deenergize it. The upper tube with the resistor with a capacitor across it carries only a transient current which interrupts momentarily the current in the second tube so that its grid gets control. This capacitor-resistance circuit will be found in many vacuum and gas-tube circuits. It is a most useful tool.

Controlled Rectifiers as Relays. There is an analogy between certain mechanical and tube relay systems, as pointed out by Rolf Wideroe in the October, 1934, *Electrical Engineering*. He starts with a simple overload and underload relay, showing how a tube may be used in place of a mechanical circuit breaker. The first, naturally, consists of a rectifier whose grid permits the flow of current when a certain voltage is reached. The next step toward making an under-voltage relay is to rectify the voltage to be controlled, using it to overcome a positive bias put on the grid from a battery or other source. When the voltage falls too low, the bias battery will permit the tube to fire.

By combining the over- and under-voltage relays, a percentage differential relay or an under-impedance relay may be made. Still other more complex circuits are given in the reference cited in the previous paragraph. Also discussed are the effects of disturbances and temperature upon such relays, noting that the mercury-vapor tubes will be at a disadvantage in such circuits because of their temperature characteristics. Argon-filled tubes have fired at a grid voltage within approximately 0.2 volt over a long period, and varying the anode voltage by 10 per cent will not cause a variation of more than ± 5 per cent in the firing grid voltage.

The literature on this simple function of thyratrons is very extensive and indicates that this phase of thyratron development is now fairly stable.[1]

The Inverter.   In the earlier days of the application of tubes to industrial processes the inverter was thought to be of very great potential value. The inverter is a tube mechanism for converting direct current power into alternating current power. To date the inverter has not come into very great use except for small amounts of power. The dream of transmitting power at high direct voltages rather than in the form of alternating current has not come to fruition. The advantages are great and a glance at the literature will show the bases for early work on this subject.[2]

The Inversion Process.   Any scheme for converting direct current into alternating current may be called inversion. Thus a

---

[1] W. K. Kearsley, A Vacuum-tube Time Switch, *General Electric Review*, February, 1931; C. C. Holloway, *Electronics*, August, 1933, p. 220, on a time-delay relay for a coil-winding machine.   Additional circuits and data will be found in A. W. Hull, *General Electric Review*, December, 1932, p. 628; Baker, Fitzgerald and Whitney, *Electronics*, April, 1931, p. 581; and George Mucher, *Electronics*, April, 1936, p. 38.

[2] See C. H. Willis, B. D. Bedford, and F. R. Elder, *Transactions of the American Institute of Electrical Engineers*, January, 1935; *General Electric Review*, February, 1935, and May, 1936; see also talk delivered by C. W. Stone before the American Society of Civil Engineers, New York, Feb. 15, 1933.

simple vacuum-tube oscillator may be considered as an inverter; but in the stricter use of the term, an inverter is a thyratron or several such tubes used for converting large amounts of d-c power to a-c power.

In the simplest form of gas-tube inverter direct current is fed into it; then by some means the grid voltage is varied so that alternating current will flow in the anode circuit. In the high-frequency oscillator this commutation is produced by the tuned circuit which is an electrical analog of the fly wheel in mechanical systems. It is, in effect, an energy-storage device. In thyratron inverters some form of energy storage is necessary, and this may be the charge stored in a condenser, or the field built up around an inductance. With two-tube inverters, a commutation system is necessary to shift conduction from one tube to another. Thus one tube may be used to shut the other off when it conducts. If the tubes are arranged back-to-back, the total plate current will resemble that produced by an a-c generator.

Although most inverter circuits involve two tubes, there are several single-tube circuits for performing the function of getting alternating current from a d-c source.[1] Consider Fig. 19A. Assume the switch to be closed on a d-c source at a time when C is discharged. Since no voltage exists across C, the cathode of the tube is at the same voltage as b, the negative side of the line. The grid is positive because of its position on the voltage divider, a-b. If this positive voltage is of the proper magnitude, the tube starts to conduct.

The current passes through L, R_1, the tube, and C shunted by R_2 and back to the line. If R_2 is high enough, and R_1 is low enough, C will charge quickly, and the voltage across it will soon equal the line voltage. Ordinarily the current flow would cease at this instant, but because of the inductance, current will continue to flow because of the collapsing flux about the coil which induces an emf, forcing current to flow through the condenser.

As a consequence of this continued flow, because of the inductance, when the current finally ceases, the condenser is charged higher than line voltage and the anode is now more negative than the cathode by this voltage. Therefore, until this charge leaks off through R_2, the tube will not conduct current again. When, however, the voltage across C has decreased to the point where

[1] See Lord and Livingston, *Electronics*, April, 1933.

the difference in potential between grid and cathode is equal to the critical voltage, the cycle will be repeated.

The overcharging of the condenser enables the grid to retain control of the discharge for a period long enough for deionization to take place.   Thus the tube commutates the flow of current.

The second fundamental single-tube inverter is shown in Fig. 19*B*.   In this case when the switch is closed, the cathode and anode are at almost the same potential (the condenser is

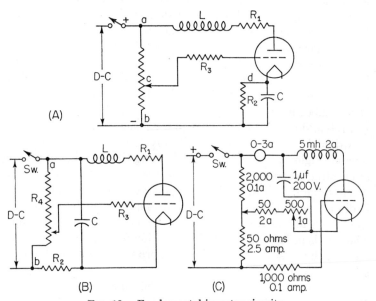

FIG. 19.   Fundamental inverter circuits.

uncharged), and the grid is at a negative voltage by the amount of the drop along *a-b*.   While *C* is charging through R_2, the tube does not conduct.   Charging *C* lowers the voltage of the cathode, and when it reaches the value which will give the grid-cathode potential the critical value, the tube will conduct.   At this point the condenser discharges through the inductance and R_1.   The voltage across *C* is now reversed, because of the overcharging effect, making the anode negative long enough for deionization to occur and give control to the grid again.   Now *C* charges again and the cycle is repeated.

Occasionally the circuit is used without the potentiometer, the grid being connected to the negative side of the line. The lack of the potentiometer removes the ability to control the frequency with which the condenser and tube discharge and it tends to make the timing more susceptible to error.

In Fig. 19C are typical constants of a single-tube inverter circuit described by E. D. McArthur, *General Electric Review*, November, 1933.

Single-tube Inverter Applications. After setting R_2 and R_4 (Fig. 19) to produce the proper frequency, a small synchronizing voltage introduced in series with the grid circuit will maintain the proper frequency of inversion so that the tube may be run in synchronism with some other circuit. Multiple or submultiple frequencies may be synchronized in this manner.

In practice L and R_1 would probably be a transformer, from the secondary of which would be taken the desired alternating current. The leakage inductance is usually sufficient to overcharge the condenser. If the voltage ratio of the transformer is of the correct order, the circuit may be used to light neon signs, the circuit then becoming an interrupter induction coil.

If R_2 is replaced with an emission-limited vacuum tube to maintain a constant charging or discharging current through the condenser and the time of conduction is made very small, a sawtooth wave form will be secured, useful in cathode-ray tube work, for television, or for other purposes where a sharp break is desired. In welding control by grid-controlled rectifiers this method of timing is used.

A d-c potential may be used in series with the saw-tooth wave which, varied in amplitude according to some desired time function, will control the proportion of the time the resultant voltage is positive. This voltage applied to the grids of other tubes will control the ratio of the time that current is passed to the time it is off. The number of welding spots per second may be varied by changing the frequency generated by the inverter.

Another use of the inverter technique is for stroboscopic work. If a gas tube illuminates the rotor of a motor and if, acting as an inverter, it is synchronized from the source which drives the motor, the shaft and rotor will seem to stand still; or the rotor of an induction motor will seem to run backward at a speed proportional to the slip frequeney. If a shaft to be observed is not running in synchronism with any a-c source, a small synchronizing voltage may be introduced into the grid circuit by the use of small contacts or by inducing a voltage in a small pick-up coil once a revolution.

There is a very extensive literature on inverters, and the references at the end of the chapter will give one the essential background.[1]

The Ignitron.   A new and highly important type of controlled rectifier resulted from the discovery by Slepian and Ludwig of a new method of initiating the discharge in a gaseous controlled rectifier.   Tubes making use of this discovery are called ignitrons. By immersing certain materials, a carborundum crystal, for example, in a mercury pool and then passing current from the crystal to the mercury the start of an arc is forced.   At a definite value of voltage and current a small spark occurs at the junction and immediately grows into the cathode spot of an arc.   If an anode is properly placed and held at a positive potential with respect to the arc, the latter will be transferred to the anode and thereby initiate the discharge.   This process may require only 25 microseconds.   Thus the discovery made possible a mercury-pool controlled rectifier with the advantage of practically unlimited emission and therefore a high overload capacity. Furthermore, it requires no delay when put into service.   The life of the cathode, and therefore the tube, is longer than the hot cathode, or thermionic type.   Compared to the conventional mercury-pool tube, the ignitron is simpler and has much less tendency to arc back.

Each pool of a conventional pool-type rectifier requires a starter of some kind to form the arc and a keep-alive transformer and reactor to maintain the arc.   At least 5 amp is required in the keep-alive circuit to insure stability.   In addition to the consumption of energy, this keep-alive circuit tends to produce ionization in single-anode tubes, and therefore on the inverse cycle it tends to increase troubles from arc-back.   The anodes are placed in anode arms to prevent arc-back, thereby complicating the structure and increasing the size, especially since each pool requires keep-alive equipment.

The ignitron has no keep-alive and no anode arms.   Three such tubes (one for each phase) will replace a conventional recti-

[1] Some very useful material will be found in the "Engineering Manual" of Electrons, Inc., Newark, N.J.

fier with less auxiliary equipment, lower replacement cost, and better performance.

Silicon carbide and boron carbide are the two materials most generally used for igniters, although other materials may be used. The igniter current for starting the cathode spot is usually less than 20 amp, and the igniter voltage for this current about 50 volts.

In use, a properly timed current pulse is given to the igniter at the beginning of each desired current-carrying period. At the end of each period the cathode spot automatically goes out and is not reestablished until the current pulse is given again to the

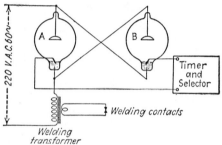

FIG. 20.   High-current ignitrons are generally employed in industrial circuits requiring control of extremely high currents.

igniter at the beginning of the next following current-carrying period. Thus in each current-obstructing period there is no cathode spot on the mercury to induce arc-backs on the adjacent anode.

Ignitrons are now used extensively for controlling the currents used in spot welding stainless steel, aluminum, and other metals. In this application, pulses of current of large magnitude but carefully controlled short duration must be fed into the weld. Two ignitrons placed in the primary circuit of a welding transformer as in Fig. 20 permit the large currents to be controlled by merely controlling the grid potentials of the auxiliary thermionic cathode tubes. Glass ignitrons can pass single-cycle pulses of 1,000 amp for making spot welds at 60 spots per minute. For larger powers, water-cooled metal ignitrons are used. These can pass single-cycle pulses of 3,500 amp sixty times per minute.

The most convenient method of obtaining the proper current pulses to the igniter is usually to connect the igniter terminal to the anode externally through a small thermionic cathode tube. For example, in a simple rectifier circuit, as in Fig. 21, the igniter tubes may be simple rectifiers. When a main anode becomes positive, current flows through the auxiliary thermionic cathode to the igniter, and at 10 to 20 amp a cathode spot forms on the mercury, and the arc in the ignitron shorts the thermionic cathode tube out of the circuit. When the main anode becomes negative, no current flows to the igniter, and no cathode spot forms. Thus the current-obstructing property remains unimpaired.

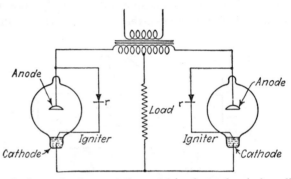

Fig. 21. Ignitron circuit especially useful in electrochemical applications.

The current carried by the auxiliary thermionic cathode tube need never exceed that sufficient to start a cathode spot upon the mercury. In case of a short circuit in the external circuit, for example, the heavy current is all carried by the ignitron with mercury-pool cathode. The auxiliary tube is then protected from any severe duty by the ignitron itself, and its life is very long. At the same time, because of its small size, its renewal is inexpensive.

If the auxiliary thermionic cathode igniter tube is provided with a control grid, then additional possibilities in power conversion become available. Now, for sending current to the igniter it is necessary not only for the main anode to have the proper positive polarity but also for the grid of the auxiliary thermionic tube to have the proper excitation. Thus, for example, by retarding the moment of excitation of the igniter, the current-carrying intervals in the circuit of Fig. 21 can be shortened, and the current supplied by the rectifier controllably reduced, with control equipment that needs to handle only the minute currents of the grids of the auxiliary. This characteristic should be extremely valuable in electrochemical applications.

With control of the grid of the auxiliary thermionic cathode tube, we may not only control rectification or conversion of alternating current into direct current but also effect inversion or conversion of direct current into alternating and also conversion of alternating current of one frequency into that of another frequency. Circuits for accomplishing these functions are well-known and have frequently been described using discharge tubes with grids interposed between the main electrodes for controlling the initiation of the current-conducting interval. The ignitron with its small grid-controlled auxiliary igniter tube may be used in all these circuits in place of the directly grid-controlled power tubes, with the great advantage that the controlling grid is no longer in the path of the main discharge so that loss in efficiency due to the presence of this grid is avoided.

REFERENCES

Alexanderson, E. F. W., and A. H. Mittag, Thyratron Motor, *Electrical Engineering*, November, 1934, p. 1517.

Alpert, N., Linear Thyratron Control Circuit, *Electronics*, December, 1949, p. 184.

Bowlus, O. E., and P. T. Nims, Thyratron Frequency Changers, *Electronics*, March, 1948, p. 126.

Cage, J. M., Theory of the Immersion Mercury Arc Ignitor, *General Electric Review*, October, 1935, p. 464.

Craig, P. H., *Electronics*, May, 1933, p. 639.

Dow, W. G.. and W. H. Powers, Firing Time of an Igniter Type of Tube, *Electrical Engineering*, September, 1935, p. 942.

Hafner, H., Grid-controlled Mercury Valve Used as Rectifier and D.C.-A.C. Converter, *Bulletin Oerlikon*, August-September, 1932, pp. 725–728.

Heins, H., Hydrogen Thyratrons, *Electronics*, July, 1946, p. 96.

Ignitron, *Electrician*, June, 1934, p. 792.

Improved Welding Timer Expands Spot-welding Use, *Electrical World*, Mar. 24, 1934.

Inverter for Projector Lamps (in German), *Allgemeine Electricitäts-Gesellschaft Mitteilungen*, January, 1932, pp. 11–13.

Jaeschke, R. L., Thyratron Braking for Oil Drilling Rigs, *Electronics*, April, 1948, p. 92.

Knowles, D. D., and E. G. Bangratz, The Ignitron, *Electric Journal*, December, 1933.

Knowles, D. D., The Ignitron—A New Controlled Rectifier, *Electronics*, June, 1933, p. 164.

Laub, H., Discharge Tubes for Rectification, Inversion and Frequency Changing (in German), *Elektrotechnik und Maschinenbau*, vol. 50, pp. 317–325, May 29, 1932.

Ludwig, L. R., F. A. Maxfield, and A. H. Toepfer, An Experimental Ignitron Rectifier, *Electrical Engineering*, January, 1934, p. 75.

May, J. C., H. J. Reich, and J. G. Skalnik, Thyratron Phase-control Circuits, *Electronics*, July, 1948, p. 107.

McArthur, E. D., *General Electric Review*, November, 1933.

Prince, D. C., Direct-current Transformer Utilizing Thyratron Tubes, *General Electric Review*, vol. 31, pp. 347–350, July, 1928.

Reich, H. J., *Review of Scientific Instruments*, October, 1932; March, 1933; *Electrical Engineering*, December, 1933.

Silverman, Daniel, and J. H. Cox, A High Power Welding Rectifier, *Electrical Engineering*, October, 1934, p. 1380.

Slepian, J., and L. R. Ludwig, A New Method for Initiating the Cathode of an Arc, *Transactions of the American Institute of Electrical Engineering*, vol. 52, p. 693, June, 1933.

Stoddard, R. N., A New Timer for Resistance Welding, *Electrical Engineering*, October, 1934, p. 1366.

Technical Principles and Applications of Controlled Rectifiers and Inverters (in German), *Electrolectinische Zeitschrift*, vol. 53, pp. 770–786, Aug. 11, 1932.

Tompkins, F. N., The Parallel Type of Inverter, *Electrical Engineering*, April, 1933.

Wagner, C. F., and L. R. Ludwig, Ignitron Type of Inverter, *Electrical Engineering*, October, 1934, p. 1384.

Westendorp, W. F., An Inverter-lamp for the Conversion of 60-cycle Power into 1,000-cycle Modulated Light, *Physics*, vol. 3, No. 4, pp. 193–202, October, 1932.

Willis, C. H., Harmonic Commutation for Thyratron Inverters and Rectifiers, *General Electric Review*, December, 1932.

Willis, C. H., A Study of the Thyratron Commutator Motor, *General Electric Review*, February, 1933, p. 76.

CHAPTER 7

RELAYS AND RELAY CIRCUITS

It has been pointed out that electron tubes are, in general, low-power devices. For vacuum tubes, currents of several hundred milliamperes may be considered high. Gas tubes can control currents of the order of amperes. Many industrial applications, however, require the control of higher values of power than can economically be handled by electron tubes.

The relay is an electromagnetic device; that is, it contains a coil of wire wrapped around a core so that a magnetic force will be exerted when a current is passed through the coil. The magnitude of magnetic force produced by an electromagnet is proportional, among other things, to the product of the amount of current flowing through the coil and the number of turns of wire that make up the coil. By using relatively large numbers of turns of wire on the coil only small currents are required to produce a substantial electromagnetic force. Thus large pieces of magnetic material can readily be caused to move by the flow of small currents, such as those associated with vacuum tubes. As might be expected, the large pieces of magnetic material that are made to move are the contacts of a high-power switch. The larger the cross-section of any current-carrying element, the less will be the losses occurring in that element, so of course large contacts have advantages for the large current values involved in high-power applications.

The power-multiplying capabilities of a relay are limited by the resistance of the wire that forms the relay coil. A relay that can be operated by currents of the order of microamperes (extremely sensitive relays) can only be expected to control currents in the neighborhood of a few hundred milliamperes, because the amount of power supplied to the relay coil is small, and thus the electromagnetic force available to move the relay contacts is small. In fact, relays of this type consist primarily of sensitive indicating-meter elements, the pointer of which serves as the moving contact. Relays that require several milliamperes for their operation will handle contact currents of a few amperes, and so on. These values are given for general cases. Many times certain factors enter into the picture that limit the power-multiplying capabilities. In these cases the power-multiplication ability of the relay is not the important property, as will also be explained later.

Relay Terms. In the relay business there are a great number of terms with special meanings applicable to relays only. A few of the most common of these are presented here.

Armature—The movable part of a relay that is mechanically coupled to the moving contact.

Break—The opening or interruption of a circuit.

Chatter—Undesirable opening and closing of relay contacts.

Cycle—With reference to relays a cycle is the complete program of operation required to make a relay perform its desired function and then return to its original condition.

Deenergize—This means to disconnect from a power source. In relay talk this means interrupting flow of current in relay coil. The relay is then said to be deenergized.

Drop-out—In relay language drop-out refers to the time when the relay coil current decreases to a point where the electromagnetic force is no longer sufficient to attract the armature. For instance, when the coil is deenergized, the relay "drops out."

Duty cycle—The working time compared to the idling time of a piece of equipment. The power rating of the equipment, such as the coil of a relay, is based on the load it will carry without overheating. Where a device is only called on to carry a load for a few seconds once every few minutes, for example, it has a relatively long time to cool between operations. Therefore while it is operating it can carry a larger load than it could carry continuously. A small device, such as a relay, will achieve its maximum temperature after about 20 minutes of continuous operation. Thus for periods of 20 minutes or more, operation is said to be continuous despite the length of subsequent idling periods. Duty cycles are usually given as *momentary* (working period so brief that almost no temperature rise occurs), *intermittent* (where the device must dissipate excessive heat during idling periods), and *continuous*.

Make—Two contacts are said to "make" when they touch so as to establish an electrical circuit.

Normal position—This term refers to the position of the relay contacts when the relay coil is deenergized.

Normally open—A term used to describe a pair of relay contacts that are open when the relay is in its normal position.

Normally closed—A term used to describe a pair of relay contacts that are closed when the relay is in its normal position (see Relay Symbols).

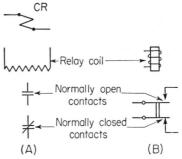

Pull-in, or pick-up—This term refers to the energizing of the relay by application of power to the relay coil to operate the contacts. The relay picks up when it is energized.

This list is incomplete, but it presents the relay terms most commonly used. There are actually many more terms[1] that will be encountered by anyone specializing in relays and circuits involving relays.

Fig. 1. The symbols for relays shown in *A* are used extensively in industrial power circuits; those in *B*, in periodicals dealing in general electronic circuits.

Relay Symbols. There is considerable disagreement as to how relays should be represented in schematic diagrams. Figure 1 shows several different symbols that are in common use in modern industrial schematics. The type shown in *A* has the advantage of making diagrams look less complicated because the contacts can be placed anywhere that is convenient on the drawing. The type shown at *B* presents a more involved problem to the draftsman, but it gives a clearer presentation of the relay function. In the first system the relay contacts are associated with their respective coils by numbers and letters, and contacts and coils are located wherever convenient on the diagram.

Figure 2 shows several of the multitude of possible contact combinations. As might be expected, a large number of com-

[1] Charles A. Packard, "Relay Engineering," Struthers-Dunn, Inc., Philadelphia.

binations of contacts are available. The type shown in Fig. 3 illustrates the use of a locking circuit with a relay. By the use of this device, which merely consists of an extra pair of contacts that are closed when the relay is energized, the relay may be energized by a momentary switch and held in its energized position until the coil circuit is interrupted by an auxiliary switch (reset) that is normally closed.

Contact Arcing. Most high-power industrial circuits, in which relays are used to interrupt the flow of current, have some inductance; that is, they have the property of trying to maintain whatever current is flowing through them. If normal rated current is flowing through an inductive load and also through the closed contacts of a relay, the inductance of the circuit will tend to keep that current flowing even when the relay

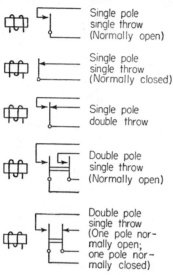

Single pole single throw (Normally open)

Single pole single throw (Normally closed)

Single pole double throw

Double pole single throw (Normally open)

Double pole single throw (One pole normally open; one pole normally closed)

Fig. 2. A wide variety of contact arrangements is possible. Several typical combinations are illustrated here.

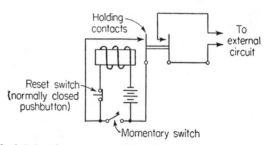

Fig. 3. The left-hand contacts on this relay form a locking circuit. When the relay closes, these contacts short the momentary actuating contacts, and the relay remains closed until the reset (momentarily open) switch is actuated.

contacts are opened. This action takes place because a certain amount of energy is stored up in the electromagnetic field of the inductance. When the flow of current is interrupted, this field collapses and generates a voltage that tends to maintain current flow. When this voltage appears at the contacts of a relay, a certain amount of power must be dissipated. The resistance across the open, or partially open, contacts is high—the resistivity of air being high. Thus all of this power is dissipated when the contacts first part. This rapid discharge takes place in the form of an arc between the terminals until the stored energy is dissipated in the form of heat in the arc.

This heat, if excessive, can damage the contacts of the relay. Thus the inductance of the circuit being interrupted also enters into the design or selection of a relay for a particular application. The amount of heat produced by an arc is dependent on the amount of current that flows during the arc and the time duration of the arc. Special contacts are available for breaking circuits that have extremely high inductances—one system uses two separate breakers, one pair actually breaks the circuit, while the other is designed to withstand the arcing and takes the heat produced by the arc. This type is called the double-break type. A relay whose action is very fast will be better suited for breaking high inductance circuits, because the arc is quickly extinguished as the contact spacing increases.

A-C versus D-C Relays. Relays are available for operation on either alternating or direct current. An a-c relay operating on a 60-cycle source will actually attract its armature 120 times a second, once for each half cycle of current through the coil. The characteristic of the armature must be such that it will be attracted on both halves of the cycle (will have low residual magnetism), and the contacts connected to it must have inertia and flexibility to stay closed continuously while the coil is energized.

Most a-c relay coils are only rated for voltage. In most circuits involving a-c relays a fixed source of a-c power is used, and a small switch used to connect the relay coil to this source. In electronic applications, a-c relays may either be operated by low-voltage power from filament voltage supplies or directly from 115-volt power lines. Of course, contact ratings for both types of relays must be sufficient for any specific application.

Where a source of d-c voltage of the proper magnitude is available, d-c relays are preferable. An a-c relay is prone to vibration and sometimes to chatter, when the frequency is sufficiently low.

Resonant Relays. One special version of the a-c relay is the resonant relay, which will operate only if the voltage applied to its coil is of a certain frequency. Relays of this type are useful in multiple-circuit remote-control applications and telemetering devices. For instance, if two relays are available, one resonant to 200 cps and the other to 400 cps, then a single pair of wires may be used to operate either relay at some remote point by the application of a voltage of the desired frequency at the sending end.

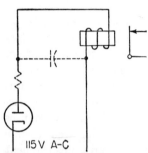

These relays operate as simple tuned circuits. The inductance of the coil is resonated with enough capacitance so that the combination has a low impedance at the proper frequency. Thus high current flows at resonance, and the relay is energized. When the coil is not resonant to the frequency of the applied voltage, the relay is not energized.

Fig. 4. Dotted lines represent the position of resistance and capacitance sometimes included in tube-relay circuits to prevent chatter and other undesirable effects.

D-C Relay Operation. It should be mentioned that since the current-carrying contacts are independent of the current actuating the electromagnet, a d-c relay can control alternating or direct current by its contacts, and, of course, an a-c relay can also control either direct or alternating current. Relays having d-c coils may be operated from a-c lines by the addition of simple rectifying circuits. Such a setup is shown in Fig. 4 which shows a diode rectifier and the coil of a d-c relay. If 60-cycle a-c voltage is applied to the input terminals of this circuit, the current flowing through the relay coil will consist of pulses of d-c current flowing for $\frac{1}{120}$ second once every $\frac{1}{60}$ second. Depending on the design of the relay, chatter may occur. The armature will actually only be attracted half of the time and to varying degrees. To avoid chatter, the armature may be made quite heavy so that its inertia will be sufficient to prevent movement for the short intervals when no current flows through the coil. Another means for using this type of circuit with a d-c relay and avoiding chatter is to provide some filtering, that is, to smooth out the pulsations. The inductance of the relay coil itself provides a certain amount of filtering, and the addition of a capacitor across the terminals will usually provide more than sufficient protection from chatter. The capacitor charges up on voltage peaks and provides the coil with current during the interval when the source current supply is cut off.

A typical value for this filtering capacitor is 4 μf. Larger values will further reduce tendency toward chattering but the relay will become increasingly sluggish in pulling in upon application of power. The reason is that the voltage across the relay coil cannot rise quickly when shunted by the large capacitor. The capacitor voltage will rise at a rate depending on the size of the capacitor and the resistance in the circuit in series with the applied voltage. When voltage is first applied, most of the drop occurs across the series resistance (which may be the internal resistance of the source) due to the flow of current that charges the capacitor. As the capacitor charges, more and more of the source voltage appears across it (and the relay coil) and less appears across the resistance, until the relay finally pulls up.

Time-delay Relays. The effect mentioned above is frequently used where an intentional time delay is desired between the application of power and the pulling up of a relay armature. By placing resistance in series with the power lead and by putting capacitance across the relay coil, a wide range of relay closure time delays may be obtained. Sometimes a small resistance must be placed in series with a capacitor-filtered relay to limit the surge current that would otherwise be prohibitively large when power is first applied to the capacitor. The maximum current rating of the rectifier must not be exceeded.

Another type of time-delay relay device takes advantage of the time required for the filament of a rectifier tube to heat after current has been applied. The rectifier tube is connected in the circuit in the usual manner and when energy is applied to the filament, it slowly heats up and starts making electrons available. Thus the closure of the relay contacts is delayed by the length of time required for the filament to heat sufficiently to produce enough electrons to energize the relay coil. This is an unorthodox application of an electron tube, and the performance of tubes in such an application must be measured experimentally by the user.

Uses of Time-delay Relays. There are many uses of time-delay devices. One particularly useful application is overload protection.   Relays or a form of relays are frequently used to prevent overloads to pieces of equipment.   The coil of the relay is placed in series with the electrical load, and when the load current exceeds a specified limit, the relay armature moves and disconnects the load from its power source.   In most cases instantaneous overloads can be tolerated—in fact they are expected, for instance when the load is initially applied.   In this case if one uses a delay device which has a delay period longer than the expected instantaneous overload that can be tolerated, the relay will not interrupt the circuit at all, unless the overload is sustained.   Any place where some action is required for sustained conditions but not for momentary conditions dictates the use of a delay relay of some sort.   There are, of course, delay circuits using tubes which are capable of more accurate time delays than are possible with relays.   However their accuracy is only an advantage in certain applications, and where relay control is of sufficient accuracy, the added complication of the tube versions is seldom justified.

There are also a great many thermal and mechanical delay devices in use.   A bimetallic strip will bend when heated and may thus be used as a relay.   Current may be allowed to run through the strip and thus heat it, or the current may be run through a heating coil that heats the strip indirectly.   In either case the strip bending occurs gradually, and thus a time delay occurs between the application of the high current and the closing or opening of the contacts.

Mechanical delay devices may take many forms.   A heavier armature will move more slowly than a light one, and an armature that has to move over a considerable distance will make (or break) more slowly than one whose contacts are separated only by a small distance.   Another device, called the *dashpot*, resembles an automobile shock absorber.   A piston is mechanically coupled to the moving contact.   When the armature moves, the moving contact (which is usually connected to the armature through a spring) tends to follow the movement.   However, the piston is placed in a closed cylinder, and before it can move, the air pressure (sometimes liquids are used) must equalize.   As the air slowly creeps around the tight-fitting piston, the piston slowly moves and allows the moving contact to move.

Fail-safe Operations.   In many applications it is essential that the equipment provide some sort of indication when anything

is wrong.   In other words it must be self-policing.   Relays provide a convenient means for doing this.

Consider, for example, a burglar alarm.   It would have relatively limited use if it were ineffective when the power was disconnected.   A thief could simply pull the plug or disconnect the
power to the circuit by some other means.   Most devices of this
kind employ an alarm relay that is always energized under normal
conditions.   As a burglar trips the detecting device, the relay is
deenergized through the auxiliary equipment and an alarm is
sounded.   Thus in the event of power failure, the relay will automatically be deenergized and the alarm will again be sounded.
The cause of the alarm is then determined and appropriate action
taken.

Many such fail-safe devices are used in modern aircraft devices,
where correct operation is essential to safe flight.

Supersensitive D-C Relays.   As mentioned before, relays are
available for closing circuits as the result of the flow of a few
microamperes of current through their coils.   These types are
modified coil-type microammeters, with platinum-iridium contacts mounted on the moving pointer and with adjustable contacts on either or both sides of the pointer.   Platinum contacts
are used because platinum does not oxidize or tarnish in air.   For
less expensive relays, contacts made of silver are often used.

The principle of a supersensitive relay of the type described is
shown in the drawing of Fig. 5.   The arrangement shown is
designed to provide an indication whenever the current flowing
through the coil rises above or falls below a certain specified level.
When the current is exactly at this desired level, the pointer
(moving contact) is midway between the upper and lower limit
contacts.   When the current varies either way, contact is made
with one or the other.

Even though platinum-iridium alloys are good conductors, the
current that can be passed by these contacts is small because of
their relatively small cross-sectional area and that of the wires
connecting them to the external circuit.   The customary practice is to use a second relay between the supersensitive unit and
the device to be controlled.   Several milliamperes of current can
be controlled by the contacts of the supersensitive relay, and such
a value is ample to operate the larger relay.

By proper placement of the fixed contacts on a relay of this
sort, other functions can be obtained.   A fixed contact at the

high-current end of the meter movement will act as a normally open relay; and a fixed contact at the no-current end will be contacted when the flow of current through the coil is interrupted so that it operates as a normally closed relay.

Relays of this kind have numerous disadvantages. In the first place they are intricate and require protection against mechanical damage, jarring, and so on. They are also quite prone to chatter when the current in the coil is just enough to close the contacts. This may cause undesirable operation of the

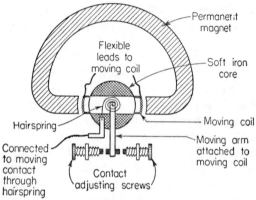

Fig. 5.   A supersensitive relay is essentially a current-meter movement with contacts arranged to be opened or closed by the "needle."

device being controlled, and it may also cause damage to the contacts by arcing. This disadvantage is overcome in the Weston Sensitrol relay, the basic contruction of which is similar to that shown in Fig. 5 except that a piece of soft iron replaces the moving contact, and a small, but powerful permanent magnet replaces the fixed contact. When the arm swings toward the closed position, the permanent magnet attracts the moving element and draws it into contact with a solid snap. In this way permanent and sure contact is made. To release, or reset, the relay, the moving contact is either returned to its off position manually or by means of an electrically operated solenoid. Relays of this sort are available in many different types, with a variety of current ratings and contact arrangements. Of course, they have their greatest advantage where positive, but not continuous, control is necessary.

Applications of Supersensitive Relays. These supersensitive relays find somewhat limited use in industrial applications because of their fragility and cost, but they are very useful where no other relay will serve the purpose.

For example, certain types of photocells generate sufficient current when irradiated with light to energize a supersensitive relay. In botanical and agricultural research accurate records of the length of time certain temperatures or certain values of illumination are maintained are of vital interest and value. By connecting a photocell and a supersensitive relay so that the relay turns on a clock whenever the critical value is exceeded, accurate records may be made.

Sensitive Relays. Sensitive relays usually refer to those that require currents from 0.5 to 3 ma for their operation. They are the most common types in the field of electronics, because they may be used directly in the plate circuits of vacuum tubes, which may in turn be caused to conduct the required values of current by the application of small values of voltage on the grid of the tube. The operation is fundamentally the same as with the supersensitive relays, but in this case the extra sensitivity is supplied by tube amplifiers instead of by the increased sensitivity of the relay movement.

Figure 6 shows a drawing of a typical "telephone-type" sensitive relay. The armature is made of soft iron and is allowed to pivot. In effect, as in most relays, the function of the relay is to overcome the force exerted on the armature by a spring.

The force that is exerted by the spring is, for all practical purposes, constant. However, as the current increases in the relay coil, the force exerted by the electromagnet increases proportionally. As the electromagnetic force approaches the force of the spring, the armature begins to move. At the moment when the armature first begins to move, the space between the armature and the electromagnet decreases. This further increases the electromagnetic force applied to the armature (the distance being smaller) and increases the unbalance in favor of the electromagnet, until the armature snaps into its energized position.

When relay current decreases, the electromagnetic force decreases, but the armature does not spring back immediately, as in the case of the supersensitive relay. The current must decrease considerably before the spring tension will overcome the electromagnetic force, which is high because of the small spacing between coil and armature.

The difference in current between the value required to energize a sensitive relay and the value at which the relay will drop out is called the *operating differential*. This value is often given as a percentage; for example, the drop-out current may be 20 per cent of the pull-in current.

These sensitive relays are capable of pulling up on relatively low current because of the great number of turns of wire. The large number of turns causes the resistance of the coils to be high.

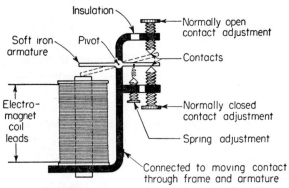

FIG. 6.   Typical "telephone-type" sensitive relay construction.

In fact, resistances of 10,000 ohms are common. A mean value might be in the neighborhood of 8,000 ohms. For maximum efficiency in utilizing sensitive relays, it is best to select a relay whose coil resistance is equal to the output plate resistance of the vacuum tube with which the relay is to operate. Under these conditions a maximum transfer of energy will occur between source and load.

Relay coils are generally given a power rating which must not be exceeded in normal operation. In designing a tube circuit for a sensitive relay, it is important that the current flowing under maximum current conditions, that is, with the tube conducting the most current expected, does not exceed the power rating, which can be computed by the formula

$$W = \frac{E^2}{R} = I^2 R$$

where W is the power in watts, and E the voltage that appears across the relay coil (which is equal to the power supply voltage minus tube voltage drop and the drop across any other resistance in the circuit). The relay coil voltage will be maximum when the voltage drop across the tube is lowest, that is, when the tube is conducting and allowing current to flow through the relay coil.

Sensitive Relay Adjustments. There are three basic adjustments which must be made for optimum operation of sensitive relays. They are:

1. The amount of force exerted by the spring (spring tension)
2. The position of the normally closed contact
3. The position of the normally open contact

The tighter the spring tension, the greater the electromagnetic force (coil current) required to energize the relay. Also, the greater the spacing between the armature and the electromagnet, as set by the position of the normally closed contact, the greater the required electromagnetic force for relay operation. Finally, the position of the normally open contact will determine the distance over which the armature, and moving contact will have to move to establish the energized position.

The best setting for these three adjustments is determined by experiment under operating conditions. For example, a manufacturer may provide an 8,000-ohm relay to be operated with a current of 2 ma. By reducing the spring tension the relay can be made to pull up at much lower values than 2 ma. But the drop-out current will be raised considerably, and undesirable chatter may result.

An excellent discussion of sensitive relay adjustment is presented by Fisher.[1] He reports that the best way to achieve maximum contact pressure for rated current conditions is to make use of a paper gauge. The procedure is as follows: (1) Insert the paper gauge between the armature and magnet. Energize the coil sufficiently to hold the armature firmly against paper and magnet. (2) Move the normally open contact until it just closes (electrical indication, such as small lamp and battery or ohmmeter may be used). See that the paper is still held firmly between armature and magnet. A working air gap for the

---

[1] R. T. Fisher, Adjusting Sensitive Relays, *Electronics*, February, 1947, p. 71.

energized position is now set.   The normally open contact is not
moved again.   (Any convenient gauge may be used if the paper
thickness is not right.)   (3) Pull out paper gauge and reduce
coil current until the value is reached at which relay drop-out is
desired.   Then reduce spring tension until armature actually
does drop out.   Reenergize, and check again.   (4) Now increase
the coil current until the desired pull-up value is reached.   Now
adjust the normally closed contact until armature pulls in open-

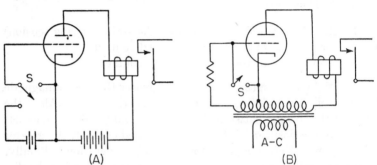

(A)   (B)

Fig. 7.   Use of electron tubes permits control of fairly rugged relays by
extremely low power switches.

ing normally-closed contacts.   Reduce coil current, deenergize
relay, then increase again to check for desired operation.
    The relay is now completely adjusted.   The currents for
adjustment can be provided by the actual circuit into which the
relay is to be placed, or by an auxiliary circuit consisting of a
battery, a current-indicating meter (milliameter), and a variable
resistance to set the proper current flow.
    Relays in Vacuum-tube Circuits.   Figure 7A shows the basic
circuit of a vacuum tube with a relay coil as its plate load.   Tube
curves may be consulted to determine the correct operating voltages for proper relay operation.   In the circuit, switch S is
thrown up to energize the relay.   When this switch is closed, it
removes the grid bias of the tube, which has been limiting the
flow of anode current to some low value.   When this bias is
removed, the anode current immediately rises, and the flow of
current through the relay coil causes the relay to pull up.   This
circuit is shown with a d-c plate-voltage supply.
    A modification of this circuit is shown in Fig. 7B.   Here an a-c
plate-voltage supply is furnished by a transformer.   This system

can be connected directly to the a-c power lines.   Here the triode not only controls the relay coil current, but it rectifies the a-c voltage and sees that the current through the relay coil is unidirectional.

Both of the foregoing examples are on-off control types. Actually most vacuum-tube and relay circuits employ one of these two principles, the only differences being the way in which the grid voltage of the relay control tube is varied.   It might be varied gradually by means of a variable resistance in place of the switch, which might in turn be adjusted by a liquid level float. When the float reaches a predetermined low level, the contacts of the relay close and turn on the supply to refill the tank. Many applications of this nature are in daily use.

Usually power pentodes and tetrodes, rather than triodes, are used for relay control tubes, because their current ratings are higher, and the ratios of plate-current change to grid-voltage change (transconductance) are greater.

To determine ahead of time how a particular tube will work with a certain relay, it is only necessary to construct on the $E_p - I_p$ characteristic curves a load line corresponding to the relay-coil resistance, as explained in Chap. 3.   Once the load line is located, it is possible to determine plate current values for various values of grid voltage.

As an example, assume that a pull-up current of 10 ma and a drop-out current of 5 ma are given as ratings for a particular relay, whose resistance is, say, 8,000 ohms.   The load line is first drawn, and then the values of grid voltage corresponding to these two plate-current values are determined.   The activating device must, by some means, cause the grid voltage to change between these two limits.

Special Relays.   Certain applications preclude the use of standard types of relays for one reason or another, and a great many special types of relays have been developed for specific jobs. Telephone relays, which may be classified broadly as the sensitive type, make use of mechanical coupling between armature and a moving contact.   The mechanical coupling is performed by an insulating material in a way that the armature of the relay is not involved electrically with the contact system.

Some relays make use of complicated systems of springs and ratchets to accomplish certain tasks.   Most sensitive relays use a system of mechanical levers either to amplify the distance over which the moving contact moves, or to insure good contact by amplifying the pressure exerted by the relay coil.

Relays are available with contacts sealed in a vacuum to prevent fires where severe contact arcing might be expected. Power relays capable of handling many kilowatts of power are sometimes made of an evacuated capsule, with contacts at either end and a globule of mercury, which is free to move within the capsule, depending on its position. The capsule is then coupled mechanically to the armature of a relay or solenoid so the mercury establishes contact between the two terminals for one position and breaks the contact in another.

The number of specialized types is almost as limitless as the number of applications that have been found for relays. Basically all of them perform the same function—their contact systems control an electrical circuit.

Care of Relays. Care should be taken to see that sparking does not occur at the contacts of a relay, or at least that it is held to a minimum. Sparking will drastically reduce the life of a set of relay contacts if allowed to occur regularly.

Contacts must be kept clean. This will prevent burning of foreign matter that may form a high resistance on the contacts. If relays cannot be kept in a dustproof housing, they should be cleaned periodically with a good solvent, such as carbon tetrachloride. Pitted or worn contacts may be refinished by the use of a flat file held between the contacts and drawn back and forth while exerting slight pressure to hold the contacts together. Crocus cloth can also be used to advantage in rejuvenating worn or pitted contacts.

Moving parts of relays are designed to operate without lubricants, and the application of oil or graphite may be very damaging. Supersensitive relays must be treated like fine watch movements, and their care should be entrusted only to a trained expert.

Capacity Relay Circuit. The introduction of a device known as the capacity relay caused quite a sensation in the early days of electronics. Store owners put signs in their windows asking passers-by to place their hands near a metallic plate attached to the window pane. As they did this, a display in the window started to move, with obvious attention-getting results.

The capacity relay has since been applied to many a useful job.

It is especially useful as an alarm circuit, for it is capable of detecting the approach of objects.   Certain burglar alarms operate on this principle, and safety devices for some types of machinery use the capacity relay idea to remove power from the machinery when the body of the operator is in a dangerous position.

The circuit of a capacity relay is shown in Fig. 8.   Actually, there is more than just a relay involved—two tubes are used.   A feeler, or antenna, is attached to the grid of the oscillator tube. Standard broadcast-receiver oscillator coils may be employed. The frequency of oscillation is determined by the coil in the grid

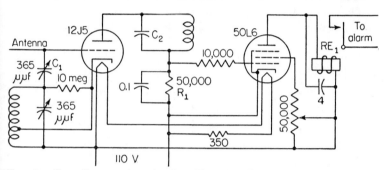

Fig. 8.   Capacitance relay circuit.   The relay is closed until an object approaches the antenna.   This type of circuit is used widely in window displays and in burglar-alarm applications.

circuit of the 12J5 and by C_1 and C_2.   When the coil and condenser in the plate circuit of the oscillator are tuned to the resonant frequency of oscillation, the plate current will be very low.   If the frequency is changed, the plate current of the oscillator circuit rises sharply, and the voltage across R_1 increases in such a direction as to cause the current flowing through the 50L6 to increase to a value sufficient to close relay RE_1.

The circuit is adjusted as follows: Set C_1 at maximum value (all the plates meshed).   Then adjust C_2 for minimum plate current (which indicates that the plate circuit of the 12J5 is tuned to the frequency of oscillation).   The relay is then adjusted (the spring tightened or loosened) until it just fails to make.   Then C_1 is decreased slightly until the relay makes.

Whenever a body comes near the antenna, the capacitance is, in effect, increased, the frequency of oscillation goes down and approaches the value at which the relay will drop out.   Here a fail-safe feature has been incorporated.   In the event of a power failure the relay will close (drop out) and an alarm will sound. The relay should be a d-c type with a pick-up rating of 3 ma and a drop-out value of about 1 ma.   The rating of the contacts are, of course, dependent on the size and type of alarm used.

R-F Operated Remote-control Relay.   The circuit of Fig. 9 is very useful in that no standby power is required.   The relay is actuated by energy supplied by a radio transmitter.   Thus when the circuit is deenergized, no power is supplied to it, which means that it can be left for long periods of time without wasting power.

The basis of the instrument is a Weston supersensitive relay that closes with a current of 2 μa flowing through a 1,000-ohm

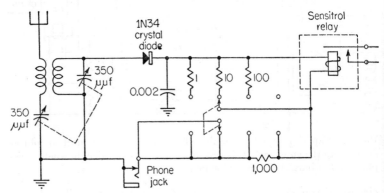

Fig. 9.   Circuit using a supersensitive relay requiring no stand-by power and actuated (powered) by the energy contained in radio waves.

coil.   The contacts of this type of relay are capable of carrying 50 ma.   Where additional current must be controlled, another relay can be used with its coil current furnished by the a-c power line through the contacts of the supersensitive relay.   This device is useful as a monitor that warns radio station engineers when the carrier of the station is off.   In this case the antenna input circuit would be tuned to the carrier frequency.

The crystal diode rectifies the r-f power and supplies d-c current to the relay coil.   Since signals of widely varying strength may be encountered, a sensitivity control is provided.   This is in the form of an adjustable shunt across the relay to reduce its sensitivity by factors of 10, 100, or 1,000 times.   The phone jack permits the use of headphones for initial adjustments and for identifying the carrier to which the circuit is tuned.

Additional details on this circuit are given by Fink.[1]

REFERENCES

Clement, A. W., Relay Contacts . . . Their Ailments, *Electronics*, December, 1938, p. 29.

Dlouhy, F. S., New Electronic Timing Relay for Reducing Outages on Power Circuits, *Electrical Engineering Transactions*, July, 1946, p. 407.

Dudley, Beverly, Relays for Tube Circuits, *Electronics*, May, 1938, p. 18.

Ellwood, W. B., J. T. L. Brown, and C. E. Pollard, Recent Developments in Relays, *Electrical Engineering*, November, 1947, p. 1105.

Fisher, R. T., Adjusting Sensitive Relays, *Electronics*, February, 1943, p. 70.

Fisher, R. T., Graphic Solution of Design Problems Involving Sensitive Relays, *Electronics*, October, 1943, p. 125.

Furst, Ulrich R., Relays in Industrial Tube Circuits, *Electronics*, December, 1944, p. 134; January, 1945, p. 136.

Halman, T. R., Voltage Surges in Relay Control Circuits, *Electrical Engineering*, April, 1949, p. 327.

Harder, E. L., Principles of Protective Relaying, *Electrical Engineering*, November, 1948, p. 1075.

Lamb, A. H., New Fields for Magnetic Contact Relays, *Electronics*, December, 1940, p. 34.

MacPherson, R. H., A. R. van C. Warrington, and A. J. McConnell, Electronic Protective Relays, *Electrical Engineering*, February, 1949, p. 122.

Mercury Contact Relays, *Bell Laboratories Record*, April, 1949, p. 132.

Packard, Charles A., "Relay Engineering," Struthers-Dunn, Inc., Philadelphia.

Waidelich, D. L., Capacitive Relay Oscillator, *Electronic Industries*, July, 1948, p. 17.

[1] D. G. Fink, R-F Operated Remote Control Relay, *Electronics*, September, 1947, p. 115.

CHAPTER 8

ELECTRONIC MOTOR CONTROL

In the past 10 years electronic motor control has come out of the laboratory and into the shop, where today it is in evidence in practically every phase of industry. Through the use of electronics innumerable machine operations of every conceivable description have been simplified, and the quantity and quality of processed materials have undergone marked improvement with reduced first costs and operating expense.

Electron tubes with appropriate circuits can be used to control practically any motor function, such as speed, acceleration and deceleration, starting torque and current, overloads, and so on. The following paragraphs will describe methods for controlling some of the more common motor characteristics—the types of control most frequently needed in industry.

D-C Shunt Motor Control. By far the most commonly used motor control setup is built up around a d-c shunt-wound motor fed from a tube rectifying system which is in turn fed from standard a-c distribution lines. The reasons for the popularity of this motor control system will become evident when its versatility and efficiency are understood.

Basically these d-c motor control setups are comprised of three main parts: the motor itself, with its armature and field windings; and two tube-rectifier units, one for supplying the necessary field power, and the other for rectifying the necessary armature power. The control circuits are usually incorporated as integral parts of the rectifying systems.

Shunt-motor Theory Review. Before the operation of an electronic motor control can be understood fully, it is necessary to review the general theory of the shunt-wound d-c motor. The circuit for such a motor is shown in Fig. 1. The field coil actually consists of a large number of turns of relatively small wire wound on radial poles around the periphery of the motor. It is shown schematically, however, simply as a single coil. As d-c current is forced through these field coils by the application of a voltage across them, a magnetic field is set up along the axis of the poles around which the coils are wound.

The armature winding consists of several turns of relatively heavy wire or strap wound on the rotatable member of the motor, and as d-c current is forced through this winding another mag-netic field is produced. These two fields are of such magni-tude and direction that they cause the armature to rotate about its axis.

The armature winding offers very low resistance to the flow of current while the motor is standing still. When it begins to revolve, and the segments of

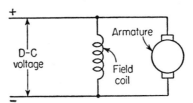

FIG. 1. Diagram of a shunt-con-nected d-c motor, showing the field coil and armature.

the armature winding begin cutting the magnetic lines of force set up by the field coils, a voltage is induced in the armature winding which opposes the original voltage applied to the armature and acts to cancel out the effect of a portion of that applied voltage. This opposing voltage or "back emf" limits the current through the armature by reducing the effective voltage that causes the flow of current.

The speed of the motor is determined by the balance point at which the effective armature voltage (which is approximately the applied voltage minus the induced voltage) is just sufficient to cause enough armature current to flow to drive the mechanical load and make up for friction losses in the motor and transmission system.

Speed Control. It can be seen that if the magnetic field set up by the field winding is decreased, the induced canceling volt-age in the armature winding will be less. Thus the *effective* armature voltage will be greater, the armature current will increase, and the motor will speed up.

On the other hand if the armature applied voltage is reduced, the effective armature voltage is decreased, and less current flows. The motor will thus slow down.

These two speed-changing phenomena are the basis for motor speed control. Where it is desired to have a motor run at some speed slower than its normal speed, control of the armature current may be used. Where the speed is to be increased, field current control may be used. Combinations of both types of control are commonly employed to obtain speed regulation over very large ranges.

Typical Speed-control Circuit. A greatly simplified motor speed-control circuit is shown in Fig. 2. Here the d-c voltages

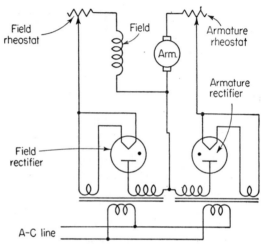

Fig. 2. Schematic for controlling the speed of a d-c motor by using gas rectifiers to convert a-c line power to direct current.

for the field and armature are supplied by two separate rectifier systems. The voltage applied to each may be varied by the addition of resistance in series with the windings. Special power rheostats are available for this type of circuit, but these components are usually bulky and expensive. They are also difficult to maintain because of the large amounts of power they must dissipate.

By substituting thyratrons for the diode rectifiers shown in Fig. 2 and adding suitable electronic circuits to control the rectifying action of the thyratrons, armature and field currents can be adjusted at less expense and with numerous other advantages.

Figure 3 shows a basic electronic control system, again greatly simplified. The thyratron grids are connected to phase-shifting

devices.   The phase of the grid voltage is made variable so that
the thyratrons may be caused to conduct for different portions
of the half cycle during which the thyratron anodes are positive.
Note that when diode rectifiers were used to supply direct current
to the field and armature, they conducted current for the full
positive half cycle, affording no control.

If a thyratron grid is allowed to swing positive at a time when
the plate of the tube is just going positive, the tube will conduct

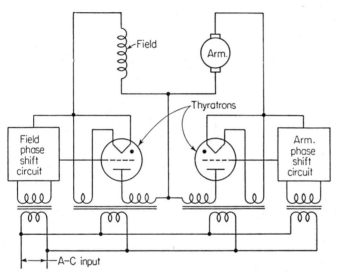

Fig. 3.   Simple circuit showing the use of grid-controlled gas tubes to vary
voltages applied to the motor field and armature.

over the entire positive half cycle.   Any load connected to that
tube will draw power during these positive half cycles.   If the
grid voltage is retarded, however, so that the grid is in some portion of its negative half cycle at the time the plate voltage starts
its positive half cycle, the firing of the tube will be delayed until
the grid voltage swings to a value which will permit the tube to
conduct.   Thus the tube conducts during only a portion of its
positive half cycle, and current in the load will flow for shorter
intervals of time.   The *average* current, that is, the total of the
instantaneous current divided by the time, will decrease.   If it
is the armature current which is decreased in this manner, the
motor speed will decrease.

It is worth noting that if a single thyratron is used to control the armature or field, current cannot flow more than half the time, because the tube will not conduct during the half cycles of the applied a-c voltage which make the anode negative with respect to the cathode. This, then, is the condition which will produce the maximum average current through the tube and the load. With two tubes in a full-wave rectifier circuit it is possible to force current through the load at all times if desired.

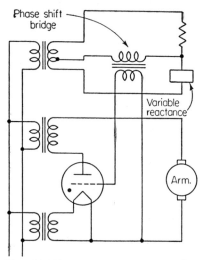

Phase shift bridge

Variable reactance

Arm.

FIG. 4. Diagram of means for retarding the phase of thyratron grid voltage for varying the current supplied to the motor armature.

Phase-shifting Methods. The armature portion of an electronic control system which uses the phase-shift principle is shown in Fig. 4. Here the d-c armature current is obtained from the a-c distribution lines by means of a single thyratron rectifier circuit. The grid of the thyratron is connected to a transformer whose primary is connected across the output terminals of a special phase-shift bridge circuit.

In such a circuit, as the value of the variable reactance is increased, the a-c grid voltage is retarded in phase. Thus instead of being positive when the plate becomes positive, the grid voltage lags behind by a certain amount. The tube does not conduct as soon as the plate goes positive but at some time later in the positive plate excursion as determined by the time when the grid voltage goes positive. This latter is determined by the tube characteristics. The result is that the thyratron will conduct for shorter and shorter periods of time and the average current will be less as the phase lag increases.

If the armature were rotating in a fixed field, its speed of rotation would be decreased by increasing the amount of reactance in the phase-shift bridge.

Actually the circuit shown in Fig. 4 is applicable only to small motors, since only half-wave rectification is employed. To supply adequate armature power for larger motors, high values of peak rectified current would be required. The circuit in Fig. 5 employs a full-wave rectifier with exactly the same type of phase-shift arrangement but with a more practical type of variable reactance in the bridge.

Saturable Reactor Phase Shifter. The variable reactance shown in Fig. 5 is a saturable reactor. The inductive reactance

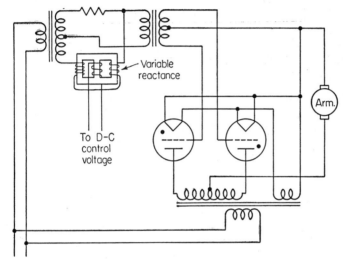

Fig. 5. The use of saturable reactors greatly increases, or amplifies, the amount of control possible.

introduced into the circuit by the saturable reactor is determined by the amount of d-c current flowing in the d-c winding.

The advantage of the saturable reactor is that only a small change in d-c power is required to cause a large change in its inductance. The small d-c change can be achieved by a potentiometer connected across a source of d-c voltage, or it may be derived electronically by a circuit such as the one shown in Fig. 6, where a potentiometer is used to determine the amount of bias on a control tube. As the arm of the control rheostat is moved up, making the grid more negative with respect to its cathode, the plate current of the tube will decrease, reducing the current which flows through the d-c winding on the reactor. The a-c side of the reactor will present more inductance in a grid phase-shift circuit, causing less armature current to flow and the motor speed to decrease.

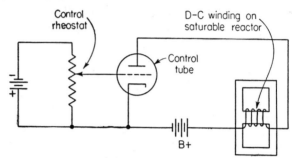

FIG. 6. Simple circuit for varying the direct current applied to the d-c winding of a saturable reactor.

Thus we have effectively added resistance in the armature circuit. However instead of requiring a large power rheostat with a great power loss, we have accomplished the same effect with a small potentiometer having almost negligible power loss.

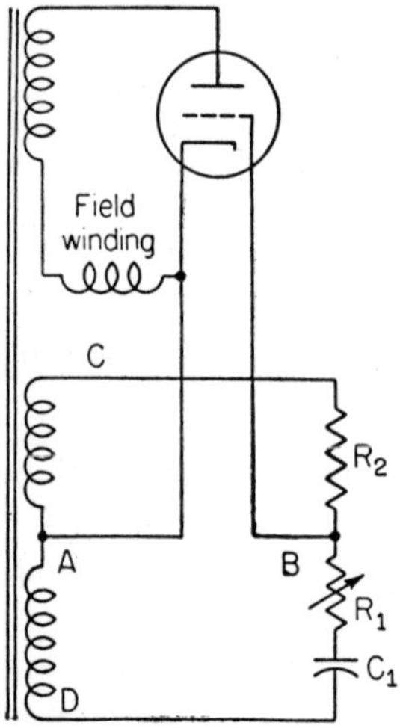

Variation of Resistance. In explaining the phase-shift bridge used to control the armature current in the previous section, it was shown that the phase of the grid voltage was changed by varying the inductance of one of the arms of the bridge. Phase-shift variation also may be accomplished by varying the resistance in the arm containing the reactance.

This system is illustrated in Fig. 7. The circuit is shown connected to the field winding of a motor. The basic phase-shift bridge is still present, but in this case the reactance used for phase shift is a capacitor, and the element used to vary the phase shift is actually a variable resistance or rheostat in series with the capacitor.

FIG. 7. Basic phase-shift circuit shows a bridge configuration.

In the chapter on basic circuits we saw that the voltage across a capacitor was 90 deg out of phase with the current flowing through it. Therefore, since the voltage across a resistance is in phase with the current flowing through that resistance, the voltage across the capacitor and the voltage across a resistor in series with it are 90 deg out of phase with each other.

Thus if the value of the resistor R_1 in Fig. 7 is chosen so that its effect is very much greater than that of the capacitor C_1, the voltage across that arm of the bridge will be practically in phase with the current flowing through it and consequently in phase with the voltage across the other arm of the bridge which is made up of R_2. The voltage between A and B is then nearly in phase with the voltage across points C and D, since little phase shift occurs around the bridge.

If now the value of R_1 is decreased, so that its effect is quite small as compared to the reactive effect furnished by C_1, then the voltage across that arm of the bridge will be made up primarily of the voltage across the capacitor, and it will be out of phase with the voltage across the other arm of the bridge which is still caused by the pure resistance R_2. Thus decreasing the value of R_1 effects a phase shift in the voltage output taken from points A and B.

So by decreasing the resistance in the capacitor arm of the phase-shift bridge, the field current can be decreased and the motor speed increased.

Continuous Control. We have seen that the speed of a motor can be increased by lowering the field voltage and decreased by lowering the armature voltage. In many cases a given d-c motor with a certain rated speed is to be used in a system where speed control above and below the rated speed is desirable. It is possible to maintain smooth control over the entire range of speeds with a single speed-changing knob by using the rheostat shown in Fig. 8.

If the motor is designed to run at its rated speed when the full voltage is applied to both the armature and the field, it will operate under this condition when the arms of the rheostats are straight up and no resistance is in either circuit.

Moving the knob counterclockwise places some resistance in the field circuit, but at the same time makes the arm of the armature rheostat move onto a copper segment which provides a direct path to the power line. The armature circuit will continue to have full voltage applied to it. However, the resistance added to the field circuit reduces the field current, and the motor speeds up.

To decrease the motor speed the knob is rotated clockwise, thereby taking resistance out of the field circuit. When the rated speed point is passed, resistance is added in the armature circuit, while the field current remains unchanged.

Speed Regulation. We have seen that motor speed can be controlled by a d-c voltage. We have also seen that the speed of rotation of a motor determines the amount of induced voltage in the armature and thus the effective voltage across the armature. It would seem that we should be able to devise a loop arrangement such that if the motor speed were reduced, due to some

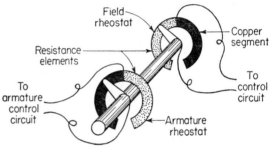

Fig. 8. Special dual potentiometer provides continuous speed control with a single knob for low-power applications.

external load change for instance, the voltage change in the armature winding caused by the speed change could be used to restore the motor to its original speed, thereby providing a degree of regulation.

A circuit capable of doing this is shown in Fig. 9. The voltages shown applied at the left side of the diagram are assumed to be provided by some regulated source—they serve as reference voltages in the speed-regulation circuit, as will be explained shortly.

V_1 is a triode connected across the upper half of the regulated voltage supply, with the d-c winding of a phase-shift saturable reactor in its plate circuit. The grid voltage of V_1 is determined by the three-resistor voltage divider which is connected across the entire regulated voltage supply. For the moment let us assume that V_1 is conducting, because its grid voltage is relatively positive with respect to its cathode. The current flowing through the d-c winding of the saturable reactor reduces its a-c reactance, and the armature rectifier thyratrons conduct over a maximum

portion of the positive half anode cycle.   Suppose that the motor
tends to speed up, as might happen if its load were decreased.
As the armature accelerates, the induced voltage increases, causing the total voltage across the armature to increase.   A portion
of this armature voltage increase is applied to the grid of V_2
through R_4 in such a way that the grid becomes more positive.
As the grid of V_2 becomes more positive, that tube conducts more
current.   The V_2 plate current flowing through R_1 lowers the

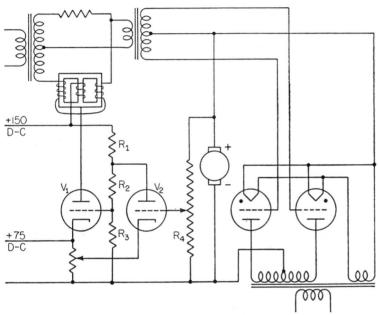

Fig. 9.   Circuit providing regulation of the speed of rotation of a d-c motor.

voltage at the grid of V_1 causing that tube to conduct less current.
Thus the current in the d-c winding of the saturable reactor
decreases and the reactance in the phase-shift bridge is increased,
causing the grid voltage of the rectifier thyratrons to be retarded
in phase and the armature current to be decreased.   The motor
speed drops until the original speed (before the load decrease
occurred) is attained.
    It is well to remember that the speed regulation is accomplished
by comparing the voltage across the armature with a known fixed
voltage.   To have perfect regulation the armature voltage would

necessarily have to vary exactly linearly with the armature speed.
Such is actually not the case, because the total armature voltage
is determined by the applied voltage, the opposing induced voltage, and the IR drop caused by the current flowing through the
armature resistance.   This third factor, the IR drop, is directly
proportional to the armature current, since the resistance is con-

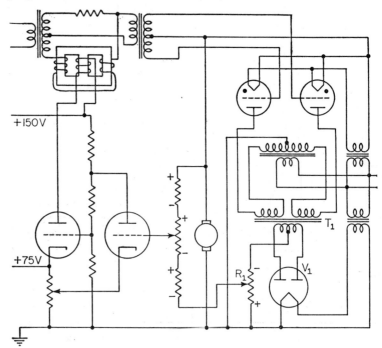

+150V

+75V

R_1

V_1

T_1

Fig. 10.   Speed regulation and IR-drop compensation are provided by this
circuit.

stant.   It is the factor which prevents the armature voltage from
deviating in direct proportion to motor speed.

IR-drop Compensation.   The discrepancy in speed regulation
caused by the armature IR drop may be compensated by the circuit shown in Fig. 10.   Another transformer, T_1, has been introduced.   Its primary windings are connected in the armature circuit in such a way that the voltage across its secondary increases
as the armature current increases.   The secondary transformer
voltage is rectified by V_1 and the portion of the resulting d-c
voltage appearing across the lower portion of R_1 is applied in

series with the armature voltage divider in the speed-regulation circuit. By proper adjustment of R_1, the voltage added in series to this circuit will be exactly equal and opposite to the voltage discrepancy caused by the armature IR drop (since both are proportional to armature current). The voltage tapped off for the regulator circuit will be exactly proportional to machine speed.

This IR-drop compensation circuit also serves as an armature current-regulating device, since a large armature current will cause the addition of a large negative voltage into the speed-regulator voltage divider across the armature. The result will be a reduction in armature current through the speed-regulation circuit.

An armature current-regulating circuit operating on the above principle is shown in Fig. 11. Here the armature current flows through the regulation transformer primary as before. However, instead of using the rectified regulating voltage in series with the armature voltage divider, as in the IR-drop-compensation circuit, here the voltage is used directly to control the firing time of the armature thyratrons through V_1 and the saturable reactor connected in its plate circuit. The circuit of Fig. 11 shows the field of the motor being supplied by the same anode transformer, but with straight diode rectifiers and a series potentiometer for controlling field current.

Motor Reversing. If the voltage applied to either the field or the armature of a d-c motor is reversed, the direction of rotation will be reversed. However, this reversal cannot be accomplished instantaneously.

For instance, quickly reversing the polarity of the armature voltage would cause the armature current immediately to rise to a dangerously high value. The reason for this high current is that the applied voltage (having been reversed) would now add to rather than oppose the induced voltage in the armature. This induced voltage depends upon the direction of rotation, and the armature would not immediately reverse.

Several methods for avoiding this heavy current have been devised. Probably the commonest and simplest method makes use of a large magnetic contactor which disconnects the armature voltage and connects a resistance across the armature, giving the effect of dynamic braking. Once the armature has come to rest,

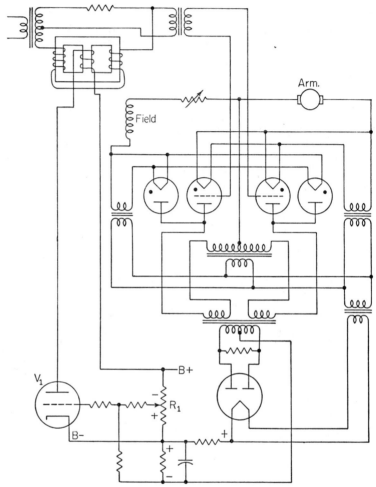

F<small>IG</small>. 11.   Circuit providing adjustable speed control with IR-drop compensation and armature-current regulation.

the same, or another, contactor may be operated to apply the reverse polarity voltage to the armature circuit, thereby causing the motor to begin accelerating in the opposite direction.

Where more rapid direction changing is required, a regenerative system is employed whereby the kinetic energy stored up in rotation of the armature is forced back into the power lines. This system is found more frequently in nonelectronic setups, however. It becomes quite involved in electronic versions because of the fact that electrons can flow in only one direction in a tube rectifier.

Additional Refinements. Thus far we have discussed only general motor control circuits. It must be kept in mind that in commercial control units many additional refinements are necessary to provide protection against overloads and make it possible for inexperienced personnel to operate the motors without damage to the equipment.

In many cases thermally-operated overload relays are integral parts of electronic control units. They are seldom necessary with fractional horsepower motors, since usually these motors have sufficient internal impedance to limit the starting and accelerating currents to values which will not damage the motor or paralyze the d-c power supply.

Starting-current limiting devices may be placed in the circuit in a number of different ways. Some setups use a starting button which is depressed and held until the motor reaches a certain speed, at which time the button is released. With this type the limiting device is connected in the circuit while the start button is depressed.

An automatic system involves a centrifugal switch or some other means for cutting the starting-current limiting device out of the circuit when the motor reaches some safe speed. These starting-current limiting aids may be separate units, such as a resistance in series with the armature, or they may be part of the speed-control or speed-regulation systems.

Throughout this chapter we have been pointing out various ways to change motor speed and other characteristics by the use of electronic circuits. It must be kept in mind that in almost every case the alteration of one motor characteristic will be accompanied by an alteration of some other characteristic; this may be unimportant, advantageous, or extremely disadvantageous, depending on the application.

For instance, when we say the speed range of a d-c motor is extended by the use of current-reducing devices in series with the motor elements, we must understand that the rated horsepower available for rated speed may not be available when the motor is slowed down. At very low speeds the armature current must be reduced below its normal value, because the air cooling usually produced by armature rotation is reduced. However, this would be true not only of electronically controlled motors but of all types running at reduced speeds.

The twisting effort, or torque, will remain constant in a motor the speed of which is regulated by variation of the armature voltage alone, but the horsepower varies. If, on the other hand, speed control by variation of the field is employed, the horsepower output available remains constant, but the torque decreases as the field is weakened and the speed increases.

It will be noticed that in d-c machinery circuits the armatures and fields are supplied directly from the rectifying system. No d-c smoothing reactors or other external means are used to absorb the instantaneous differences between the output voltage of the tube and the counter voltage produced in the armature. Thus the armature current actually flows in pulses during the interval when the instantaneous applied voltage exceeds the counter voltage in the armature. The armature winding reactance affords some filtering of these pulses. Some circuits incorporate a separate reactance in the armature circuit to smooth the pulses.

In some cases filter sections are required to prevent hunting. Electronic circuits are almost instantaneous in operation, whereas the equipments they control usually have finite time delays before they respond to control. These circuits are often found between the grids and cathodes of rectifying thyratrons.

In this electronic motor control discussion we have limited descriptions to single-phase applications in the interests of simplicity and ease of explanation. The circuits described are applicable to larger multiphase equipment with, of course, correspondingly more electronic components. In fact motors up to 200 hp in rating have been furnished with electronic control devices.

Reversible Motor Control. Many types of industrial machinery, such as milling machines, shapers, lathes and variable-depth boring machines, require motors which move work repeatedly between two points—in other words the drive motor is continually reversing.

The electronic circuit shown in Fig. 12 is capable of reversing a motor when the load on the motor reaches a preset limit. Thus it qualifies for the job described above. Either limit can be set without regard to the other by means of potentiometers R_1 and R_2.

Potentiometer R_3 is geared to the turning mechanism of the load so that its full resistance is traversed with the complete range.

Relay 1 controls the direction of travel of the motor. The load will move one way when it is energized and return the other way when it is deenergized. With the potentiometers in the positions shown, RE_1 will initially be deenergized and the motor will move the load to such a position that R_3 picks off a voltage equal to that set on R_1. RE_1 will then be energized by the firing

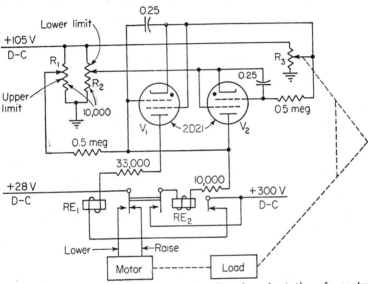

FIG. 12. Circuit for rapid reversal of the direction of rotation of a motor

of V_1 and the motor will reverse. The other extreme reversal will occur when the load moves to a point where the voltage tapped by R_3 equals that set at R_2 causing V_2 to conduct and RE_1 to be deenergized again. The values shown were chosen to reverse the direction of an automatically rotated radio dial, but by proper alteration of components it could easily be adapted to heavier operations—in fact any reversible motor setup which can be controlled by the action of a relay can be used in conjunction with such a circuit. A more detailed description of the operation of the circuit is presented by Stephenson.[1]

[1] J. G. Stephenson, Reversible Motor Controller, *Electronics*, September, 1947, p. 93.

Tachometer Speed Regulation. Figure 13 shows a circuit containing a tachometer generator mechanically coupled to the motor which is being electronically controlled. The output of such a generator is a d-c voltage which is directly proportional in magnitude to the speed of rotation of the motor.

A little imagination will reveal a simple means for controlling and regulating motor speed by taking advantage of this type of device. The voltage may be applied to the circuit supplying motor current in such a way that a decrease in the tachometer

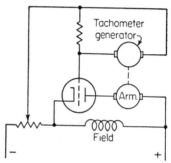

FIG. 13.   Tachometer generator provides the reference signal for this speed-regulation circuit.

output, such as might be caused by a decrease in motor speed, would cause an increase in armature current so that the motor will regain its original speed.

Of course the setup shown in Fig. 13 would have extremely limited usefulness because of the small power handling capabilities of a tube which might be controlled by the voltage of the tachometer generator. Actually, the voltage derived from the tachometer would be used in one of the circuits discussed previously to control the motor.

REFERENCES

Alexanderson, E. F. W., M. A. Edwards, and C. H. Willis, Electronic Speed Control of D-C Motors, *Electrical Engineering*, June, 1938.

Cockrell, W. D., Electronic Control . . . Maintenance and Trouble-shooting Tips, *General Electric Review*, September, 1943, p. 489.

Dalton, B. J., Electronic Motor Control, *General Electric Review*, May, 1945, p. 12.

DeWolf, F. T., D-C Motor Operation with Rectifier Power Supply, *General Electric Review*, April, 1947, p. 15.

Fendley, S. D., Electronic Motor Control, *General Electric Review*, April, 1943.

Fendley, S. D., Motor Control by Means of Tubes, *Electronics*, March, 1943, p. 138.

Harris, W. B., Industrial Applications of Rototrol Regulators, *Electrical Engineering Transactions*, March, 1946, p. 118.

Heumann, G. W., Speed Control Systems for High-speed Squirrel-cage Motors, *General Electric Review*, February, 1948, p. 28.

Leigh, H. H., Simplified Thyratron Motor Control, *General Electric Review*, September, 1946, p. 18.

Livingston, O. W., Constant Current Systems for Electronic Control of D-C Motors, *General Electric Review*, May, 1947, p. 38.

Moyer, E. E., Electronic Control of D-C Motors, *Electronics*, May, June, July, September, and October, 1943.

Poole, A. B., Flea Power Industrial Synchronous Motors, *Electrical Manufacturing*, January, 1949, p. 74.

Puchlowski, K. P., Electronic Motor Control, "Industrial Electronic Reference Book," John Wiley & Sons, Inc., New York, 1948.

Ryder, J. D., Electronic Control Circuits for D-C Motors, *Electronics*, December, 1938, p. 20.

Schmidt, A., Jr., Operating D-C Motors from Controlled Rectifiers, *Electrical Engineering*, June, 1948, p. 516.

Stephenson, J. G., Reversible-motor Controller, *Electronics*, September, 1947, p. 93.

CHAPTER 9

ELECTRONIC MEASUREMENT AND CONTROL

A large part of the rapid progress that has been made in industry in the past 50 years is due to man's ability to produce great quantities of commodities. The key to mass production is standardization. The key to standardization is measurement. The requirements for making accurate measurements quickly and without interruption of the manufacturing process presented a logical problem to electronics engineers.

The science of measurement is sometimes as incomprehensible as is the extent of the universe. There is no end point. Nothing is perfect. All physical measurements as we know them today are relative. For instance, our units of length are based on a set of arbitrary standards. In effect, when we say that a piece of string is a yard long, we imply that the piece of string is as long as the distance between two scratches on a certain piece of platinum-iridium in a temperature-controlled room in Washington, D.C. Of course we don't know if this is true, but we do know that the string compares in length with, say, a yardstick, and we assume that the yardstick was originally scaled after an accurate steel yardstick which might have been calibrated from a standard yardstick which was once calibrated from the world standard in Washington.

Our units of the presence or absence of heat are based arbitrarily on the temperature at which water freezes under certain fixed conditions. Some industrial processes require very exacting temperature measurements. But, to set a process in operation in Chicago in accordance with plans drawn up in Cleveland, again we must compare. The convenient basis for temperature comparison was logically chosen as the freezing point of water, since, under prescribed conditions, water always freezes at the same temperature.

The Electronic Measuring Stick. In introducing electronics into the field of measurement, we simply add another intermediate comparison like the steel yardstick. Sometimes this electronic measuring stick takes the form of a voltage which exists between two points. The magnitude of this voltage must in some way be related to the magnitude of the phenomenon being measured. As an example, suppose we have a system for producing a voltage of 12 volts which corresponds to a distance of 1 ft in some electronic distance-measuring system. Suppose that through appropriate circuitry, we have established the fact that the voltage is exactly proportional to the distance being measured. Having established these two conditions, we may safely say that if the voltage drops to 11 volts, something has happened to the spacing of our two reference points and they are now 11 in. apart instead of 12.

The electronic measuring stick can actually be any phenomenon which is capable of being measured. Instead of the 12-volt example, the distance information mentioned above might have been converted into a currrent of 12 ma, and the same proportion used. Or the 12 in. could be converted into a measurable time interval, say 12 milliseconds, between two electrical impulses of current or voltage.

In other words whether the basis for comparison is a voltage, current, unit of time, change in frequency or phase, change in the tuning of an LC circuit, or a change in resistance, inductance, or capacitance, as long as it is measurable and as long as it bears some definable relationship to the magnitude of the phenomenon being measured, we have a workable system.

The advantages of introducing the electronic measuring stick are numerous and will become more and more evident. For a brief example, however, consider convenience. Measuring the depth of liquids in a large number of widely dispersed storage tanks can be accomplished at some central station. Measurement of the fuel in automobiles is a good example of an extremely simple electrical measuring system, but consider the time, energy, and danger that is eliminated by having such a remote indicator of fuel depth.

One of the great virtues of the use of tubes in measurement and control operations is the fact that the measuring device can be arranged to have almost no effect on the quantity being measured.

For example, a low-resistance voltmeter of the conventional type will not read voltage correctly unless the voltage source has low internal resistance. Otherwise the current required by the voltmeter, flowing through the internal resistance of the source, will produce a voltage drop so that the meter actually indicates a value that is lower than the voltage that exists under normal circumstances without the meter load.

A vacuum-tube voltmeter has an extremely high resistance, which means that the current required for its operation is practically zero. Therefore it will read the open-circuit voltage of any source much more accurately than will a conventional meter.

Electron-tube meters can be located at a distance from the quantity being measured, they act instantly (no lag), they consume extremely little current, and they can be arranged to measure practically any physical, chemical or electrical quantity.

Measuring Light Intensity. The phototube is one of the most universally used electronic measuring aids. The phototube produces an electrical change which is proportional to the illumination falling upon it. Once the tube and its circuit have been calibrated, they form a very simple and accurate measuring device for determining illumination levels.

It is a simple step to go from the measurement of illumination to the control of illumination. Suppose that the circuit is arranged to ring a bell when the output of the phototube falls below or increases above some arbitrary limit. Then an attendant can adjust the illumination to the desired value. The next step is to make the circuit turn on more light if the illumination has fallen below the desired value and turn off lights if the illumination has become too high. In this manner street lights may be turned on when daylight falls below a desired limit. Another simple application of this general idea is to open one's garage doors when the headlights of the car are turned on.

Dimension Control. Since the phototube responds to light, many devices have been developed for controlling physical dimensions by its use. For example, the length of an object can be controlled as follows: In Fig. 1A is shown a method for cutting sheets of uniform length from a continuous strip of material. Here the material is fed into a cutter from the left. As soon as the end of the strip interrupts the beam of light between the light source and the phototube, a relay in the phototube unit operates a cutter. The accuracy of such a system depends on a number of factors. This system is applicable to any job where a large piece of material is to be divided into small equal-size units. Variations of this simple scheme are often necessary. For example, suppose it is impossible to position the light source and the phototube on opposite sides of the sheet. A mirror may be used to reflect the light as shown in Fig. 1B, or a light-absorbing background may be used and the reflectivity of a glossy material employed to actuate the cutter. In this case the

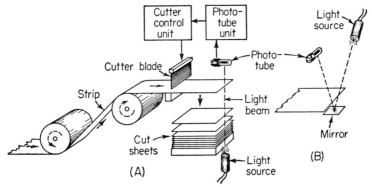

Fig. 1. Example of an electronic control setup. When the strip interrupts the light beam, a phototube signal actuates the cutter through the cutter control unit. Thus sheets are cut to uniform lengths.

circuit is so arranged that an increase in illumination falling on the phototube surface would cause the relay to act.

The problem just described is more than a measurement problem. In fact it is a good example of the compatibility of electronic *measuring* and electronic *control* systems. Once the quantity to be measured is translated into an electrical quantity —voltage, current, frequency—or into time intervals, it can be measured by electronics. Control devices are initiated by this measured electrical quantity.

THICKNESS GAUGES AND CONTROLS

Imagine a continuous process in which a material is being shaped into sheets and the thickness of these sheets must be held within close limits. The thickness might be controlled by the pressure exerted between two rollers through which the material passes as shown in Fig. 2A. This pressure is controlled by a motor-driven screw arrangement such that if the motor turns in one direction the pressure will be increased with resultant decrease in thickness of the sheet. When the motor reverses its motion, the thickness increases.

By using the system of Fig. 2A, automatic thickness control is possible. The type of thickness gauge employed depends on

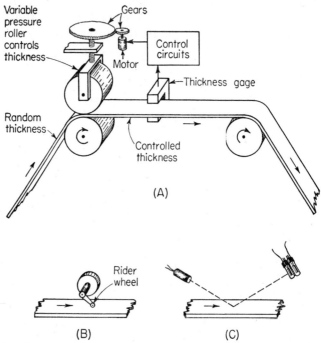

(A)

(B)   (C)

Fig. 2. Control setup for maintaining constant thickness of strip material. When the thickness gauge "tells" the control circuits that the strip is too thick, more pressure is applied to the rollers, which in turn squeeze the strip to the proper thickness.

several things: the type of material being measured, the desired thickness, the speed of travel, its roughness or surface configuration, and the degree of accuracy required. A simple rider wheel connected to the arm of a potentiometer might suffice (see Fig. 2B). In some cases the double phototube arrangement would have some advantage (Fig. 2C). When the material passing through the inspection point is of the desired thickness, the reflected light beam falls between the phototubes. If then the thickness increases, the angle of incidence between the light source and the reflecting surface changes, and the light beam falls on one of the phototubes. A signal will result, and with suitable electronic circuitry this signal can be used to vary the mechanical adjustment which controls the thickness in such a way that the thickness is corrected to the proper value.

These simple systems provide limited accuracy. Numerous mechanical-movement amplifiers can be applied to increase the electrical variation caused by the mechanical variation.

Radioactive Thickness Gauge. A simplified diagram of a radioactive thickness gauge especially suited for the measure-

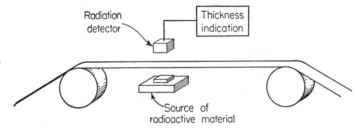

FIG. 3. Radioactive substances give off particles that pass through the materials and form the basis for measuring the strip thickness.

ment of sheets traveling at high speeds is shown in Fig. 3. A small sample of some radioactive substance is placed in a container below the surface of the moving material. The amount of radiation which passes through the material to the radiation detector is directly dependent on the thickness of the material and its absorption characteristics. The choice of the radioactive material depends on the application.

Ultrasonic Applications. Another type of thickness gauge makes use of a relatively new branch of the science of electronics called *ultrasonics*. Sound waves travel away from their point of origin at a uniform speed, the exact speed depending primarily on the material through which the sound transmission is taking place. It has been known for some time that sound waves are reflected by any change in density of the medum. If you yell across an open canyon, the sound of your voice will travel until it reaches the other side which represents a wall of material with a different physical make-up than the air through which the sound has been traveling. When these sound waves reach such a plane of different density, an echo will occur, and some of the sound energy will be reflected back toward the origin. The principle is the same as that used in radar, but in this case radio waves are used instead of sound waves. The frequencies most commonly used for this type of measurement lie in and just above the limit of human hearing.

A simplified diagram of an ultrasonic thickness gauge is shown in Fig. 4. The sound waves originate as electrical impulses in an ultrasonic oscillator. These impulses are amplified electrically and applied to a transducer which converts them into mechanical sound vibrations and passes these sound vibrations into the material whose thickness is to be measured. The sound waves are sent out in the form of short-duration pulses. When these pulses reach the other side of the material, they meet a

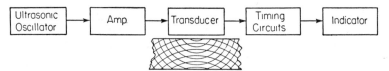

FIG. 4.   Block diagram of an ultrasonic thickness gauge.

plane of different density, and an echo results. A portion of the reflected sound energy finally returns to the transducer, which is also capable of converting such reflected echo pulses back into an electrical impulse. Thus we have two electrical impulses— the one sent out originally, and the one caused when the transducer picks up the returning echo. By electronic means, the time elapsed between the two pulses can be accurately determined. If the speed of sound within the material is known, the distance the original sound pulse traveled can be calculated. The thickness of the material will be equal to half of that distance, since the sound energy had to travel out and back.

This sounding system can be used for detecting and locating internal flaws, such as bubbles and impurities in a material, whether it is transparent or not, since any flaw or impurity represents a different density and gives rise to an echo. The position of the foreign particle or flaw in the material can be determined the same way the thickness of the material is calculated.

Portable Ultrasonic Thickness Gauge.   This is an instrument designed primarily for determining the thickness of tanks, pipes, process vessels and similar structures.[1]   It also employs ultrasonic energy for thickness measurement, but a slightly different and less complicated technique is used.   The basic circuit is shown in Fig. 5.   It comprises a variable-frequency self-excited oscillator which generates an alternating voltage.   This voltage is applied to an X-cut quartz crystal.   When this crystal is held against the surface of the material whose thickness is to be measured, it transmits a continuous ultrasonic wave into the material.

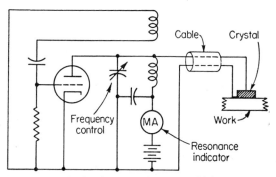

FIG. 5.   Basic circuit of an ultrasonic thickness gauge.

If the oscillator is tuned to a frequency that is an integral multiple of the fundamental frequency of the wave in the thickness of the material, there will be a sharp increase in the amplitude of the mechanical vibration in the part of the material directly beneath the crystal.

This condition is indicated by an increase in the current measured by the milliammeter.   When this increase is detected, the frequency of the wave is noted.   From the frequency the thickness of the material can be determined, since the thickness or physical size of an object determines its resonant frequency, just as the frequency of the organ pipe depends on its length.   The velocity of sound waves in a material is easily determined from tables or by running test measurements on known thicknesses of the same material.

The circuit used for the actual instrument employs five miniature tubes and is powered by self-contained batteries.   Instead of a meter, earphones are used as a resonance indicator.   Since

[1] Norman G. Branson, Portable Ultrasonic Thickness Gage, *Electronics,* January, 1948, p. 88.

the frequencies employed lie within the audio range, the operator can easily tell when critical frequencies are reached.

X-ray Thickness Gauge. Another system for measuring thickness without contact makes use of X rays and the fact that these rays are capable of penetrating opaque materials such as metals. Such a system was designed by W. L. Lundahl[1] of Westinghouse for measuring the thickness of cold-rolled steel and cold-rolled copper.

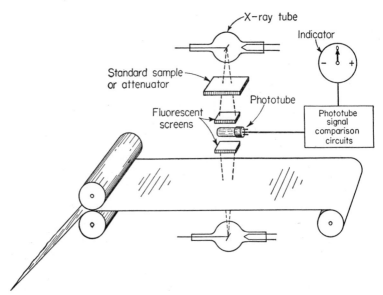

FIG. 6. Setup of an X-ray comparison thickness gauge. The amount of X-ray absorption by the strip material is compared to the amount of X-ray absorption by the standard or sample.

The gauge consists of two X-ray sources and a phototube pickup, as shown in Fig. 6. The phototube unit *sees* two pieces of fluorescent material which emit light when bombarded by X rays, the amount of light being proportional to the intensity of the X rays. The two X-ray tubes are energized alternately so that for one moment the phototube views light resulting from the radiation of one tube and at the next instant, of the other tube.

To reach the fluorescent material, the X rays coming from

[1] W. L. Lundahl, X-ray Thickness Gage, *Electronics*, March, 1948, p. 154.

the bottom tube must pass through the material being gauged. Thus a certain amount of ray attenuation will be expected. The rays from the top tube are attenuated by a calibrated standard which interrupts a known amount of X radiation. If the standard is of the same material as that being gauged, and its thickness is made equal to the desired thickness, then the amount of radiation and illumination reaching the phototube will be equal from both sources. If the thickness of the moving strip varies, for some reason, the ratio between the signals from the two sources will be changed, and the change in phototube signal may be used to indicate the error or to introduce corrective measures.

With this type of system a calibrated, tapered-disk attenuator may be used as a standard. This consists simply of an X-ray-absorbing wedge that can be moved in and out between the standard X-ray tube and the phototube unit. By placing in the gauging beam a known thickness of the material to be measured and sliding the wedge to a point where the phototube signals are balanced, calibration is accomplished.

Thus the device is an exact analog of the density-measuring instruments (densitometers) employed by photographers, engravers, and spectroscopists to determine the amount of light that can pass through photographic materials.

Contact Thickness Gauge. In certain applications it is possible to make actual contact in determining thickness measurements. Where the material is a conductor of electricity, it is possible to tell when contact is established by allowing a current to pass from one contact to the other through the material. This system is especially valuable in gauging soft metals where extreme accuracy is required. Where contact is determined by feel, the pressure exerted by a gauge might deform the piece.

Figure 7 shows an example of an electron tube micrometer which was devised for measuring the movement of loud-speaker elements. This combination of a vacuum-tube voltmeter and an Ames gauge[1] permits determination of physical position to within 0.000025 in. The Ames gauge is graduated in 0.0001-in. divisions and is mounted on a suitable fixture with its movable foot in a position to come in contact with the piece being gauged. When contact is established, the grid circuit of the vacuum-tube

[1] R. P. Glover and T. A. Hunter, Loud Speaker Deflection Measurements, *Electronics*, January, 1931, p. 474.

voltmeter circuit is grounded and current flows in the plate circuit meter.

In the course of developing the electron-tube micrometer described above, a low-voltage lamp and battery were tried as a means for contact indication. It was found, however, that the lamp would glow over a range of about 0.002 in., which was not sufficiently accurate for the application. The heavy current that must flow through the contacts causes this difficulty. The less the current, the more accurate will be the contact indication.

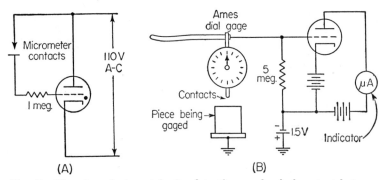

Fig. 7. Use of an electron tube for detecting mechanical contact between two metallic parts. The flow of current through the contact points is negligible when a vacuum-tube amplifier is used between the contacts and the indicating instrument.

The vacuum-tube arrangement provides a very definite indication with an extremely small current flow through the contact. Many applications of tubes to micrometer measurements will be found in the literature.

Loop Control. The thickness of a strip of material can be adjusted by controlling the tension or pulling force applied to it and thereby controlling the stretching experienced by the material. One of the most common systems for applying the proper reel torque for winding or pulling the material at the proper tension is shown in Fig. 8A. The system is described basically as a loop-control system, since tension is measured by determining the amount of slack or the size of the loop which appears in an unsupported section of a strip of the material. Of course, a big loop, or a great amount of sag, indicates low tension. The reeling motor must be speeded up to increase the tension. A small loop means too much tension.

Several systems are available for translating sag into electrical energy capable of automatically adjusting reeling motor speed and thus maintaining constant tension. The first method, shown in Fig. 8*A*, is the simpler of the two shown and affords only an on-off type of control. If the phototube sees its light source, a relay is actuated which will slow down the reeling motor. If the loop sags, however, so that the light beam is interrupted,

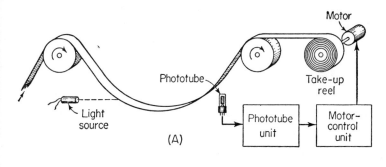

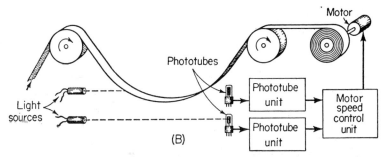

FIG. 8. Phototubes may be used to maintain tension in strip operations. When tension is too great, the sag decreases, allowing the phototube to "see" the light source. This produces a signal which decreases the pulling tension and restores proper tension.

the phototube initiates a speeding-up process which will reduce the loop by increasing the tension on the strip. Thus the control system is either on or off depending on whether or not the phototube sees its light source. The motor is constantly in the process of speeding up or slowing down, depending on the path between phototube and light source. Actually, in this system the motor runs at the proper speed for only short periods of time as it passes through that value in speeding up or slowing down. But, the average speed and thus the average tension on the strip will be the desired value. Figure 8*B* shows a slightly more elaborate system. No motor-speed correction is applied when sag is within desired limits.

Most electronic control systems are instantaneous in operation, but quite often the mechanical processes they control are not. As in the case just cited, there is a certain amount of mechanical lag. When the phototube sees its light source, it sends an electrical impulse to the motor control unit, which in effect tells

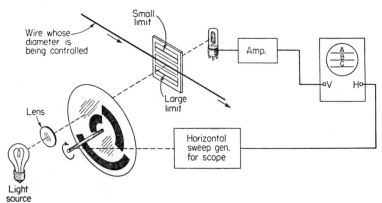

Fig. 9. Comparison system for measuring the thickness of wire continuously while the wire is traveling at high speeds. The same principle may be used to maintain constant thickness by use of proper control circuits.

the motor to slow down. But the motor, having a certain amount of momentum, can't slow down instantaneously, so for a brief instant the loop continues to decrease until the motor speed decreases.

Wire or Tube Thickness. The thickness of any wire or tube can be measured accurately, continuously, and without physical contact by the system shown in Fig. 9. It consists of a light source, a scanning wheel, three windows, a phototube and its control circuits, and an oscilloscope, which serves as an indicator.

The system employs the comparison technique. The scanning wheel rotates at a uniform speed and directs light from the light source periodically and in sequence through the three windows. The top window contains a sample wire the diameter of which corresponds to the smallest wire that can be used, while the lower window contains a wire which represents the maximum allowable thickness. The wire being measured passes by the center window.

The phototube signal will depend on the amount of obstruction offered in each window. A line is produced on the screen of a cathode-ray oscilloscope, the height of which depends on the phototube signal. For example, when the thin wire window is illuminated, the line might appear at A, and the thickest wire might cause a line at C in Fig. 9. Then the line representing the thickness of the test wire will fall somewhere between these two limits if its size is between the required limits.

This system is able to measure with splendid accuracy regardless of the speed of the wire passing the center window. Variations in supply voltages will not seriously affect the operation, since sensitivity changes will be felt also by the standard channels. Care must be exercised in aligning the scanning wheel, the windows, phototube, and light source for accurate operation. This equipment is manufactured by the Wilmotte Manufacturing Company of Washington, D.C. The example shown in the figure is, of course, simplified for the purposes of explanation.

Reluctance Thickness Gauge. It is well known that a current will be induced in a closed coil which is positioned with certain physical relationships to another current-carrying coil. The amount of induced current will depend on a number of factors, among them being the nature of the material which separates the two coils. This fact suggests another system for measuring thickness. Consider the diagram of Fig. 10A.[1] The alternating current in coil 1 induces alternating currents in coils 2 and 3. If the induced currents in these two coils are equal and opposite in phase, their effects will be cancelled in the primary of transformer T, and no current will be induced in its secondary. If, on the other hand, something happens to disturb this balance condition, a current will flow in the secondary of transformer T, and its magnitude will be proportional to the degree of unbalance. Such unbalance might be caused by introducing some foreign material between coil 1 and one of the two pickup coils, as shown at X. The degree of unbalance depends on the nature and thickness of this foreign material. By putting a piece of known

[1] R. C. Walker, "Electronic Equipment and Accessories," Chemical Publishing Company, Inc., Brooklyn, 1945.

thickness at Y, we again have a comparison system for determining the thickness of materials without physical contact.

Elevator Leveling. In effect the GE elevator leveling system utilizes a variation in reluctance. The circuit is shown in Fig. 10B. Here a tube as an oscillator draws grid current in the oscillating condition. This grid current flows through a resistor which biases the tube so that the plate current is low. If the tube stops oscillating, the plate current increases.

The various devices comprising a single tube, the necessary coils, condensers, etc., are mounted in a single box carried by

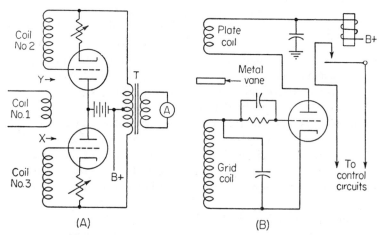

(A)   (B)

Fig. 10. Reluctance thickness gauges. The coupling between coils is varied by the presence of metal.

the car. As the car approaches the proper floor, a metal vane mounted in the hatchway is brought between the plate and grid coils by the movement of the car, thus shielding them from each other. This shielding removes the feed-back voltage from the grid circuit. The tube thus ceases to oscillate, and the plate current goes through a change of approximately 15 to 1. This change in current operates a relay which in turn controls the elevator motor. The vane enters the space between the plate and grid coils, and at approximately the center line of the coils a maximum movement of $\frac{1}{8}$ in. is required to cause the relay contacts to open or close. As the car movement varies directly as the position of the vanes, a car movement of $\frac{1}{8}$ in. maximum is sufficient to cause the control to function.

Use of a phototube and light beam is a natural method of elevator control and levelling. The phototube is also employed to keep the doors from closing until they are clear of traffic.

Register Control. The literature on this subject is voluminous, and many ingenious and complex arrangements have been developed for keeping the flow of cloth or paper through a process even and free from wobble. Where labels are to be cut at a definite place so that the pattern is not cut into, register control comes into use; and in multicolor printing, phototubes have performed some of their most elegant jobs.

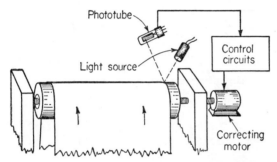

FIG. 11. Phototube setup for maintaining the correct position of a strip on a roller.

For example, in a sheet-reeling operation, electronic devices can be put to good use. The setup shown in Fig. 11 shows how a phototube will keep a web of material from moving sideways so that the coil formed will have straight sides. Its application is widespread, especially in the textile and paper industries where the material cannot be kept even by mechanical guides.

Here again control is an on-off process. If the phototube sees its light source, the reeling shaft is moved axially until the material interrupts the light beam. Then the opposite axial motion is imparted to the reeling shaft, and so on. The overall effect is to keep the sides of the coil even, since the material always enters the coil at the same place.

The mechanism for moving the shaft axially may take any of several forms. Again, we work from an electric signal, or voltage; in this case the signal from the phototube may be used to operate a double-throw relay to reverse the direction of a motor. Suitable gearing is then applied for converting the rotational energy into lateral motion, as suggested in the drawing. A hydraulic piston and a pump could be rigged up so that the phototube relay controls the opening and closing of a suitable hydraulic valve.

Photoelectric Contour Tracer. Another ingenious industrial electronic device makes use of the same principle. Where a large number of pieces are to be cut from sheet stock according to a template, automatic contour tracing can be accomplished by the system shown in Fig. 12. Here a paper template is made of the desired shape. A motor-positioned phototube head is mounted above the white template, which is placed on a dark

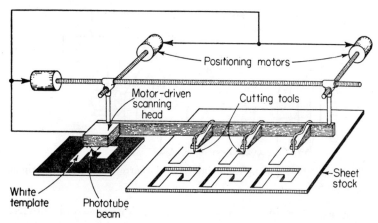

FIG. 12. Photoelectric contour follower. Cutting tools automatically trace out the contour represented by the paper pattern on the table.

table. When the phototube is over the white template, light is reflected from the light source, and the phototube signal is used to activate the motor-positioning setup in such a way that the phototube moves toward the edge of the template. When it reaches the edge, the light reflected to the phototube decreases. The resulting decrease in phototube signal causes the motor control to move the phototube unit toward the template again. The phototube unit therefore effectively follows the contour of the template, though actually its path consists of a zig-zag line around it. The accuracy with which it follows the pattern is, however, adequate for rough work. If a series of cutting torches is connected mechanically to the scanning phototube unit, as shown in the drawing, the pieces cut out will be practically identical in shape to the template used.   Once started, the equipment is self-operating.

MECHANICAL MOTION GAUGING

In a sense, when we measure the thickness of anything, we measure the physical position of one of its sides with respect to the other.   If we set up a device that will detect a *change* in the thickness of the piece, we in effect have a device capable of measuring mechanical position or *change* of position, which is, of course, motion.

There are three general classifications of devices for detecting mechanical motion—capacitance, inductance, and resistance gauges.   Photoelectric systems, in which motion is measured by a change in the angle of reflection of a beam of light, are discussed elsewhere.   Of the three general types, capacitance and inductance are usually applied to the more specialized applications in which for some reason the more widely used resistance gauges are unsuitable.

A capacitance gauge, as might be expected, measures mechanical motion in terms of a change in capacitance.   For instance, two plates separated by a dielectric such as air form a capacitor. If the distance between the plates is decreased by the movement of one plate toward the other, the capacitance increases.   Thus any device capable of measuring this change in capacitance may be calibrated in terms of mechanical motion and used to indicate relative position.

Inductance gauges are of two types.   One makes use of a coil of fairly springy wire, which is caused to move by the mechanical motion to be measured.   The movement imparted to the coil is such that the individual turns of the coil change position with respect to other turns and thus change the effective inductance. Another system couples the mechanical motion with a piece of some material whose permeability differs from that of air.   A simple example is shown in Fig. 13A.   An iron vane is connected to the moving element in such a way that if the element moves to the right, the vane moves farther into the coil.   A movement in the opposite direction will cause the vane to move away from the coil.   Iron in the presence of a coil of wire will increase the value of the coil inductance.   Thus if we can measure the coil inductance, we can determine how close the iron vane is to the coil.

A slight variation of this scheme is the transformer version in which the energy coupled from the primary of a transformer to its secondary is changed by a vane moving in and out between the two windings. In this case, however, the transformer is not of the physical appearance one generally associates with transformers. It has two coils, usually wound on the same axis, with a space between them through which the iron vane can pass as a result of motion of the element to which it is connected. An

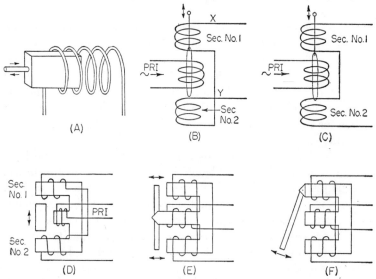

FIG. 13. Differential transformers provide a good link between mechanical and electrical phenomena.

alternating voltage is applied to the primary winding. The magnitude of the current induced in the secondary is measured to determine the position of the vane.

Differential Transformers. Another motion-measuring device is the differential transformer, which is illustrated in Fig. 13B through 13F. These are only a few of the possible configurations, but they are representative of the setups used in industrial instrumentation to detect the position of objects.

The differential transformer consists essentially of a primary coil, two secondary coils, and an armature of magnetic material. The armature is coupled mechanically to the object whose motion is being observed.   The primary coil is energized by some source of a-c power, and the two secondary windings usually are connected (except for the setup shown in Fig. 13*C*) so that the voltages induced in them are 180 deg out of phase.

If the coupling between the primary and each of the secondary windings is equal (the armature centered), no voltage will appear between points X and Y.   If, however, the magnetic armature is moved slightly toward one of the secondary windings, it will increase the coupling to that secondary, and decrease the coupling to the other.   Thus the voltage induced in the first secondary will predominate and a voltage will appear between X and Y.   If the armature moves in the other direction, a similar voltage will appear, but since that secondary is 180 deg out of phase with the voltage in the first secondary, the over-all voltage will bear that phase relationship.

These characteristics of the differential transformer make it very useful in the measurement of mechanical displacement.   If an object is to be kept in position at some given spot, it can be coupled to a differential transformer, and the voltages generated when the object moves can be used to initiate the mechanical positioning devices to bring the object back to its proper position. An excellent discussion of differential transformers as applied to the measurement of straight-line motions is presented by W. D. MacGeorge in the June, 1950, issue of *Instruments*.

Resistance Motion Gauges.   As implied in earlier paragraphs, resistance gauges are the type most generally used.   They are, in general, less sensitive than the capacitance and inductance type. That is, the percentage change in signal which is produced by the movement of a resistance gauge element is smaller than the change in signal that would be produced by an equal mechanical movement of the elements of one of the other types.

However, because of their low cost, the ease with which they may be attached to equipment, and their reliability and adaptability, they have won great favor among instrumentation and measurement engineers.   Properly applied, resistance strain gauges can be relied upon to detect and measure mechanical motion of less than 0.001 in., provided the necessary signal amplification facilities are employed.

Figure 14 shows a group of resistance devices which have some important characteristics in common.   In each case there is a pair of terminals and a mechanical arrangement that converts motion into a change in resistance between these terminals.

Figures 14A and 14B are similar—both depend on a sliding conductor moving along a piece of material which represents a finite and measurable resistance. For instance in A, if one terminal is the supporting block at the left and the slider the other, the resistance measured between the two terminals will be directly proportional to the distance between the place where the contact rests on the slide wire and the end of the slide wire which is connected to the left-hand terminal.

Figure 14C shows a stepped device, as contrasted to the continuous devices just described. Here we have set up a means for determining the height of a bar L. The resistance between M and N, if none of the contacts are immersed in the mercury, will be the sum of the resistances connected in series between the two points. The same will be true when just the left-hand contact touches the mercury. When the second one makes contact, the resistance between O and P is shorted out (since mercury is a good conductor of electricity), and the total resistance between M and N decreases. As the bar L moves down, the resistance between the terminals decreases and constitutes a means for determining the height of the bar. If L were stationary, this would provide a means for measuring the level of the mercury.

A modification of this arrangement is shown in Fig. 14D.

Figure 14E through 14I shows resistance gauges which employ carbon as the resistance-changing element. Carbon has the property of changing its resistance radically when it is compressed. The carbon particles are irregular, and they contact adjacent particles only on the tips of the ragged points and rough edges. Compression squeezes these sharp points into better contact with adjacent particles, and the cumulative effect is to lower the resistance of the over-all mass to the flow of electric current. The four carbon gauges differ only in the form that the carbon element takes. In E it is in the form of granules, in F disks, and in H and I it has the form of a strip. The way the conducting terminals are connected to the strip is the only difference between H and I.

Figure 14G shows a device for detecting and measuring rotational motion. A piece of resistance wire is fused to the inside of a doughnut-shaped glass tube, which is half filled with mercury.

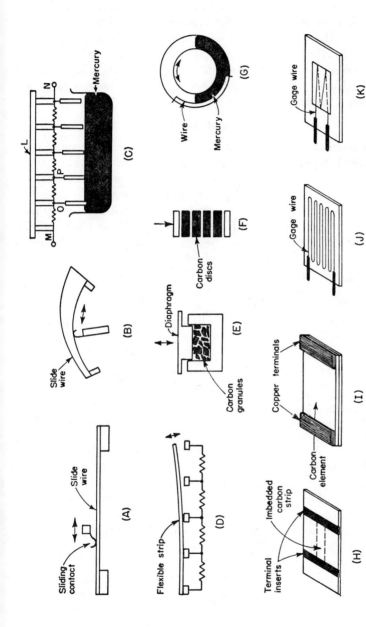

Fig. 14. Typical schemes for converting mechanical changes into resistance changes.

When the doughnut is rotated in such a way that the resistance wire is completely out of the mercury, the resistance measured between the two terminals A and B is the resistance of the wire. If the doughnut is rotated so that part of the wire is immersed in the mercury, the resistance of the immersed portion is effectively shorted out. Thus the resistance appearing between terminals A and B is less.

STRAIN GAUGES

A movement between two points on a common piece of solid material represents a strain in the material. Strain gauges therefore find their most common use in measuring the amount of strain experienced at different portions of materials as they are subjected to various types and degrees of mechanical loads.

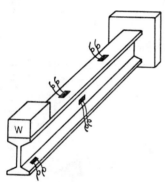

Fig. 15. Placement of resistance strain gauges along a beam under test provides valuable information about stresses and strains resulting from weighting and other influences.

Wire strain gauges may be of either of the forms shown in Fig. 14J and 14K. A length of gauge wire is securely fastened to a piece of flexible cardboard or some kind of cloth in such a way that if the cloth is stretched or compressed, a physical deformation will be felt by the gauge wire. Gauge wire has the property which makes its resistance increase as the wire is stretched, and decrease when compressed.

An example of a typical use for this type of gauge is shown in Fig. 15. A steel beam is being made to support a weight W at one end, while the other end is assumed to be fixed. By placing strain gauges at convenient intervals along the steel beam, it is possible to determine the effects of the loading at those points as the weight W is applied to the end of the beam.

Frequently, it is desired to study strains at different portions of such a beam simultaneously. For this purpose, and other more elaborate applications, many ingenious commutating devices have been devised. In fact one packaged unit[1] contains

[1] Electron Tube Corp., Philadelphia.

a four-channel oscillograph outfit for just this purpose. It is used primarily in testing aircraft parts. Needless to say, such testing devices have been responsible for the saving of many lives and much property.

Resistance Measuring Circuits. None of these devices whose resistances change as a result of mechanical movement would be of value if we couldn't measure the resistance changes. Sometimes the resistance changes involved are a small percentage of the resistance of the gauge being used. For example, a 10,000-ohm gauge under one condition might be called upon to register a substantial mechanical motion for a change in resistance of say 100 ohms, or a 1 per cent change.

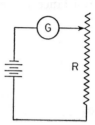

A basic circuit for measuring resistance is shown in Fig. 16. The gauge and a sensitive current-measuring galvanometer G are connected in series with a voltage source, which may be a simple battery or some other source of voltage. The choice of voltage source de-

Fig. 16. Simple circuits for measuring changes in resistance.

pends on the type of current-measuring device used. In the following discussions d-c galvanometers are indicated for simplicity. The main requirement is that the indicating device show different readings for each possible change which might occur in the resistance.

The disadvantages of the simple circuit shown in Fig. 16 are many whenever very accurate and dependable operation is required. It will be remembered that the resistance of materials changes as the temperature of the air surrounding them changes. If for some reason a warm current of air were to pass over the resistance gauge element, the effect would be to raise the resistance of the gauge, and the indicator would register an erroneous movement. Likewise, a temperature change along the wire connecting the gauge to the measuring equipment can have an effect. Another source of error in the simple circuit is the fact that whenever the voltage of the source changes, the instrument will go out of calibration, and the readings will become meaningless.

The circuit of Fig. 17 overcomes these difficulties to a certain extent. The gauge might be of the type illustrated in Fig. 14B,

with both ends of the resistance element and the slider connected
to the measuring equipment through long wires or perhaps slip
rings if the measuring gauge were mounted on a piece of rotating
machinery.

Let us assume that when this instrument is first put into operation it is calibrated so that when a voltage of three volts is
impressed on the gauge the voltmeter will read 1.5 volts when the
slider is in the center of the resistance element.   If the variable
resistance R were not in the circuit, the entire voltage of the

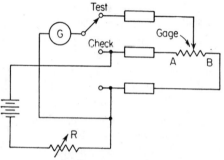

FIG. 17.   A more accurate method for measuring remote resistance values.
Three wires must be used between the resistance element and the measuring
circuit, but a calibration or checking circuit is provided.

battery would be impressed across the gauge.   If the battery
voltage happened to be 3 volts, the instrument would be in
calibration.   But suppose the battery ages, and its voltage drops
to 2 volts.   Then the voltmeter will indicate half of that value,
or 1 volt, when the slider is at the center of the resistance element.

To compensate such voltage fluctuations the two-position
switch is added and a variable resistor placed in series with the
voltage source.   Before a measurement is made, the switch is
turned to the *check* position.   This places the terminals of the
voltmeter across the resistance gauge.   The voltage across the
gauge may now be set by means of R to the desired value, say
3 volts.   When the switch is turned to the *test* position, the
calibration of the indicator dial will be accurate.

Wheatstone-bridge Circuit.   The circuit shown in Fig. 18 is
known as a Wheatstone bridge.   The basic components are four
resistors, one of which is the resistance element of the measuring

device; a voltage source, which may again be either alternating or direct current; and a current-indicating instrument.

The circuit shows the voltage source connected across the top and bottom of two sets of resistors in series. The other two junctions (*A* and *B*) are connected by the current-reading instrument which, if a battery is used, may be a sensitive milliammeter, or where better accuracy is desired, a microammeter or galvanometer.

If all four of the bridge resistors had exactly the same value, the voltage at points *A* and *B* would be equal to each other and also equal to half of the voltage applied to the circuit. Since the voltage applied across the terminals of the current-measuring device is zero, no current will flow through it, and the circuit is said to be balanced.

Now assume that R_3 is the resistance gauge whose value we wish to determine. If its value is lower than that of, say, R_1, then the voltage drop across it will be less than that across R_1, and a voltage difference will exist between points *A* and *B*. The galvanometer will deflect and the bridge is said to be unbalanced. If we change the value of R_1 until the galvanometer again reads zero current, we know that the value of R_1 has been set to equal that of the unknown resistance. If we know the value of R_1, we know the value of R_3. Accurately calibrated resistors are available for such purposes.

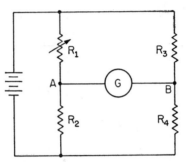

Fig. 18.   Bridge circuit for measuring unknown resistance values.

Although the bridge circuit shown is perfectly usable, and if proper care is taken it will yield extremely accurate measurements, a great many refinements can be added to increase its usefulness. If a highly sensitive indicating instrument is used, the full-scale or full-current limit is a very small value. If a high degree of bridge unbalance is brought about by a large change in the gauge resistance, a large amount of current will flow, and it might prove fatal to the instrument. Shunt resistances are frequently employed to by-pass part of the current around the meter until the bridge is brought near balance.

When the bridge is nearly balanced, the shunt resistance is removed and the full sensitivity of the meter employed.

Also it may be useful to have more than one value of resistance available for R_2 and R_4. Different values of R_1 might be needed if a wide variety of gauge resistances must be measured with the same bridge.

Many ingenious systems for automatic balancing of bridges have been devised. A few of these are mentioned in the chapter on phototube applications. An exceptionally complete treatment of bridge circuits and the mathematical equations for them can be found in Volumes 17 (1944) and 18 (1945) of *Instruments* in a series of articles by H. C. Roberts.

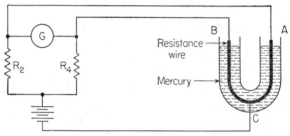

FIG. 19. The mercury shorts out sections of the resistance wire in differential fashion. Note the similarity to the circuit shown in Fig. 18.

Differential Resistance Gauges. Figure 19 shows a slightly different type of gauge. The application illustrated is that of determining pressure by means of a manometer. As the pressure on the surface of the mercury in tube A becomes greater than that applied to the surface of B, the mercury will tend to rise in tube B and consequently to fall in A. As this happens, more of the resistance between B and C is shorted out by the mercury, while less is shorted between C and A. Thus we have in effect a Wheatstone bridge in which R_3 (the resistance of the wire from B to C) decreases, and at the same time R_1 (A to C) increases. The bridge is thus unbalanced twice the amount that it would be if just one resistance changed.

With this type of indication the bridge is balanced when the two mercury columns are equal, and the voltage, or the values of R_2 and R_4, is adjusted so that the indicating instrument is approximately at maximum when the pressure difference is a

maximum.   By this means the meter reading becomes a direct
indication of the pressure difference.

Compensation for IR Drop.   Although very small in comparison, the resistance of the wires used to connect the resistance
gauge to the measuring circuit has a finite value, which may cause
an erroneous reading.   This is especially true when the resistance
gauge is located some distance from the reading station.   Figure
20 shows two schemes which can be used to compensate this
error.

Study of Fig. 20A will reveal that basically it is still the same
Wheatstone bridge.   If, however, the right-hand side of the

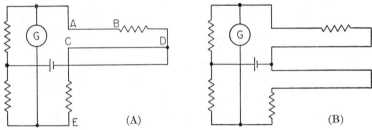

(A)   (B)

Fig. 20.   Two schemes for compensating for disturbing influences caused by
variations in conditions between an unknown resistance element and the
measuring equipment.

voltage source were connected at point C instead of point D, the
resistance between points C and A would be greater than that
between C and E by an amount equal to the resistance of AB
plus CD.   By the arrangement shown the wire resistance is
shared equally by the two arms of the bridge, and the effect of
this undesired resistance is canceled out.   If we simply added a
resistor in series with CE equal to that of the connecting wires,
we would accomplish a degree of compensation for the IR drop.
But any temperature change that occurred along the connecting
wires would cause a change in their resistance and destroy the
compensating effect.   The circuit shown in effect places the
compensating resistor in the same circumstances as the wire
resistance, so temperature-effect compensation is automatic.   It
is a simple matter to cut a piece of the same type wire to the
right length—much easier than trying to set a resistor to the
proper value.   Figure 20B is similar but uses one extra wire.

RCA Triode Transducer. Figure 21 shows a special type of vacuum tube which provides a direct link between mechanical motion and an electrical signal. Called the 5734, the device contains a cathode and grid, which are similar in function to the corresponding elements of a conventional vacuum tube. The plate is suspended at only one point—the center of a metal diaphragm which forms the end of the tube. This diaphragm is thin and flexible, though its rim is firmly connected to the

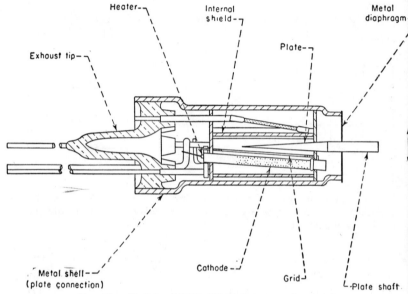

FIG. 21.   Sketch of RCA 5734 triode transducer tube.

walls of the tube. A short nipple juts out from the diaphragm and can be moved within small but finite limits. Movement of this nipple results in movement of the diaphragm which in turn causes the plate of the triode to move within the tube. The mechanical motion is thus translated directly into a change in current through the tube. The amount of current that flows depends on the spacing between the cathode and the plate, so when the plate moves toward the cathode, the current increases, and vice versa.

The sensitivity, that is the change in voltage which results from a given deflection of the plate shaft, is 40 volts for every degree through which the plate shaft moves. The maximum

deflection possible due to the construction of the tube is ½ deg.
This tube is especially applicable to studies of vibration and,
among other advantages, offers extremely small size and low
inertia of the moving element. The movable plate structure
has a mechanical resonance near 12,000 cps, which places an
upper limit to its usefulness as a vibration measuring device.

Power-line Fault Locator. The use of a varying-frequency
alternating current to determine the location of grounds and of
open and short circuits in power transmission lines has been
made by many power companies. An oscillator and amplifier
capable of supplying frequencies from 1 to 100 kc are connected
to the faulty line, and the frequency is increased while the current
in the line is recorded on a graphic milliameter, which automatically records variations.

It will be found that sharp peaks occur at equally spaced intervals as the frequency is increased. The frequency interval is
then measured. This interval indicates the distance between
the fault and the application of the voltage in terms of the equation $L = V/2d$, where L is the distance in miles, V the wave
propagation in miles per second (determined for each circuit by
test), and d is the average difference in frequency between current
peaks. By means of such measurements the accuracy of location
in most cases can be made within 2 per cent. The cause of the
current peaks is the reflection and phase shift which the alternating current undergoes at the fault in the line, the result being
that certain frequencies are reinforced by the reflection, while
certain others suffer destructive interference. In the apparatus
used, the entire oscillator-amplifier, power supply and recording
instruments are mounted on a portable truck containing all the
necessary apparatus.

Measuring Commutator Roughness. An interesting application of the grid-controlled rectifier is the measurement of commutator roughness by determining the voltage variations when
current is passed through a brush riding the surface of a commutator. If the surface is smooth, the voltage variations across
the brush and commutator are of the order of 2 volts with 110
volts applied. If a complete break occurs, as would happen if
the brush were lifted from the surface and let fall on the commutator, the voltage variation would be 110 volts.

The tube is supplied with grid voltages varied in steps of 1

volt from 0 to 100 volts. The brush voltage drop is in series
with this voltage and in opposition to it. If the grid voltage is
slowly decreased from some high negative value until the tube
glows, it is easily possible to determine the brush-voltage drop
by noting the voltage at which the tube broke down and by
referring to a curve showing the required grid voltage, for the
particular plate voltage used, to make the tube conduct.

This device will measure roughness of the order of 0.0001 in.
when the commutator is rotating at a peripheral speed of 5,000 to
10,000 ft per minute and at a temperature of about 100°C.

Watch-tick Amplifier. Many attempts have been made to use
electronic circuits for the rapid regulation of time pieces. A
chronograph system,[1] making use of the techniques of facsimile
transmission, has been developed into a watch-analyzing mechanism which checks timepieces and automatically prints a case
history of any trouble. By this means the timekeeping capacity
of a watch, to an accuracy of within 1 second per day, can be
determined in 1 minute. The device uses a temperature-controlled tuning fork as a standard of time. The fork controls
the speed of a driving motor which rotates the paper upon which
the record is to be kept. The watch ticks are picked up by a
microphone and are amplified to operate a printer recorder which
makes marks on the paper. An error of one part in a million
may be recorded and measured in about 1 minute.

TEMPERATURE MEASUREMENT

The importance of measuring and controlling temperature in
industrial processes has increased in recent years. In many cases
temperature can be measured adequately by liquid or metallic
thermometers. Temperature is actually measured indirectly by
measuring its effect on certain substances which demonstrate
known characteristics under varying degrees of the presence or
absence of heat.

A few examples of such effects are:

1. Expansion of solids, liquids, or gases by increased molecular
   activity in the presence of heat
2. Generation of an electric voltage by a thermocouple
3. Change in electrical resistance of a material in the presence
   of heat

[1] C. J. Young and Maurice Artzt, *Electronics*, July, 1935, p. 220.

4. Difference in the amount of expansion between two mechanically bonded dissimilar metals

5. Changes in radiation characteristics. It is well known that a piece of white hot iron is hotter than a similar piece which is only red hot. The accompanying table provides a rough means for estimating temperature by eye.

Degrees Fahrenheit	Degrees Centigrade	Color
2200	1200	White
1975	1070	Light yellow
1820	1000	Yellow
1550	840	Light red
1370	740	Cherry red
1250	675	Medium cherry red
1160	630	Dark cherry red
1050	560	Blood red
990	530	Black red

By proper calibration, instruments capable of measuring any of these changes can be made to measure temperature, or more strictly speaking, changes in temperature.

A common temperature-measuring device is the glass thermometer in which a column of mercury rises as the temperature increases. In cheaper thermometers alcohol or some similar liquid is used. Another type of liquid expansion thermometer frequently used for remote indication of temperature uses a tube completely filled with mercury and fitted with a gas-filled spiral at the indicating end. When the temperature increases, the mercury volume increases and consequently the pressure of the gas in the spiral. The increased pressure causes the spiral to open somewhat and to move a pointer on the scale of an indicating dial.

Thermocouples. Thermocouples are extensively used in the measurement of industrial temperatures. A thermocouple consists of a pair of dissimilar wire conductors. These wires are joined, as shown in Fig. 22. The free ends are connected to a high-resistance voltmeter. When the temperature at the measuring junction differs from the temperature at the voltmeter (reference junction), a voltage appears at the terminals of the voltmeter. The magnitude of the voltage is proportional to the difference in temperature at these two locations. This voltage might be a few millivolts. The measuring junction may be brought in contact with the material whose temperature is being measured, or the heat energy can be conveyed to the thermocouple by conduction or radiation through air or some other medium.

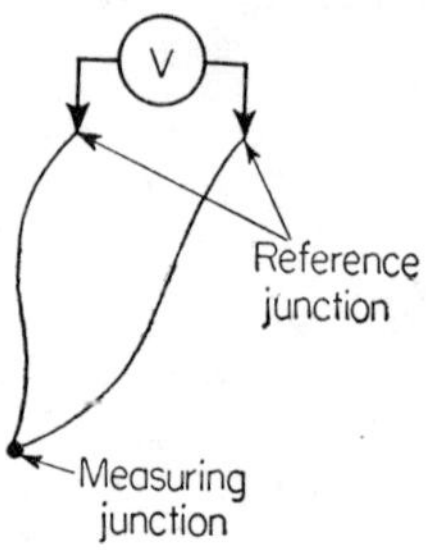

Reference junction

Measuring junction

FIG. 22. Basic thermocouple circuit for measuring temperature.

Modern thermocouple instruments employ many refinements for increasing the speed and accuracy of indications. Since the thermocouple voltage depends on the difference between the temperature at the measuring junction and the reference junction, some accurate means must be provided for determining the temperature of the reference junction. A standard thermometer will usually suffice.

Thermocouples are especially valuable in determining temperatures at very small spots in or on materials. Where the voltage of one junction is insufficient for a particular job, several such units may be connected in

Materials	Range, °C	Degrees per millivolt
Constantan and iron.....................	−200 to 1000	24 to 17
Chromel and P-alumel..................	−200 to 1400	35 to 25
Constantan and copper.................	−200 to 400	36 to 19
Platinum and platinum with 10% rhodium	0 to 1750	0 to 95

series. A few typical thermocouple characteristics are listed in the accompanying table.

Resistance Thermometers. The electrical resistance of metals changes as their temperature changes. Thus for a given piece of metal wire the temperature surrounding it may be determined by measuring its resistance. Converting the resistance values to temperature units may be accomplished either by calibration curves, or by the formula $R_2 = R_1\alpha(T_2 - T_1)$, where R_2 is the resistance of the wire at the measured temperature T_2, and R_1 is the resistance of the wire at some known temperature T_1.

The factor α is the temperature coefficient for the particular type of metal used.

Platinum and nickel have very desirable characteristics for use in resistance thermometers. They are probably the most widely used metals for that purpose. Because corrosion is accelerated by exposure to high temperatures and also because it decreases the cross-sectional diameter of the wires thereby increasing the resistance permanently, the resistance thermometer is limited to measurements below about 300°F. The low limit is about

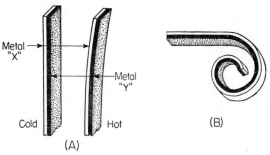

Fig. 23. Bimetallic strips transform temperature changes into mechanical changes.

−150°F. The nickel version is generally incorporated in a Wheatstone bridge arrangement in conjunction with some null-detecting device.

Bimetallic Strips. The difference of expansion of various metals is often used as a yardstick to measure temperatures, especially in domestic heating systems. The home thermostat is of this type. A strip made of two pieces of metal having different expansion coefficients welded or bolted back to back will curl with a change in temperature. If one end is held stationary, the other end will move. The reason for this movement is illustrated in Fig. 23A. Metal X, let us say, expands more than metal Y for a given change in temperature. Thus metal X will *push* metal Y, and metal Y will *pull* metal X. The strip may also be coiled in a spiral, as shown in Fig. 23B, and a spiral or rotational motion will result. A pointer connected as shown may then be used to indicate temperature on a circular dial.

A very simple and early use[1] of a tube for temperature control

[1] C. H. Sharp, Electronic Devices in a Testing Laboratory, *Electronics,* September, 1932, p. 284.

is illustrated in Fig. 24. Here the tube serves only to reduce the
current that must be handled by the bimetallic strip, so that a
slight movement of the latter is sufficient to operate the control.
Although this system will control temperature to within 0.1°C,

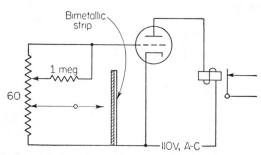

Fɪɢ. 24. Basic circuit for using a bimetallic strip with a relay. Movement
of the strip resulting from a change in temperature causes part of the grid
resistor to be shorted out, with a resulting increase in plate current and the
closure of the relay.

more complex electronic circuits will enable much greater control
to be effected.

Radiation Pyrometers. The temperature of a body may be
determined by observing its radiation characteristics. A
thermocouple, a phototube, or a
thermistor may be used to measure radiation and thus temperature. Another scheme makes use
of direct comparison. Here the
current flowing through an incandescent filament is adjusted
until the brightness of the filament
is the same as that of the hot body.
By measuring the current and
referring to a calibration chart,
the temperature of the filament (and the body) can be determined. The calibration chart is made by comparing the filament
at different temperatures with known temperatures. This
system is called optical pyrometry and is, of course, limited
to bodies which are sufficiently hot to give off visible heat
radiation.

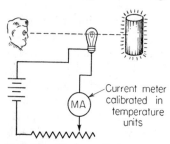

Fɪɢ. 25. Basic optical pyrometry arrangement.

Electronic Control. Electronic circuits are used in temperature control for the same reason they are used in other applications. They can perform certain types of operations better, faster, more reliably or cheaply than mechanical or straight electrical methods.

As in other electronic control problems, temperature control by electronics requires the temperature to deviate from the desired value before the controlling action goes into play.   Corrective

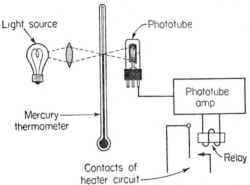

Light source

Phototube

Phototube amp

Mercury thermometer

Relay

Contacts of heater circuit

F<small>IG</small>. 26.   Simple method for maintaining a fixed temperature.   When the mercury rises in the tube, it cuts off the light to the phototube.   The phototube circuit releases the relay and turns off the heater.

control measures may then be applied.   The simplest temperature-control instrument permits heat to be applied until the temperature reaches the desired value or a little higher.   Then the heat supply is removed until the temperature falls to some lower predetermined point, at which heat is again applied and the cycle repeats.   The temperature then varies periodically between a pair of upper and lower limits.

Another system is that of proportional control in which heat input is proportional to the demand.   Then if heat is being lost at a low rate, heat is applied at a low rate.   If heat is being lost rapidly, thereby reducing the temperature by a considerable amount, the heat input is automatically set at a correspondingly high rate.   The system is continually balancing itself at some temperature.

Phototube System. An extremely simple system of temperature control is shown in Fig. 26.   It uses a phototube in conjunc-

tion with an amplifier and a simple mercury thermometer. A
light source and lens system is mounted on one side of the thermometer and the phototube on the other side at a level corresponding to the desired temperature. If the mercury column is
below that level, the phototube sees its light source and passes a
current which causes the relay to operate. The heat is then
turned on. When the mercury column rises above the phototube
level, the light beam is cut off, as is the heat source, since the
relay is deenergized.

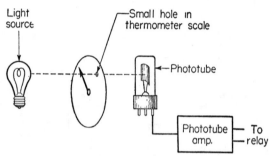

FIG. 27. Another simple means for actuating control functions at some
desired temperature. The needle of the thermometer cuts the light beam.

This type of phototube device may also be used on circular
scale thermometers as shown in Fig. 27. Here a hole is placed
in the thermometer scale at the desired temperature. As the
temperature rises, the pointer covers the hole, thereby cutting
off the light beam. The relay is then deenergized and the heat
source disconnected.

Another electronic device is shown in Fig. 28. A light metallic
vane is attached to the arm of some conventional temperature-
measuring device. As the temperature increases toward the
control temperature, this vane moves between two coils of a
simple feedback oscillator. Under normal conditions the circuit
is not oscillating, but the presence of the vane increases the
feedback from the plate coil to the grid coil, and the circuit starts
to oscillate. In so doing, the plate current of the tube, which
flows through the coil of the relay, decreases from about 10 ma
to 5 ma, and the relay is deenergized, turning off the heater.

In another oscillating-tube system the presence of the vane in
the coil area shifts the frequency of oscillation, which again

causes a difference in the plate current flowing through the relay coil.

Self-balancing Potentiometers. Probably the most precise method for measuring temperature makes use of a potentiometer to measure the voltage generated by a thermocouple. A typical

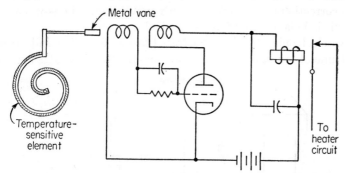

FIG. 28. A metallic vane attached to the temperature element moves into the coils as the temperature rises and completes the feedback circuit which causes oscillation. The accompanying drop in plate current lets the relay drop out.

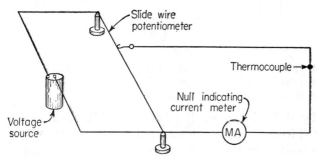

FIG. 29. When the voltage picked off by the potentiometer slider equals the thermocouple voltage, current flow ceases in the thermocouple circuit, and the position of the slider is the measure of the thermocouple voltage, or temperature.

circuit is shown in Fig. 29. The thermocouple voltage is accurately determined by measuring the length of a slide wire whose voltage drop is equal to the voltage generated by the thermocouple.

When the slider is set to a place where no current flows through the indicating instrument, the circuit is balanced. This type of circuit offers maximum accuracy, because there is no voltage drop due to current flow, since no current is flowing when the reading is made.

Self-balancing potentiometers are available for keeping permanent records of changing temperatures. The undesired current flowing in the indicating circuit is used to initiate mechanical correction forces on the potentiometer arm. Thus when the circuit is balanced, no force is applied.

An electronic system is illustrated in Fig. 30. The indicating instrument is a light-beam galvanometer, which indicates current

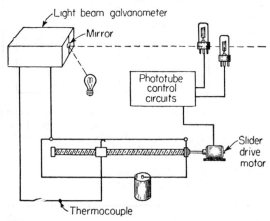

FIG. 30.   Phototubes initiate controls to restore balance conditions when the light beam reflected by the galvanometer mirror moves from its position between the phototubes.

flow by deflecting a small mirror. A thin beam of light is reflected from the mirror in such a way that very small changes in the position of the mirror will cause the reflected light beam to move several inches or so.

As shown in Fig. 30, the reflected light beam falls between the two phototubes when there is no current flowing through the galvanometer. Thus no mechanical force is applied to the potentiometer driving motor. If a current begins to flow, as might occur if the thermocouple voltage changed, the mirror will be deflected one way or the other, depending on the direction of the current flow. The reflected light beam will fall on one of the phototubes and the phototube control circuits will cause the potentiometer drive motor to reposition the slider until balance is again achieved.

This system can be used to maintain very accurate continuous measurement of temperature. It may be altered to provide similarly accurate control of temperature. In the control application the phototube signals are used to turn on heat or to turn on a cooling system so that the temperature of the specimen changes and brings the circuit to balance.

Another system uses the unbalance voltage indirectly. Techniques discussed in the phototube chapter are used to convert

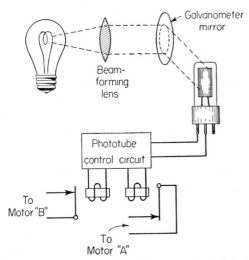

FIG. 31. Another form of control circuit for use with a light-beam galvanometer. Relays control the functions to restore balance once it is disturbed.

the d-c unbalance voltage to an a-c voltage, which may be amplified by conventional amplifiers and used to initiate control devices.

Figure 31 shows the light-beam type. During periods of temperature change small currents pass through the galvanometer and deflect the light beam away from its balance position. When the light beam is partly on and partly off the phototube cathode, the current is such that one of the relays is open and the other is closed. Thus both motors are inoperative. When the light beam is entirely off the cathode of the phototube, or when it is entirely on it, the relays are either both open or both closed, and the proper motor is energized to correct the position of the arm on the potentiometer. As described, this system is simply a

measuring circuit. To effect control, the relays are not connected to balancing motors but to temperature controlling devices
such as a combination of fan and electric heater.   Bridge unbalance causes one or the other to operate to return the bridge to
balance by lowering or raising the temperature and thus the
voltage read by the thermocouple.

Figure 32 shows a system which converts the unbalance voltage
into alternating current for effecting bridge balance or operating

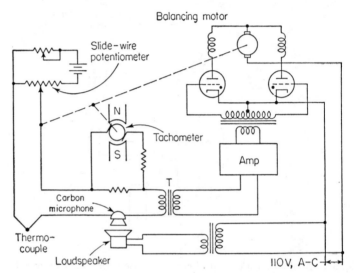

FIG. 32.   Unbalance voltage is converted into a-c voltage which is amplified
by conventional means and applied to control devices.

control devices.   An interesting feature of the circuit shown is
the tachometer, which causes control to be made smoothly and
positively without undue lag or hunting back and forth around
the desired value.   The motor speed control is such that the
speed of the motor is proportional to the degree of unbalance of
the system.   Thus, as the balance point is neared, the balancing
motor slows down and comes to a smooth stop at balance.

To explain the operation, consider the circuit to be unbalanced
so that a d-c voltage exists between the thermocouple and the
potentiometer.   This d-c voltage is converted into alternating
current by means of a simple carbon microphone which is furnished with a 60-cps sound wave by a vibrator or oscillator.   The

resulting a-c voltage is stepped up by transformer T and a voltage amplifier and applied to the thyratrons.

Depending on phase, one or the other thyratron will fire and drive the balancing or control motor in the proper direction to rebalance the circuit. The anodes of the two thyratrons are connected directly to the two field windings of a d-c series-wound commutator motor. The tachometer voltage is introduced into the circuit so that the speed of the motor is controlled to maintain the sum of all three voltages at zero. This system is used by

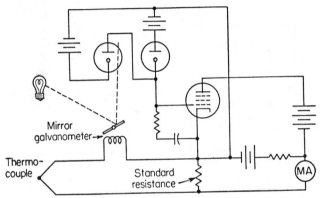

Fig. 33. Version of an automatic potentiometer system for measuring thermocouple voltages.

Leeds and Northrup in a temperature-measuring unit. A similar unit is made by the Brown Instruments Company.[1]

In the photoelectric potentiometer manufactured by the Weston Electrical Instruments Corporation, a variable current is passed through a fixed resistor, the voltage drop across which is used to balance the thermocouple voltage, as shown in Fig. 33.

The plate current of a pentode amplifier flows through a standard resistor in opposition to the thermocouple voltage. When the two voltages are balanced, the galvanometer is undeflected. If unbalance occurs, the galvanometer deflects and its mirror reflects a light beam to one of the phototubes through a system of prisms. The phototubes act as variable resistances in the grid circuit of the pentode amplifier to vary the grid voltage depending upon the direction and amplitude of the

[1] R. D. Towne and D. M. Considine, Continuous Balance Potentiometer Pyrometer, *Electronics*, August, 1942, page 92.

unbalance. This causes more or less current to flow through
the tube and also through the standard resistor to rebalance the
circuit. The milliammeter in the plate circuit measures the
current required to balance the input voltage and may be calibrated directly in temperature units. Or this circuit may be
used to operate control relays, as in previous examples.

Gas-tube Voltmeter. A method using a gaseous triode for
measuring small a-c voltages has been described by Hughes.[1]

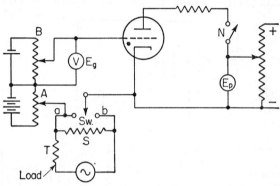

Fig. 34.   Peak voltmeter using a gas triode.

This makes use of the fact that the characteristic of such a tube,
that is, the relation between grid voltage and plate voltage for
current to flow, is very steep. The voltage to be measured is
added to a fixed grid bias, which is then reduced until the tube
fires. The circuit in Fig. 34 shows the arrangement for determining the peak value of an alternating current through a given
load. The alternating current is passed through a standard
shunt (resistor) S. By means of a two-way switch Sw the
alternating potential across the shunt can be applied to the grid.
The function of potentiometer A is to give a constant negative
bias such that when Sw is on a, only a very small extra bias is
required from another potentiometer B to prevent the anode
glow appearing in the tube.

The test procedure is as follows: with switch N open, E_p is
adjusted to, say, 100 volts, and the grid bias of B is made greater
than the critical value. Then N is closed and B reduced until

[1] Hughes, Edward, The Measurement of Peak Values of Alternating Currents and Voltages by Means of a Thyratron, *Journal of Scientific Instruments*, June, 1933.

the tube suddenly glows. The reading on E_g just before the appearance of the glow is noted. Once the ionization has commenced, positive ions are attracted to the grid, and consequently there is a decrease in the reading on E_g. The critical voltage on B may be checked, however, by opening N, thereby eliminating the grid current.

Switch Sw is next moved over to b and the test repeated. The difference between the readings on E_g with Sw on a and b respectively gives the maximum potential difference across S.

This method has been used with frequencies varying from 20 to 500 cycles. With a low-reading voltmeter for E_g it is possible to determine the critical grid voltage within 0.01 volt.

The method has been used mainly for measurement of the potential drop across a standard shunt; this did not exceed 2 volts and could be determined within 0.02 volt. There appears to be no reason, however, why the same method could not be applied to determine (1) the maximum value of much larger alternating voltages either directly or indirectly by connecting two unequal condensers in series and measuring the maximum potential difference across the larger unit (2) the maximum value of a current of any magnitude in a high-voltage circuit by means of a current transformer having the standard 5-va secondary loaded by a noninductive resistance of about 1 ohm. With only a 5-va load on a standard transformer, it has been found that even for very distorted wave forms the shapes of the primary and secondary currents are practically identical. Hence the maximum value of the primary current can be determined by substituting the secondary load of the current transformer for S in the circuit diagram.

Tube Control of Wire Drawing. An example of the control of electric equipment during operation by means of grid-controlled rectifiers is found in the GE wire-drawing shops. Very fine wire is reeled under a strain that is a large percentage of its ultimate strength.

The wire must be kept at the proper tension while it is being reeled, and this tension is maintained by the use of electron-tube equipment as described below.

The wire passes from a large reel through the wire-drawing equipment where it is drawn down to the desired size, and thence to a small spool where it is rereeled. As the wire is drawn at a constant rate, the speed of the rereel spool must be constantly decreased to compensate for the increasing diameter of the surface on which the layers of wire are being wound.

The rereel spool is driven by a small d-c motor, the armature of which is supplied with power by the rectifying action of gaseous triodes. A small reactor is included in the grid circuit of these tubes. The reactance of this solenoid determines the phase relationship between grid and plate of each tube and thereby governs the average current taken by the motor through the tubes.

To correlate the tension of the wire and the reactance of the coil, the wire passes under a pulley that is held down by an adjustable spring so that the pulley goes up when the tension increases. To the pulley is attached the core of the reactor, the coil of which is in one side of the grid-control bridge. The loop on which the rider pulley rides decreases when the rereel motor runs too fast, drawing the core into the reactor, increasing its reactance, and varying the phase of the grid so that the tubes pass less current, thus slowing down the motor. Hence the motor torque varies instantly with the wire tension. Copper wire three mils in diameter is reeled at 4,000 ft per minute. So far as the reeling device is concerned, a speed of 80,000 ft per minute could be attained.

Conveyor Synchronization. A similar application has been made in the processing of rubber by the B. F. Goodrich Company. In a number of the operations, conveyors are used and it is important that the speeds of the various conveyors in a chain be synchronized. On a loop of the material between conveyors (Fig. 35) ride wheels similar to the rider pulley in the wire-reeling operation. Solenoids actuated by these wheels govern the current rectified by the thyratrons and thus synchronize the speeds of the motors driving the conveyors.

Another application of the solenoid-grid-control bridge circuit is found in plants where two conveyors are feeding dissimilar materials to a hopper and it is necessary to maintain the proportions within close limits. The conveyor carrying the varying amount of material passes over a balanced weighing roller. When the roller is depressed by excess weight, it lowers a solenoid into the reactor coil and causes the tubes to speed up the motor on the other conveyor, thus maintaining the proper proportions.

Electron-tube Impact Meter. By making use of the difference in inertia of two masses and a grid-controlled rectifier, Westinghouse engineers have constructed an impact meter. The measuring part of the instrument consists of a small cylinder, 2 in. in diameter and 4 in. high and having two terminals, one at the top and one on the side. The cylinder contains a body of relatively high inertia, which is partly supported by a helical spring and partly by the electrical contacts. These contacts are located below the body and are normally closed. The contacts are connected to the two terminals mentioned above.

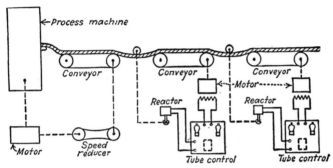

Fig. 35. System widely used for converting mechanical motion into electrical information. The slack in the web causes the core to move inside the reactor, thereby changing the reactance and speed of the conveyor motors.

This unit is placed on the object upon which the impact is to be measured. Under the force of the impact the cylinder tends to drop away from the body of higher inertia, so that the contacts between the two are momentarily drawn apart. The impact necessary to cause the contacts to open may be varied by changing either the mass of the inner body or the size of the spring.

Each of six of these mechanical units is connected to a phone jack which is plugged into one of the six receptacles in the meter. Six tubes are used, one for each unit. For each of the six circuits a potentiometer composed of small fixed resistors is connected across the power supply. These resistors are adjusted to keep the grid, which is connected to an intermediate point, at a potential too low for breakdown. However, when the external unit is subjected to an impact of sufficient intensity, its contacts open, thus opening the negative end of the potentiometer and throwing the grid more positive and causing momentary breakdown of the tube. The fixed capacitor across the potentiometer also discharges, so that when the contacts are again closed, the voltage across the tube is very low, thus stopping the discharge. This cycle of operation is repeated for each of the impacts which opens the contacts. By noting the tube or tubes flashing, the value of impact is determined.

Floating Grid Circuit. The circuit in Fig. 36 is a sensitive device for micrometer work or for detecting contacts or changes in electrical or mechanical quantities. The grid piles up a charge of electrons which cannot leak off to the cathode provided the condenser is of good quality. If, however, the grid terminal is touched or closely approached, electrons leave the grid, permitting its negative potential to decrease, with the result that plate current flows, and the relay operates. A phototube can be connected across the condenser so that the circuit operates as a standard light relay.

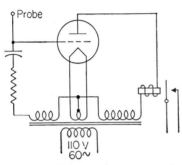

Fig. 36. Contact detector circuit. Electrons pile up on the floating grid and discharge when the probe comes in contact with a conducting object, causing the relay to operate.

If a metal probe is connected to the grid terminal, inspection of objects for size can be carried out very effectively by this circuit. The fixture holding the object to be inspected is grounded, and the grid terminal connected to the probe is brought to contact the work piece when the tube conducts. If the piece is undersize, the tube does not conduct; if it is correct, the tube conducts; and by the use of more than one probe, pieces may be sorted to within 0.00005 in. for under-, correct, and oversize.

Illumination Control. The grid-controlled rectifier operating through the medium of the saturable-core reactor has proved to be of considerable importance in the control of lighting whether for the stage, for show windows, for signs, for floodlighting exteriors of buildings or other out-of-door objects, and for the interior decoration of assembly halls, roof gardens, etc.

Such uses of electron tubes seem to offer unlimited possibilities in the art of decorative lighting. By dimming and mixing the primary colors in any desired sequence, a stage may be bathed in any hue of the rainbow, and these hues may be changed at the will of the set designer.   Delicate pastel shades obtainable in no other way are possible by the proper mixing of colors obtained from banks of lamps of three colors.

The change in color can be effected by an operator at considerable distance from the object to be illuminated, or it may be done automatically by a presetting arrangement.   Use of tubes and their associated saturable-core reactor effects considerable saving in power over a straight resistance-variation method.

The maximum effective variation of the voltage of incandescent lamps is from maximum to 20 per cent of maximum, or for Mazda C lamps from maximum current to 39 per cent of maximum.   In case the lamps are directly visible, greater variation is necessary; in this case the minimum voltage may be as low as 8 per cent or the current may go as low as 22 per cent.

In controlling lamp intensity by resistance, much power is wasted in the control rheostats.   For example, if the load current is reduced to 20 per cent, 92 per cent of the total power taken is being wasted in the rheostats.   The purpose of the rheostat in the older equipment is to reduce the proportion of power taken by the lamps.   Thus the rheostat acts as a "losser," all the power being consumed in the lamps at full brilliance and none of the power going into the resistances.   At lower intensity some of the power goes into the resistance and the remainder into the lamps.

In a typical controlled rectifier installation two buttons control the direction of rotation of a small electric motor, which changes the position of an iron core in a small solenoid-type inductor, thus varying the impedance of the solenoid and consequently varying the voltage drop across it.   The adjustable voltage from this motor-operated inductor controls the flow of anode d-c current through a saturable reactor.

For each bank of lamps to be controlled there is a panel of three tubes, a two-element gaseous rectifier, a controlled rectifier, and in the system to be described below (known as the *feedback* system) a full-wave high-vacuum rectifier.   The gaseous rectifier is used to permit current to flow during the interval between pulses of current supplied by the controlled rectifier.

The Feedback Circuit.   In Fig. 37 tube V (the controlled rectifier) supplies power in pulses to the d-c winding of the

saturable-core reactor SR. Then, during the half cycle when V
cannot pass current, the energy in the saturable-core inductance
forces current through the mercury-vapor tube P; thus full-wave
rectified current flows in the d-c winding of the reactor.

The amount of current flowing in the d-c winding is governed
by the voltage supplied to the grid of the controlled rectifier tube
from the feedback circuit, indicated in Fig. 37 by the diagram
within the dotted lines. A remotely located intensity control,
usually an inductor but here represented by the potentiometer

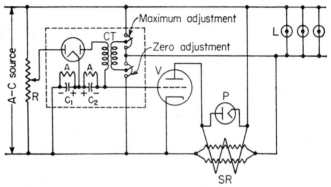

FIG. 37.   Illumination-control circuit using tubes.

R, produces a voltage whose magnitude may be varied but whose
phase is of no consequence, since the two-electrode high-vacuum
tube rectifies this voltage and charges capacitor C_1. The
voltage across C_1 for any given input from R is practically constant because of the long time constant of C_1 and its discharge
resistor A in comparison with the supply-system frequency. If
at the instant under discussion C_2 is assigned a zero charge, the
voltage existing across C_1 carries the grid of V positive, and the
latter tends to pass maximum current.

This increases the saturation of the d-c winding of the reactor,
causing its impedance to decrease and the lamp voltage to rise.
With the rise in lamp voltage the control transformer CT, which
is in effect connected across the lamp bank, charges C_2. The
polarity of the voltage across C_2 is opposite to that across C_1.
Hence, if the voltage of C_2 rises sufficiently high, the net voltage
applied to the grid of the tube V is negative, and V will cease to
pass current, thus causing the lamp voltage to drop.

Because the time constant of C_2 and its discharge resistor is nearly comparable to a half cycle of the system frequency, there is produced in effect an a-c voltage superimposed upon the difference between the two d-c voltages across the capacitors. The phase of this a-c voltage is such that as its axis is shifted by a change in the value of the difference between the d-c voltages, the phase angle at which it intersects the critical grid voltage of the controlled rectifier is shifted, thus producing phase control of the latter. Hence, as the lamp voltage nears the correct value, the tube regulates and finally passes the value of current to hold the lamp voltage at the desired value.

Potentiometers are provided to adjust the circuits properly when the intensity control is set at maximum, and at zero. These adjustments are made easily at the time of installation and are fixed thereafter.

The feedback circuit compares the voltage on the lamps with the voltage from the intensity control and acts on the grid of the controlled rectifier to hold the lamp voltage constant for any one setting of the intensity control.

REFERENCES

General

Edelman, Abraham, Industrial Applications Involving Electronic Detection, *Electronics*, March, 1943, p. 129.

Electronic Applications in Industry, *Electronics*, May, 1945, p. 92.

Fisk, D. B., Progress in Instrument Design, *General Electric Review*, October, 1947, p. 8.

Industrial Electronic Devices and Their Functions, *Electronics*, February, 1939, p. 22.

Markus, John, Electronic Applications, *Electronics*, June (midmonth), 1947, p. 102.

Middel, H. D., Electronics in Instrumentation, *General Electric Review*, November, 1944, p. 9.

Nielsen, D. M., Electric Measuring Instruments, *Electrical Engineering*, February, 1946, p. 66.

Powers, R. A., Industrial Electronics—A Progress Report, *Electronics*, July, 1941, p. 17, August, 1941, p. 33.

Serota, R. M., Typical Industrial Electronic Applications, *Proceedings of the National Electronics Conference*, 1944, p. 254.

Vore, M. P., Electronic Instruments, "Industrial Electronics Reference Book," John Wiley & Sons, Inc., New York, 1948, p. 457.

Weiller, P. G., Practical Electronic Industrial Controls, *Electronics*, March, 1945, p. 96.

Zeluff, Vin, Electronic Controls, *Scientific American*, December, 1944, p. 259.

Temperature Measurement and Control

Behar, M. F., Opportunities for Electronics in Industrial Temperature Instrumentation, *Electronics*, December, 1942, p. 72.

Behar, M. F., "Temperature Measurement and Control," Instruments Publishing Company, Pittsburgh.

Burnett, J. H., Temperature Controls, Wartime Improved, *Electrical Manufacturing*, January, 1945, p. 101.

Capacity Operated Relay Applied to Furnace Control, *Electronics*, November, 1937, p. 46.

Electronic Control of Furnace Temperatures, *Electrical Engineering*, August, 1945, p. 289.

Fairchild, C. O., and V. L. Parsegian, Photoelectrically Balanced Recording Potentiometer, *Review of Scientific Instruments*, December, 1938.

Forsythe, D. W., Color-Temperature Scale, *General Electric Review*, September, 1944, p. 26.

Fotte, P. D., C. O. Fairchild, and T. R. Harrison, "Pyrometric Practices," *National Bureau of Standards Technical Paper No. 170*, Government Printing Office, Washington, D.C.

Jupe, J. H., Control of Heat, *Electronic Engineering*, February, 1949, p. 48.

MacLaren, F. B., Electronic Pyrometer Control, *Electronics*, November, 1941, p. 50.

Rhodes, T. J., "Industrial Instruments for Measurement and Control," McGraw-Hill Book Company, Inc., New York, 1941.

Towne, R. D., Continuous Balance Potentiometer Pyrometer, *Electronics*, August, 1942, p. 92.

Walsh, Craig, Temperature Measurement and Control by Electronics, *Electronics*, October, 1942, p. 56.

Weber, R. L., "Temperature Measurement and Control," The Blakiston Company, Philadelphia.

Weiller, P. G., Electronic Thermometer, *Electronics*, July, 1944, p. 138.

Weller, C. T., Characteristics of Thermocouples, *General Electric Review*, November, 1946, p. 50.

Zabel, R. M., and R. R. Hancox, Use of Thyratron for Temperature Control, *Review of Scientific Instruments*, January, 1934.

Positioning

Fink, L. R., Position Control, *General Electric Review*, December, 1944, p. 40.

Frommer, J. C., Detecting Small Mechanical Movements, *Electronics,* July, 1943, p. 104.

Garr, D. E., Electric Positioning Systems of High Accuracy for Industrial Use, *General Electric Review,* July, 1947, p. 17.

Detectors

Blankmeyer, W. H., Metal Locaters, *Electronics,* December, 1943, p. 112.

Electronic Intrusion Detection Systems, *Electronics,* February, 1942, p. 38.

Erdman, D. C., Supersonic Flaw Detectors, *Electrical Engineering,* February, 1948, p. 181.

Markey, C. J., Cathode-ray Null Detector for Wien Bridge, *Electronics,* March, 1945, p. 125.

Weisz, P. B., Electronic Fire and Flame Detector, *Electronics,* July, 1946, p. 106.

White, W. C., Vapor Leak Detection by Thermionic Effects, *Electronic Industries,* March, 1948, p. 7.

Color

Deeter, E. L., Color Matching in the Paper Industry, *Electronics,* September, 1938, p. 18.

Photoelectric Colorimeters, *National Bureau of Standards Letter Circular,* LC-473, 1936.

Sweet, M. H., Direct-reading Color Densitometer, *Electronics,* March, 1945, p. 102.

Timers

Carlson, R. W., An Electronic Timing Device, *Electronics,* October, 1938, p. 28.

Deeter, E. L., and W. K. Dau, Interval Timer, *Electronics,* July, 1947, p. 86.

Porter, S. A., Electronic Timers, *Radio News,* October, 1945, p. 53.

Ultrasonics

Cochran, D., Ultrasonics, *General Electric Review,* August, 1944, p. 39.

DeLano, R. B., Jr., Supersonic Flaw Detector, *Electronics,* January, 1946, p. 132.

Ultrasonic Flaw Detection, *Electronic Industries,* January, 1946, p. 65.

Ultrasonics Nomographs for Industrial Use, *Electronic Industries,* July, 1948, p. 13.

Young, V. J., Supersonic Fundamentals, *Electronics,* March, 1944, p. 122.

Strain Gauges

Branson, N. G., Strain Gage Amplifier, *General Electric Review,* April, 1945, p. 55.

Fehr, R. O., Practical Strain-gage Applications, *Electronics*, January, 1945, p. 112.

McHaffey, W., Strain Gage Amplifier Design, *Proceedings of the National Electronics Conference*, 1944, p. 351.

Nielsen, D. M., Strain Gages, *Electronics*, December, 1943, p. 106.

Servo Systems

Bomberger, D. C., Servomechanisms, *Bell Laboratories Record*, November, 1945, p. 409.

Fremont, Felix, What Is the Amplidyne? How Does It Work? *General Electric Review*, August, 1943, p. 442.

Gille, W. H., and R. J. Kutzler, Electronics Sets Standard for Automatic Control, *Machine Design*, November, 1944, p. 117.

Glass, P., Electronic Position Servo System, *Electrical Manufacturing*, March, 1949, p. 100.

McCann, G. D., S. W. Herwald, and H. S. Kirschbaum, Electrical Analogy Methods Applied to Servomechanism Problems, *Electrical Engineering Transactions*, February, 1946, p. 91.

A Two-phase Voltage-to-Distance Servomechanism, *Electronic Industries*, June, 1948, p. 12.

Williams, J. R., The Amplidyne, *Electrical Engineering*, May, 1946, p. 208.

Nucleonics

Anton, Nicholas, Radiation Counter Tubes and Their Operation, *Electronic Industries*, February, 1948.

Dushman, Saul, Mass-Energy Relation, *General Electric Review*, October, 1944, p. 6.

German, L. L., Physical and Medical Aspects of Radiation, *Electrical Engineering*, September, 1948, p. 884.

Kingdon, K. H., Some Problems in the Industrial Applications of Atomic Energy, *General Electric Review*, August, 1948, p. 11.

Smith, Otto J. M., Beta-ray Thickness Gage for Sheet Steel, *Electronics*, October, 1947, p. 106.

Winne, H. A., Atomic Energy in Industry, *Electrical Engineering*, July, 1947, p. 631.

Woodyard, J. R., High-energy Particle Accelerators, *Electrical Engineering*, August, 1948, p. 759.

X-ray Applications

Atlee, Z. J., Industrial X-Ray Tubes, *Electronics*, November, 1945, p. 136.

Clapp, C. W., X-Ray Thickness Gage for Hot Strip Rolling Mills, *Electrical Engineering*, May, 1948, p. 441.

Fagen, M. D., X-Rays . . . First Electron-tube Application, *Electronics*, March, 1943, p. 148.

Lundahl, W. N., X-Ray Thickness Gage for Cold Rolled Strip Steel, *Electrical Engineering*, April, 1948, p. 349.

Woods, R. C., A New Use for X-Rays in Industry, *Electronics*, April, 1941, p. 29.

Telemetering

Burnham, W. H., New Telemetering Devices, *Electrical Engineering*, May, 1948, p. 483.

Lynch, E. E., A New Frequency Type Telemeter for Carrier-current Channels, *General Electric Review*, February, 1949, p. 28.

Factors Influencing Choice of Telemetering Systems, *Electronic Engineering*, June, 1949, p. 209.

Miscellaneous

Bovey, D. E., Variable-frequency Metals Comparator, *General Electric Review*, November, 1947, p. 45.

Bushman, R. N., Insulation-resistance Meter, *General Electric Review*, July, 1943, p. 403.

Campbell, D. A., Combustion Protective Controls, *Instruments*, December, 1945, p. 868.

Chamberlain, H. H., Tachometer Testing Facilities Increased Electronically, *General Electric Review*, May, 1948, p. 15.

Curran, F. J., Impedance Bridge for Flow-rate Metering, *Electronics*, April, 1947, p. 106.

Dalton, B. J., New Electronic Equipment for the Rubber Industry, *Electrical Engineering*, February, 1948, p. 119.

Dickinson, T. A., Electronic Control of Automatic Riveter, *Electronic Industries*, July, 1945, p. 112.

An Electronic Profilometer, *Electronics*, August, 1942, p. 94.

Electronic Recording Instruments, *Electrical Engineering*, January, 1947, p. 36.

Electron Microscopes, *Electronics*, November, 1938, p. 30.

Gravley, C. K., An Instrument for Measuring Surface Roughness, *Electronics*, November, 1942, p. 70.

Horlacher, A. F., A Magnetic Stepping Switch for Control Applications, *Electronic Industries*, March, 1948, p. 3.

Hutton, E. W., A Thyratron Controlled Half-cycle Magnetizer, *Electronic Industries*, February, 1948, p. 8.

Jaeschke, R. L., Electronic Control for Magnetic Clutches, *Electronics*, August, 1945, p. 102.

Kline, H. W., Radio-frequency Meters, *General Electric Review*, June, 1948, p. 25.

Koller, L. R., Electrostatic Precipitation, *General Electric Review*, August, 1945, p. 13.

Leonard, S. C., Measurement of Minute Changes of Capacitance and Inductance, *Electronics*, March, 1938, p. 18.

Levinton, H. L., High-voltage Measurement, *Electrical Engineering*, February, 1948, p. 154.

Nunan, T. J., The Nunan Yarn Tester, *Electronics*, February, 1939, p. 12.

Paper Tester, *Electronic Industries*, February, 1946, p. 92.

Princi, M. A., Extending the Usefulness of Laboratory Instruments, *General Electric Review*, October, 1948, p. 15.

Rabinow, J., The Magnetic Fluid Clutch, *Electrical Engineering*, December, 1948, p. 1167.

Richardson, S. C., Light-beam Wattmeter, *General Electric Review*, October, 1945, p. 59.

Rich, T. A., Self-balancing Potentiometer, *General Electric Review*, September, 1947, p. 29.

Robinson, H., Thermocouple Vacuum Gage, *General Electric Review*, May, 1946, p. 42.

Roess, L. C., Vacuum Tube Amplifier for Measuring Very Small Alternating Voltages, *Review of Scientific Instruments*, July, 1945, p. 172.

Semm, Paul, R-F Oscillator Controlled Potentiometer Recorder, *Electronic Industries*, January, 1948, p. 6.

Silverman, Shirleich, Measuring the Elasticity of Synthetic Yarns, *Electronics*, February, 1945, p. 103.

Stack, S. S., Dew Point Recorder, *General Electric Review*, April, 1949, p. 42.

Stewart, E. Y., Vibration Instrument for Gas Turbines, *General Electric Review*, March, 1949, p. 36.

Thompson, N. J., Measuring Pressures of Industrial Explosions, *Electronics*, November, 1947, p. 90.

Van Valkenburg, H. E., Application of the Ion Gage in High-vacuum Measurement, *General Electric Review*, June, 1946, p. 38.

Ware, L. A., Water Level Indicator, *Electronics*, March, 1940, p. 23.

Weinberger, J. M., Electronic Flow Meter, *Electronics*, January, 1940, p. 30.

Xerography, A Dry Printing Process, *Electrical Engineering*, January, 1949, p. 46.

Yard, E. M., Flame Radiation Measuring Instrument, *Electronics*, November, 1946, p. 102.

CHAPTER 10

COUNTERS AND DIVIDER CIRCUITS

Long before electronics entered industry to any extent, tubes were used to count events which occurred more rapidly than could be isolated and counted by mechanical devices. Tube circuits for high-speed counting and for controlling high-speed processes are now a very important tool in the electronic engineer's kit. These circuits are in common use in computers, in radiation detectors, in communication applications, and in many industrial processes where timing and synchronization of events are important.

Basically an electronic counter is the same in function as its mechanical counterpart. It is a storage device. It is quiescent until it gets an impulse of some sort; it reacts to this stimulus, and it maintains whatever condition it is left in after the arrival of the stimulus until another impulse is received. But it is inherently faster in operation than a mechanical counter since it has no inertia; and having no weight it cannot "load" the circuit to which it is attached and thus affect the operation of that circuit.

An electronic counter really acts as a slowing-down device. It can be arranged to react to every 2d, 4th, 16th, or every 100th impulse so that by interposing it between the events to be tallied and a mechanical counter, the latter simple instrument can be made to count events occurring 100 times as fast as it can handle without the addition of the electronic circuit.

Impulse Storage. If the arm of a mechanical counter is tripped twenty-three times, the number 23 appears on its indicator and will remain until another event is to be counted. It will store this number indefinitely. Of course there is a limit to the number of impulses it will record before it starts counting over again. At this point a second counter comes into action, recording the fact that the first counter has reached its limit and is starting over. The second counter is now quiescent until the first has again reached its limit whereupon the second counter records the number 2.

In the decade counting system the first counter can count up to 9, the next impulse bringing up 0 (zero). When this occurs, the second counter records number 1 so that the two will indicate that 10 events have taken place. Two counters can tally 99 impulses before they repeat.

Electronic Counters. In tube counters the actuating impulse is a voltage or other electrical stimulus and not a mechanical movement. Because the impulse is electrical, wires can connect the counter with apparatus at the place where the events occur, and a huge number of events per second can be recorded at almost any distance. An electronic counter is usually much more complex than a simple mechanical system, but it is faster and just as accurate. For each count on a mechanical counter a mechanical force must be applied to the arm of the counter. Many processes do not have sufficient physical force to trip the counter arm, thereby prohibiting the use of mechanical counters.

Electronic counters are built up from a basic unit which has only two degrees of freedom, like an electrical on-off switch. If two such switches are mechanically coupled so the second moves only when the first is turned on (and does not move when the first is turned off), then the second switch moves only half as often as the first. The counting rate has been cut in half. Addition of more switches can divide the counting rate still further.

Pulse Generators. Before any phenomenon can be counted by electronic means, it must somehow be converted into or cause a pulse of electrical energy for actuating the counter circuits. Many ingenious methods have been devised for converting mechanical processes into electrical pulses. A few are shown in Fig. 1.

In *A* a system is shown where small pieces are allowed to fall upon a plate which is attached to a microphone. The impact of the piece upon the plate causes a sound, which, by means of the microphone, is converted into an electrical voltage. In *B* the assembly-line motion is sufficient to operate a switch as each piece passes a counting point.

In *C* and *D* a phototube and light source setup is used. In *C* the light beam is interrupted as objects pass the inspection point, whereas in D a small amount of light is reflected onto the photo-tube as each paper drinking cup passes a certain point.   A means for counting revolutions of a rotating disk is shown in E.   The

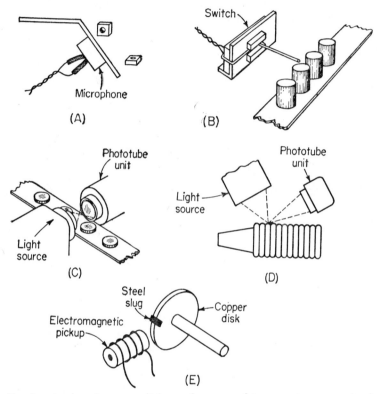

FIG. 1.   A microphone or switch may be arranged to convert some mechani-cal phenomenon into an electrical signal for counting purposes, as shown in A and B.   In C and D a phototube circuit detects movement and creates the counting signal.   A means for obtaining electrical signals for counting revo-lutions of rotating machinery is shown at E.

disk can be attached to any piece of rotating equipment.   Each time the steel slug passes the electromagnetic pickup, an electric signal is formed.

Counter Applications.   Electronic counting, timing, and con-trol instruments are mainly used in industry to measure and control such things as quantity, length, time, sequence, frequency, and revolution.   A typical application is illustrated in Fig. 2.   Here pills are being counted, but any object large enough to block a portion of the light in the phototube system could be handled in the same manner.   When the desired number of pills falls into the container on one side, the counter sends a signal to the deflection door, which diverts the flow of pills to the other side of the moving belt.   At the same time a solenoid is operated which allows the filled container to pass to a subsequent opera-

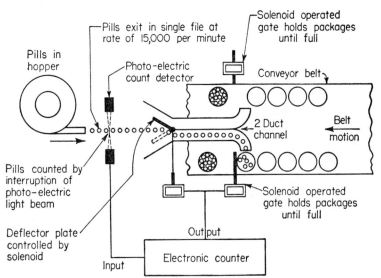

FIG. 2.   Photoelectric setup for counting pills and portioning them into lots of a predetermined number.

tion.   Thus the flow of pills is not interrupted and the passage of containers along the belt is continuous.

A similar system now in use at a shingle manufacturing plant stacks shingles in groups of predetermined quantity.   The shingles are moved on overhead conveyors and are held in place by suction or vacuum cups.   The shingles from the main assembly line cross two packaging conveyors.   A counter setup is used to divert the shingles to a second conveyor when the desired number has been sent to the first.   Thus while one stack is being bound together, another is being formed without loss of time.

The system shown in Fig. 3 is often used to measure linear footage on a continuous process.   The friction wheel or roller is brought in contact with the moving material, and its diameter is chosen so that its circumference bears some integral relationship to the desired linear dimension of the material.   Thus the counting (measuring) of these dimensions is simple.

Time and speed can be measured with extreme accuracy by the use of counters.   Very high speeds (thousands of feet per second) and very short lengths of time (down to a few microseconds) can be measured as readily as low speeds and longer lengths of time.

In measuring time intervals the counter circuit is usually used in conjunction with an extremely stable high-frequency

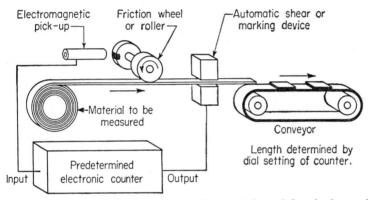

FIG. 3.   Electromagnetic pickup counts the revolutions of the wheel geared to the roller riding on the strip to actuate the cutter.

oscillator.   If the output of the oscillator is applied to the input of the counter for the interval of time to be measured and the frequency of the oscillator is known, then by counting the number of pulses or cycles the oscillator produces during the time interval to be measured, the time interval can be determined.

This is the exact system which is used to measure high velocities.   So far the science of ballistics has made the most use of the speed-measuring capabilities of electronic counters.   For example, a shell is fired past two points.   As it passes the first point a pickup arrangement starts a high-frequency oscillator.   As the shell passes the second point, the oscillator is turned off.   All that is needed for accurate determination of shell velocity is an accurate measure of the distance between the two points, the frequency of the oscillator, and an accurate count of the number of cycles that occurred during the time it took the shell to pass from one point to the other.

The use of high-frequency oscillators in conjunction with counter circuits brings up another interesting group of ideas, that is, the substitution of electronic equipment for mechanical cams and gears. By using predetermined counters to initiate operations after certain numbers of cycles, very accurate timing of operations can be achieved.

Through the use of any one of a number of simple auxiliary devices, speeds of revolution can be determined accurately and without the loading presented by less accurate and less dependable mechanical means.

The more counter applications one studies, the more possibilities he imagines. However, it is to be remembered that in many cases mechanical counters will do the job, and the cost and complication involved might be far less than that of the electronic counter. When high speed and versatility are required, however, the electronic version usually turns out to be the most dependable tool.

There are many industrial applications in which the basic counter circuits can be employed where the job of actually counting something does not occur at all. In other words the counting circuits have uses other than in counting. Basically they are "dividing" circuits; that is, they give output impulses which are some integral submultiple of the input impulses.

Numerous packaged units are available commercially but often one must build up his own system, experimentally at least, and therefore a knowledge of how such systems work is important.

Basic Circuits. The basic circuit is like an electrical switch in that it has two degrees of freedom; it can count up to 2 before it repeats. That is, it divides the number of incoming impulses by 2, thus cutting in half the rate at which the final tally must be made. In Fig. 4A tube A is either conducting or it is not. When it conducts, tube B does not. If something makes tube B conduct, then tube A goes out (ceases to conduct).

Let us suppose that before the first impulse comes along tube A is conducting, the lamp in its cathode circuit is lighted, and tube B is not conducting. Now the first impulse can be arranged to make tube B conduct, whereupon tube A and its light go out. The next impulse will make tube A go on and tube B go out.

Thus the lamp in the cathode circuit of tube A indicates every other impulse and actually notes the arrival of the even-numbered events, that is, the second, fourth, sixth, etc.

Now a second set of two tubes may be connected in place of the lamp in the circuit of tube A and arranged so that a stimulus

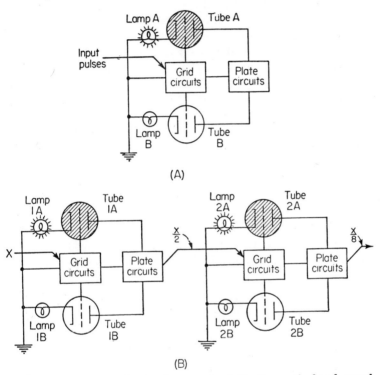

(A)

(B)

Fig. 4.   Basic flip-flop circuits show counter-indication method and cascading of basic circuits for counting higher than the basic 2.

is passed onto the second set of tubes only when tube A of the first set is changed from a nonconducting to a conducting condition.

The important thing in these circuits is not actual conduction or lack of it but the *shift* from one state to the other.   Now let us look at our four-tube system (Fig. 4B) and see how it works.

Consider V_{1B} only as a switch to turn on or off tube V_{1A}. V_{1A}, then, is the critical counting tube.   The second set of tubes is connected to tube V_{1A} and only registers when this tube is changed from a nonconducting to a conducting condition.

Nothing happens in the second set of tubes when V_{1A} goes out—only when it goes back on. Under these conditions V_{2A} will register the arrival at V_{1A} of every fourth impulse. And if a third set of tubes is connected to V_{2A} or V_{2B}, it will record every eighth stimulus that has caused something to happen in the circuits of the first set of tubes.

Now in Fig. 4B the initial condition is that tubes V_{1A} and V_{2A} are conducting. The first impulse causes tube V_{1B} to conduct and V_{1A} to go out. But since V_{2A} receives an input impulse only when tube V_{1A} reverts to its original conducting state, the arrival of the second pulse at the input of the first two-tube circuit, causes no change in the condition of the second set of tubes.

The second impulse cuts off V_{1B} and fires V_{1A}, which fires V_{2B} and cuts off V_{2A}. A counter in this tube circuit will not indicate until this tube again conducts—which it will do upon the arrival of the fourth impulse at the input to the first set of tubes.

The manner in which tube V_{2A} counts every fourth impulse can be seen from the table below, remembering that the counter in V_{2A} circuit is set at zero at the beginning when tubes V_{1A} and V_{2A} are conducting, that nothing happens to the counter when tube V_{2A} cuts off and only indicates when it goes back on. A

TUBES

Impulse	V_{1A}	V_{1B}	V_{2A}	V_{2B}
0	On	Off	On	Off
1	Off	On	On	Off
2	On	Off	Off	On
3	Off	On	Off	On
4	On	Off	On	Off

third counter circuit connected to receive a pulse every time V_{2B} returns to its original state, would return to *its* original condition after every eighth pulse, and so on.

Eccles-Jordan Pair. A simple circuit of this type just described is shown in Fig. 5. It is known as the *Eccles-Jordan circuit* and consists of two vacuum triodes. The circuit has two completely stable sets of operating conditions, and it has the further property that it can be switched from one condition to the other by the application of an electrical pulse.   The switching action is almost instantaneous.

To understand these two completely independent sets of operating conditions and the way the circuit may be switched from one to the other, a detailed study of this circuit will be made.

The circuit shown in Fig. 5 is symmetrical; that is, the components in the circuit of one tube are identical to those in the other circuit.   At the beginning let us assume that a 2-ma current is flowing through each triode.   The resulting voltage drop in each plate resistor will be 100 volts (0.002 amp × 50,000 ohms) and the voltage at each plate will be 100 volts positive with respect to ground, or cathode, potential.

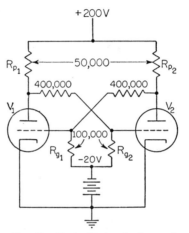

FIG. 5.   Basic Eccles-Jordan pair has two completely stable sets of operating conditions.

Suppose the transconductance of each tube is 1,000 micromhos (for each volt change in grid voltage the plate current will change 1 ma).   If perfect circuit symmetry existed, the currents in the tubes would remain equal. However, if some change takes place that causes the plate current of V_1 to increase slightly, its plate voltage would drop accordingly.   Let us say that the plate voltage of V_1 drops 0.1 volt.   The grid of V_2 experiences a drop of 0.02 volt, because it is connected on the tap of a voltage divider circuit formed by two resistors (400,000 and 100,000 ohms) in such a way that it experiences one-fifth of any changes at the plate of V_1.

The plate current in V_2 will then drop, because its grid becomes more negative, $0.02 \times 1,000 \times 10^{-6}$, or 0.02 ma.[1]   Then the plate voltage of V_2 will rise $0.02 \times 50,000$, or 1 volt.   As before, because of voltage divider action this time involving R_{P2} and R_{G1}, one-fifth of this voltage, or 0.02 volts, rise will be felt at the grid of V_1.   This voltage rise causes the plate current of V_1 to

[1] Grid voltage change multiplied by transconductance.

rise by 0.2 ma.   The resulting plate voltage drop is $0.2 \times 50,000$, or 10 volts.   The original change has thus been augmented.

The current in V_1 thus continues to increase (and that of V_2 to decrease) until stability occurs.   Let us assume the full conducting plate current to be 3 ma.   Then the plate voltage of V_1 will be 50 volts, and there will be 70 volts across the 400,000- and 100,000-ohm resistors, allowing 0.14 ma to flow through the combination.   The grid voltage with respect to the cathode voltage is then $20 - 0.14 \times 10^{-3} \times 100,000$, or -6 volts.   Cur-

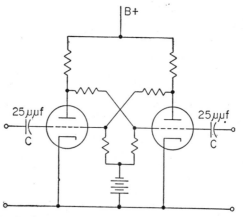

Fig. 6.   Eccles-Jordan pair with double-controlled triggering connections for changing from one stable condition to the other.

rent through the plate load resistor of V_2 is found by dividing 220 volts $(200 + 20)$ by 550,000 ohms $(50,000 + 400,000 + 100,000)$ to be 0.4 ma, assuming the tube to be completely cut off.   This establishes the plate of V_2 at a potential of 180 volts.

Triggering.   To flip the circuit to its other set of stable operating conditions, the original balance condition must be reached and then a little more voltage added so that the circuit behaves in the reverse of the example given above.

This change-initiating process is known as triggering, and it may be accomplished in a number of ways.   For example, by applying strong enough negative voltage pulses on the plate of the conducting tube, triggering could be accomplished.   However, because of the large magnitude of the required pulse, this system is seldom used.

The generally accepted method of triggering the Eccles-Jordan circuit is to apply a pulse of voltage to one or both of the grids, negative to the conducting grid or positive to the grid of the cutoff tube. This could be accomplished by shorting the grids to the cathode. The circuit diagram for double-controlled triggering is shown in Fig. 6. Either side may be triggered by the application of a pulse of the proper polarity and sufficient amplitude.

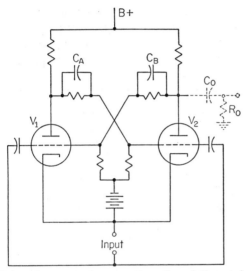

FIG. 7. Addition of commutating capacitors C_A and C_B permits the use of a single triggering input.

A circuit for single-controlled triggering is shown in Fig. 7. The only modification to the basic Eccles-Jordan circuit is the addition of C_A and C_B, called *commutating capacitors*.

To explain the action of these capacitors, let us assume the circuit to be in a stable condition with V_1 conducting and V_2 cut off. If a negative pulse is applied to the grids of the tubes, it will have no effect on V_2, since that tube is already cut off. The negative pulse will, however, decrease the plate current flowing through V_1, and its plate voltage will rise in the form of a positive pulse. This entire positive pulse is applied to the grid of V_2 since the voltage across C_A cannot change instantaneously. The positive pulse thereby delivered to the grid of V_2 is great enough to overcome the original negative input pulse, so V_2 will start conducting.   When V_2 conducts, the voltage at its plate decreases rapidly.   This decrease is felt at the grid of V_1 as a negative pulse which is sufficiently strong to cut that tube off.   Both negative and positive pulses will trigger this circuit if they are large enough.   Positive pulses, however, must be larger than negative pulses for proper triggering action.   ·

Failure to Trigger.   When a circuit fails to trigger upon the application of a pulse of the proper polarity, several factors may be responsible.   The pulse may have insufficient amplitude to push the circuit past its balanced condition.   The pulse time must be less than the time constant of the input RC combination, or the capacitor will charge and the grid will not receive enough triggering voltage.

The size of the input capacitor is subject to limitations.   If it is small compared to the input capacitance of the tube, the pulse voltage is divided and may be too small at the tube.   Also, the smaller the input capacitor, the steeper the required pulse front edge.   In other words the trigger voltage must rise to the required value almost instantaneously.   Steep-front pulses are often hard to produce and are inconvenient to handle.

If the input capacitor is made too large, it will tend to prevent changes in the grid voltage of one tube when a pulse is applied to the other.   In other words assume V_1 conducting and V_2 cut off and the coupling capacitor of V_1 too large.   A positive pulse of sufficient amplitude applied to the grid of V_2 will cause it to conduct, and its plate voltage will drop.   This drop would normally be enough to decrease the value of grid voltage at V_1 to a point where it would cease to conduct, but because of the large input capacitor the grid voltage is held fixed, and when the pulse to V_2 ends, the circuit reverts to its original untriggered condition.

There is also a limit to the closeness of adjacent pulses, but in most industrial applications this limitation is of little consequence.   By proper choice of components most of these circuits can be made to operate from input repetition rates of 100,000 per second and higher.

Counter Output.   There are several methods of taking output signals from these counter circuits.   The method employed depends on the purpose for which the output is used.   If the circuit is to be followed by another counter circuit, it is usually desirable to have the output in the form of sharp pulses, one pulse for every two input pulses. For other purposes it might be advantageous to take out a square wave, that is, a voltage which fluctuates between two definite values, one while the circuit is in one condition and the other when in the opposite state.

Figure 7 shows a method for taking either kind of output—the constants C_0 and R_0 determining the nature of the output wave. The plate voltage of V_2 is high when V_2 is cut off and low when V_2 is conducting. If C_0 is quite large, it will tend to maintain a constant voltage drop across itself, and when the plate voltage of V_2 rises, so will the output voltage. If the plate voltage remains at this raised value for any length of time, the condenser will eventually charge up (assume a voltage drop) to that value, and charging current will cease to flow. When this happens, the output voltage becomes zero. The output signal has thus suddenly gone positive and then gradually decreased to zero.

If the plate of V_2 stays positive for a brief time only, as would be the case if the input pulses were applied at a fast rate, the condenser would not have time to charge on each cycle, and the output would be almost the same as the plate voltage of V_2. That is, the output voltage would be high while V_2 is cut off and low when V_2 is conducting. This constitutes a square wave.

By making the value of C_0 very small, the charging time may be reduced to a very low value, so the output has the form of short pulses of positive voltage occurring whenever V_2 is cut off. When V_2 starts conducting again, its plate voltage decreases rapidly, but the condenser is still charged to the high voltage. When the condenser discharges through R_0, a negative output pulse occurs. Also, the choice of R_0 will have an effect on the shape of the output signal. A smaller value of R_0 will allow C_0 to charge and discharge faster and will provide a sharper pulse.

Thus for every two input pulses to the circuit of Fig. 7 we have a single output pulse which occurs when V_2 returns to its original condition. Actually, there will be two pulses: a negative pulse when V_2 conducts and the desired positive pulse when it is again cut off. However, either of these pulses can be removed from the output. Subsequent counter stages may be used that are sensitive only to pulses of one type, and in this way either the positive or negative pulses may be counted. This circuit actually registers every other pulse, or in other words, is a device for slowing down the necessary counting rate by two. A second two-tube circuit connected similarly will count every fourth input pulse and so the number of counts per second can be increased geometrically while the number of tubes goes up arithmetically. Since both triodes can be included in one envelope (and usually are used this way), the number of counts actually possible is 2^N, where N is the number of double-diode tubes employed. Thus five such tubes will count every thirty-second pulse.

Pentode Trigger Circuit. The circuit shown in Fig. 8 is sensitive only to negative pulses because, even though a positive pulse

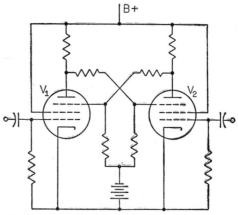

Fig. 8. Pentode trigger circuit is sensitive only to negative trigger pulses.

is applied to the control grid of the cutoff tube, the suppressor will hold the tube cut off. Interchanging the control and suppressor grid connections makes the circuit sensitive to positive pulses. Changing the cutoff voltage of the tube is accomplished by changing the suppressor voltage. With this circuit, single input triggering is possible as in the triode circuit, and triggering will occur with as little as $\frac{1}{2}$ volt.

Thyratron Counters. The circuit shown in Fig. 9 employs thyratrons and will count up to 4 million pulses an hour, or about 1,000 per second. Counters of this type are frequently used between high-speed recurring phenomena and mechanical counters which are too slow-moving or require too much energy to be actuated directly by the phenomena being counted.

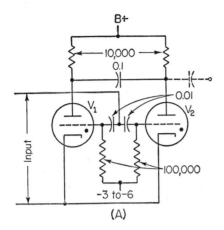

(A)

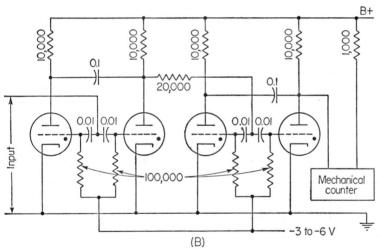

(B)

FIG. 9. Thyratron counter circuits. In *B* is shown how one thyratron counter circuit may be connected to a following stage.

In each unit the steady bias potential applied to both grids is slightly more negative than the critical negative potential required to prevent thyratrons from firing.

In explaining the circuit operation, let us assume that V_1 is conducting. As V_2 is fired by the application of a positive pulse at the input, the plate voltage of V_2 drops. This resulting voltage drop is transmitted through a capacitor to the anode of V_1, stopping the current flow in that tube. Since each thyratron responds to every other input pulse, scale-of-two operation is effected. Two tubes per stage are required. The coupling between stages is accomplished as shown in Fig. 9*B*. One of the thyratrons in each stage is coupled to the preceding unit by

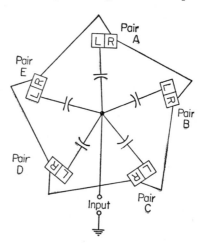

Input pulse number	Pair A		Pair B		Pair C		Pair D		Pair E	
	L	R	L	R	L	R	L	R	L	R
0	X			X		X		X		X
1		X	X			X		X		X
2		X		X	X			X		X
3		X		X		X	X			X
4		X		X		X		X	X	
5	X			X		X		X		X
6		X	X			X		X		X

X indicates conduction

Fig. 10. Block diagram of ring counter. The chart shows the condition of each tube section during progression through six counts. The counter shown is a ring of five.

connecting the input side of the grid capacitors to the plates of one of the thyratrons through high resistances.

Ring Counters. Divisions greater than 2 may be achieved by the use of several basic counters in what is known as a ring-counter circuit. A typical ring-counter block diagram is shown

in Fig. 10 along with an operating schedule for a complete cycle
of operation. In this circuit, division by 5 is possible.

In the initial condition the left side of pair A is conducting,
while the left sides of the other four pairs are cut off. Upon
receipt of the first negative pulse at the input terminals, the left
side of pair A is cut off, the voltage rise at its plate causes the
right side to conduct. The voltage drop at the plate of the
right side, which is coupled to the right side of pair B, causes
that circuit to flip. The next pulse applied to the input terminal

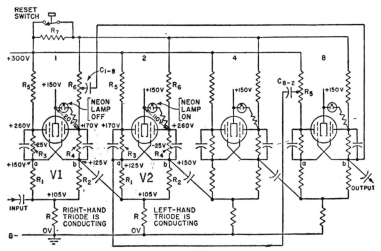

Fig. 11. Binary decade counter circuit used commercially in many applications. This system provides decade (10) counting with binary indication.

will return pair B to its original cutoff condition and flip pair C.
Subsequent pulses will pass this flipped condition around the
ring so that it is present at each tube once for every five input
pulses. Thus an output taken from any one of the five stages
will be one-fifth that of the input. Output may be taken from
the plate of either of the paired tubes, depending on the polarity
of the desired output.

The Binary Decade. The circuit shown in Fig. 11 has found
wide application in industrial electronics because of the ease
with which it may be incorporated into such an extensive variety
of counting problems. Its simplicity (it contains only four tubes
and four indicating bulbs) and its dependability are among its
other advantages.

In presenting a number, *four* neon bulbs are required *for each digit* of the number. The binary progression 1-2-4-8 is used. This system of number presentation is best understood by studying the examples shown in Fig. 12. The numbers corresponding to the lighted neon bulbs are added vertically to get the indicated number. The appropriate neon bulb or bulbs are ignited in their proper order, since two pulses from one circuit cause one pulse to be passed to the succeeding circuit.

The counter decade consists of four stages, each employing an ordinary dual-triode vacuum tube (such as the 12AT7) arranged in an Eccles-Jordan trigger circuit in conjunction with an indicat-

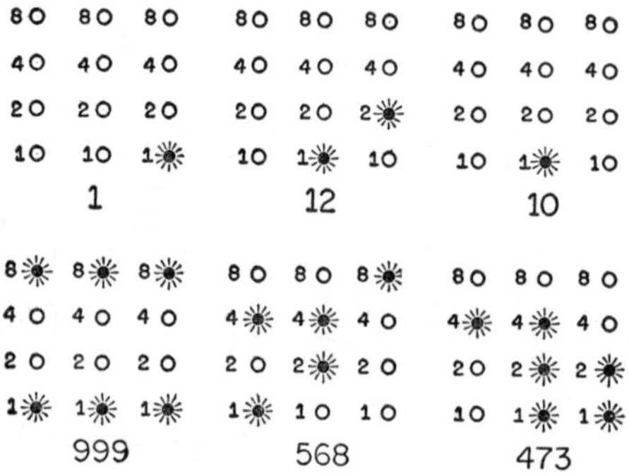

```
8 O   8 O   8 O      8 O   8 O   8 O      8 O   8 O   8 O
4 O   4 O   4 O      4 O   4 O   4 O      4 O   4 O   4 O
2 O   2 O   2 O      2 O   2 O   2 ※     2 O   2 O   2 O
1 O   1 O   1 ※     1 O   1 ※   1 O     1 O   1 ※   1 O
         1                     12                   10

8 ※   8 ※   8 ※     8 O   8 O   8 ※     8 O   8 O   8 O
4 O   4 O   4 O      4 ※   4 ※   4 O      4 ※   4 ※   4 O
2 O   2 O   2 O      2 O   2 ※   2 O      2 O   2 ※   2 ※
1 ※   1 ※   1 ※     1 ※   1 O   1 O     1 O   1 ※   1 ※
        999                   568                  473
```

FIG. 12. Six examples of binary indication of numbers used in the circuit of Fig. 11.

ing neon bulb. The basic functioning of all stages is alike and is dependent on shifting of operating potentials of each stage back and forth between the two sets of values indicated in stages 1 and 2 of Fig. 11.

Considering V_1, note first that a fixed potential of $+150$ volts is applied to the cathode of the tube at all times by the power supply. Grid and plate voltages are obtained from the resistance network included in the basic circuit and depend on relative currents through the two branches of the network $R_1R_3R_5$ and $R_2R_4R_6$.

To explain circuit operation, let us again make an initial assumption that the right hand side of V_1 is essentially at cathode potential (zero bias) and that no signal pulses have arrived. At this zero value of bias the right hand side of V_1 will conduct strongly, and its plate voltage will drop to a low value, actually about 20 volts, lower than the extinction voltage of the neon lamp connected across this particular section. For this condition, then, the neon bulb for the first stage is out.

As the right hand side of V_1 conducts, the voltage drop across R_6 is greatly increased. This leaves less voltage for R_4 and R_2, and hence point b is driven negative with respect to the cathode. A shift of 25 volts is actually produced by the resistance values shown.

The grid of the right-hand side of V_1 is connected to point a, which is at cathode potential as assumed for this explanation and required for full conduction of that portion of the tube. The grid of the left-hand portion of V_1 goes to point b, which is at $+125$ volts with respect to ground and -25 volts with respect to the cathode. Thus the cutoff bias is applied to the left hand side of V_1.

The circuit can remain in this condition indefinitely until a negative pulse is applied to the input circuit. Any positive pulse has no effect, because it is dissipated in the low impedance of the conducting triode section. When a negative pulse arrives at the input circuit, however, both grids swing in a negative direction. There is no direct effect in the cut-off side (the left-hand side), but the negative grid swing on the right-hand grid stops the plate current of that side. The resulting redistribution of the voltage drops across R_6, R_4, and R_2 places point b at cathode potential, as indicated in stage 2. The grid of the left-hand side of V_1 swings positive to zero bias, and that side starts conducting. Point a goes 25 volts negative with respect to the cathode, keeping the grid of the right-hand triode negative once it is driven negative by the negative input pulse. Thus the circuit conditions in stage 2 are reversed.

With the right-hand triode of stage 2 cut off, its plate voltage goes up to about 110 volts, above the striking value of the neon lamp. Thus the lamp glows.

The arrival of a second negative pulse again triggers the stage, the lamp goes out, and the succeeding lamp is lit, since the voltage drop at the plate of the right-hand portion of V_2 appears at the input of the third stage in the form of a negative pulse.

Count Indication. A complete counter decade consists of four identical stages with neon lamps as shown in the circuit diagram. These stages are numbered 1, 2, 4, and 8 according to the binary system; the number assigned to each stage is equal to the number of negative pulses required at the input of the decade to make the neon lamp in the stage come on the first time.

In preparation for a count a momentary displacement of the reset switch inserts a common dropping resistor R_7 in the voltage supply line to all right-hand triodes. This drives the grids of all left-hand sections negative, so that the decade is preset with all right-hand triodes conducting and all neon lamps extinguished.

When the tenth pulse is being counted, a negative pulse goes to the succeeding decade and at the same time resets the zero condition, where all lamps in the decade are out. In the binary system, however, lamps 2 and 8 should be on, and this is undesirable when indicating counts in the decimal system. Remembering that pulse 9 was indicated by lamps 1 and 8 being lit, for the count of 10 in the decimal system, lamp 8 must be extinguished and lamp 2 prevented from lighting.

After the ninth pulse the left-hand sections are conducting in both stages 1 and 8. When stage 1 is reversed by the tenth pulse, a negative pulse obtained from a tap on R_6 in stage 1 is fed through C_9 to stage 8, causing point b of stage 8 to swing negative. This drives the grid of the left-hand side of stage 8 negative, causing the flip of stage 8 and extinguishing the lamp corresponding to the number 8. The negative pulse taken from the tap on R_6 must be large enough to cause switching, but not too large, because at the eighth count it must be overpowered by the negative pulse that comes from stage 4 and correctly triggers stage 8 to turn its lamp on.

In a similar manner a positive pulse from R_5 of stage 8 fed through C_{10} to point a of stage 2 overwhelms the negative pulse sent to it from stage 1. Since the lamp corresponding to stage 2 was out for the count of 9, it stays out.

This type of counter operates reliably at pulse rates as high as 100,000 per second. It is simply necessary to supply negative pulses of approximately the proper shape and amplitude. A commercial packaged version of this circuit is available (Potter Instruments Company).

Gas Tube Counters. One extremely small commercial plug-in counter (Sylvania) uses miniature thyratrons. The unit contains 11 tubes, 80 resistors, and 23 capacitors and is capable of counting from 0 to 5,000 pulses per second. The entire circuit is contained in a package about the size of a vacuum tube, and it can be plugged into a socket like a tube. Ten of the eleven circuits are identical, and for that reason only three of these will be studied in detail. The last stage is responsible for recycling the circuit when it reaches its limit.

The basic and typical operation of three of the tubes in this counter is illustrated in Fig. 13. The resistor network composed of R_1, R_2, and R_3 is a voltage divider which places the cathode voltage to tubes V_2 and V_3 at about -4 volts and puts the grid

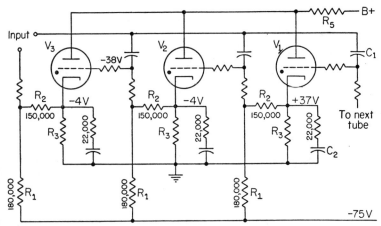

FIG. 13. Partial diagram of a commercial (Sylvania) gas tube counter of miniature design.

voltage of V_3 at about -38 volts. Assume that V_1 is conducting and that the current through it and R_3 is such that the cathode of V_1 is at about $+37$ volts, as indicated. The voltage divider R_1R_2 in the circuit of V_1 then places the grid of V_2 at -13 volts. The bias becomes -34 volts for V_3 but is only -9 volts for V_2. Since the pulse input line is connected to all the grids, each tube grid will receive the same pulse, but V_2 will be fired by a much lower pulse than V_3, say a pulse of $+15$ volts. This still leaves a considerable margin of safety, so that V_3 is still biased to about $-34 +15$, or -19 volts.

After V_1 has been conducting for a few microseconds, C_2 is charged to the cathode potential, or -37 volts. When V_2 fires, an additional current flows through the common plate resistor

R_5, and this causes a sudden drop in plate voltage, but the capacitor tends to hold the cathode at -37 volts. This allows the plate voltage to drop below the critical value long enough so that conduction stops, thus permitting the grid to regain control. The count has now advanced from V_1 to V_2 and continues through the tubes until V_9 is conducting. The circuit for V_9 is shown in Fig. 14.

When V_9 is conducting, it sets up the bias for both V_0 and the transfer tube V_{10} in exactly the same fashion as before.

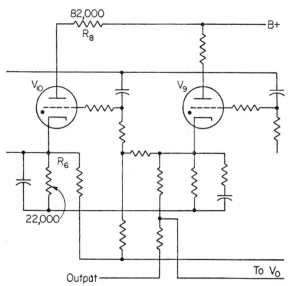

Fig. 14. Circuit showing the return of the pulse to the first stage after the count of ten.

When the next or tenth pulse comes along, V_0 and V_{10} will both conduct for a few microseconds and then go out, because $R_6 + R_8$ is quite high. A pulse is thus sent through the output to the next circuit for every 10 pulses applied to the input.

The pulses used with this type of circuit may be in the vicinity of 15 to 25 volts, and the rise times may be slightly lower than required in many commercial circuits.

Another Decade Unit. Another arrangement which produces an output pulse for every 10 pulses it receives is shown in Fig. 15. As the diagram indicates, this circuit employs a ring-type circuit, but it will be noticed that a ring-of-five circuit is

used for division by tens.   This is accomplished by following the
ring-of-five circuit with a scale-of-two circuit, so that for every
two output pulses from the scale-of-five circuit only one is
applied to the output on the succeeding stages.   Thus division by ten is accomplished.   This circuit has the advantage of
requiring fewer tubes for decade division.   For a straight ring-of-
ten circuit, ten tubes are required.   Another advantage of this
type of circuit is the fact that neon lights (NE 51) may be
arranged to read the accrued number of input pulses directly, and
several such decades may be arranged to indicate counts of
very high numbers.

In the circuit diagram of the complete unit shown in Fig. 16,
the cathode resistor R_2 is chosen to produce the desired voltage

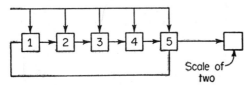

FIG. 15.   Block diagram of a simple ring-of-five scale-of-two decade counter.

on the common right-hand cathode bus with only one right-hand
section conducting.   Resistor R_1 produces the same voltage
drop with four left-hand sections conducting.   The left and
right hand cathodes are split in this manner to assure that the
odd condition will exist in only one element at a time.

Assume that V_1 is the odd tube.   (By "odd" we mean that
the right-hand section of the tube is conducting and the left side
is cut off.   The tubes are said to be in their normal condition
when the reverse is true.)   It is desired to advance the odd condition to V_2.   This can be done by a negative pulse either at the
right side of V_1 or the left side of V_2.   The negative input pulse
through C_1 appears at both places, initiating the desired change
in both V_1 and V_2.   The flip-flop action in both tubes aids the
input pulse in this respect.   Since the cathodes are by-passed,
input pulses through C_2, C_3, C_4, and C_5 are effectively shorted
out through the respective left-hand plates of V_2, V_3, V_4, and
V_5 before the transition, while during transition the pulse through
C_5 is still shorted out by the left-hand plate of V_3.   Any tendency
for the input pulse at the left-hand grid of V_3 to appear via
C_2, C_6, and C_7 to cut off the left-hand side of V_3 is overcome by

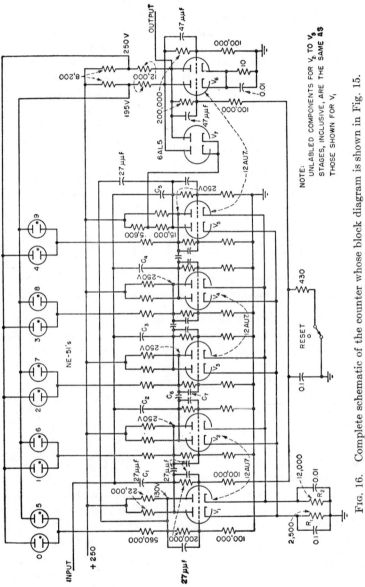

FIG. 16. Complete schematic of the counter whose block diagram is shown in Fig. 15.

the input pulse at the right-hand grid of V_3, in addition to being overridden by the positive pulse from the left-hand plate of V_2.

As long as the input-pulse rise time (before or after the pulse is differentiated by C_2 and C_3 through the left-hand side of V_2 and V_3) is short enough in comparison with the transition time and the pulse is of sufficient amplitude, wide variations may be permitted in pulse height and shape as well as in the values of interstage and input coupling capacitors.

The scale of two represented by V_6 is coupled to the ring by the diode V_7. The diode cathode will switch from $+250$ volts to 195 volts after the fifth count, and back to 250 volts after the tenth count. A complete description of the operation of this circuit is given in the reference.[1] The circuit was developed for use with radiation counting devices, but it is completely adaptable to industrial applications where high-speed counting is required.

Ring-of-three Counter. A counter circuit designed to give one output pulse for every three applied to its input is shown in Fig. 17. Only one tube is conducting at any one time. The triggering pulses are applied across R_k. Each tube has associated with it a potentiometer network R_2-R_3 to repeat a fraction of the plate voltage suitable for the following tube grid. The grids are connected into the plate circuits of the preceding tubes by resistors R_4. (All similarly labeled components have the same values for each stage.)

All of the circuits have identical component values. Therefore, when the circuit is first turned on, any one of the stages can start conducting and the remaining stages must remain cut off until the stable operating condition of the circuit is interrupted by the application of an input pulse. Assume that V_1 is conducting initially. All of the stages share resistor R_k in their cathode circuits. The value of this resistor is chosen so that when any one of the tubes conducts current, the voltage drop across the resistor will be sufficient to hold the remaining tubes cut off. The voltage drop across R_k is, of course, positive at the cathode end of each tube, thus making the grid negative with respect to the cathode.

If, then, at a particular instant V_1 is conducting, V_2 and V_3

[1] R. Weissman, Stable Ten-light Decade Scaler, *Electronics*, May, 1949, p. 84.

are cut off.   The voltage at the plate of V_1 is less than that at the other tubes, so we may say that the voltage at the plate of V_1 is negative with respect to the voltage at the plates of V_2 and V_3.   The grid of V_2 is connected by R_4 to the positive (relatively speaking) plate of V_3 and the negative plate of V_1.   The grid of V_3 is connected to one positive plate (V_2) and the negative plate of V_1.   The grid of V_1 is connected to the positive plate of V_2 and to the positive plate of V_3 and is positive with respect to the

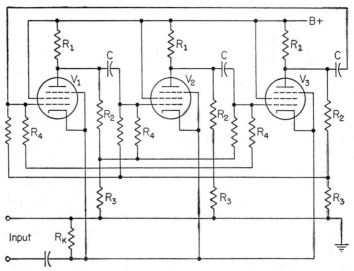

Fig. 17.   Ring-of-three counter produces one output pulse for every three input pulses.

other two grids by an amount sufficient to ensure that V_1 continues to conduct.

To change this initial condition and pass the count on to a subsequent stage, something must be done to cut off V_1 and make V_2 conduct, while V_3 experiences no change.   A positive pulse applied at the input terminals (which are connected directly to the cathodes of all tubes) will cause V_1 to be cut off momentarily because its cathode becomes positive with respect to its grid.   As current stops flowing through the load resistance of V_1, its plate voltage will rise abruptly, and a positive pulse will be sent via R_2 to the grids of V_2 and V_3.   But the grid of V_2 receives a greater share of the V_1 plate voltage rise because of the capacitor between these two points. When the input pulse subsides, the grid of V_2 is left momentarily more positive than any of the other grids. Thus V_2 conducts, and the voltage drop across R_k prevents either of the other tubes from conducting.

Subsequent pulses pass the conducting condition first to V_3 and then back to V_1 and so on, so that each tube conducts once for every three input pulses. Output may be taken from the plate of any one of the stages by coupling to the plate of the tube comprising that stage.

A ring of greater number than three can be imagined by simply adding more stages before feeding back to the first stage. The only limitation to the number of stages that can be incorporated in a circuit of this kind is the fact that the plate current of one tube must be large enough to hold all the other tubes cut off (the plate current must cause cutoff voltage to appear across R_k when one tube is conducting).

In practice, rings of five are usually sufficient and they are used in conjunction with scale-of-two circuits for decade counting. Many different combinations are, of course, possible.

Plug-in Counters. The circuit shown in Fig. 18 is a modification of the Eccles-Jordan circuit discussed earlier. It is a commercial version which may be used wherever scale-of-two division is desired. All of the necessary connections are brought out through a 9-pin plug base, and through the use of appropriate connections, the circuit is adaptable to a variety of industrial applications.

The operation of the circuit is as explained in the beginning of this chapter. This circuit will retain the last count it receives; thus it may be used for scaling random counts and for division ratios greater than two; a number of units may be incorporated and counts as high as 20,000 or 30,000 may be accommodated.

The circuit employs a single miniature 6J6 twin triode and a neon indicator, which is connected to show which side of the circuit is cut off. The neon lamp will glow only when connected across a tube which is cut off, since the voltage drop across a tube drops below its striking voltage when that tube is conducting. The neon bulb can be connected to either side by external connections. The circuit may be reset to its original conditions by the application of a bias voltage at pin 6 of the 9-pin plug or by removing B+ voltage from the plates.

The Multivibrator. According to definition, a counter circuit is one which receives pulses at some regular or irregular rate and produces an output which is an integral submultiple of the input pulse frequency. Divider circuits differ from counter circuits in that their inputs must be at a regular or very nearly regular rate. In other words there must be a fairly equal time interval between pulses.

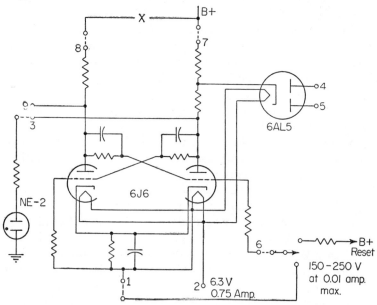

FIG. 18. Circuit of basic plug-in unit for scale-of-two operation. All connections are brought out through a standard 9-pin plug so that the units may be replaced quickly.

The multivibrator is probably the most common example of a divider circuit. It is a combination of counter circuit and oscillator. Like the counter circuit it has two sets of operating conditions, but instead of waiting for an input pulse to change from one set to the other, this switching action is accomplished automatically by the circuit itself. In other words it oscillates back and forth from one state to the other.

The usefulness of this circuit lies in the fact that this switching process can be synchronized with, for example. the voltage output from another oscillator. The resulting output from the syn-

chronized multivibrator will be some submultiple of the synchronizing oscillator frequency, and the shape of the output wave will
have certain characteristics that are advantageous in some applications. The operation of the multivibrator will be explained
by considering actual circuit values and operating conditions.
The basic multivibrator circuit is shown in Fig. 19.

If switch Sw_1 in the cathode circuit of V_2 is open, no current
will be flowing through V_2 and its plate voltage will be equal to
that of the supply, or 200 volts.
If the switch is closed, current
starts flowing and the plate voltage of V_2 drops. This drop is
applied through C_2 to the grid of
V_1. Thus the current through
V_1 drops. This causes a rise in
the plate voltage of that tube
which is applied to the grid of
V_2. This grid voltage rise
causes more current to flow in
V_2, and so on.

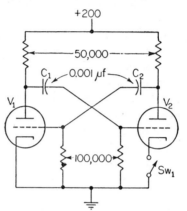

Let us assume the full con-
ducting current to be 3 ma.   Fig. 19. Symmetrical multivibra-
The plate voltage of V_2 will be   tor circuit. This circuit has two
+50 volts (the supply voltage of   unstable sets of operating condi-
200 minus the drop across the   tions, and it automatically flips
50,000-ohm plate resistor).   back and forth between them.
Then the voltage at the grid of V_1 is 150 volts negative with
respect to the plate of V_2. As C_2 charges, the negative grid voltage approaches zero, or ground potential. When the value of
grid voltage (V_1) is reached which permits the tube to pass current, that tube will again start conducting, and the voltage drop
at its plate, coupled to the grid of V_2, will cause that tube to be
cut off.

The following formula may be used for determining the period
T of oscillation (frequency $= 1/T$):

$$T = 1.5\left(R_G + \frac{R_G R_L}{R_G + R_L}\right)C$$

where T is one-half of a cycle of oscillation, R_G is the grid
resistance and R_L is the load resistance. In unsymmetrical

multivibrators the time constants are calculated for each side. The ratio of time of one-half of a cycle to the other half may vary as much as 10 to 1.

Synchronization of Multivibrators. The circuit described above is called a free-running multivibrator, since it will shift periodically from one set of operating conditions to the other without any external stimulus once it has started. The rate of this natural shifting back and forth is called the free-running frequency. Often it is desired or necessary to synchronize a multivibrator with some external source, such as a regular recurring series of phenomena to be counted. This may be accomplished by the injection of a synchronizing pulse, or signal. Synchronizing signals may be applied either through the plate, grid, or cathode of the tubes in the multivibrator.

These synchronizing pulses are usually introduced to the circuit at a rate which has an integral relationship to the free-running frequency. Since the free-running frequency is determined by the length of time the circuit spends in each of the two sets of operating conditions and the flip from one set of conditions depends on a change in grid voltage caused by a discharge of a capacitor, any change in that grid voltage will effect a change in the free-running frequency of the multivibrator. Synchronizing pulses are used to alter the normal change in voltage caused by the capacitor discharge so as to advance the time when the flip occurs. In practice, when a free-running multivibrator is to be synchronized with some signal, the synchronizing signal is first converted into pulses, say positive pulses, and these are applied to the grid of the nonconducting side of the multivibrator.

The free-running frequency of the multivibrator is adjusted to be slightly lower than the frequency of the desired submultiple of the triggering frequency. Now, as the multivibrator attempts to run at its normal frequency, the synchronizing pulses superimposed on the grid voltage cause the flip to occur in synchronism with the triggering source.

This action is best understood by studying the waveforms shown in Fig. 20. The natural discharge curve is shown in A. When the grid voltage rises above the cutoff value for the tube, the tube will start to conduct, and the circuit will flip. Under untriggered conditions the circuit will flip at T_1. Figure 20B

shows the normal grid voltage altered by the superposition of the synchronizing pulses. Again, the grid voltage must reach cutoff value for triggering. As the first pulse appears on the natural curve, we see that it is too small to affect triggering. The same applies to the second and third pulses, but the fourth pulse moves the grid voltage past cutoff just long enough for the circuit to trigger, and slightly sooner than it would have triggered in the absence of the triggering pulse.

With the triggering setup illustrated in Fig. 20 division by eight is accomplished. That is, for every eight input or syn-

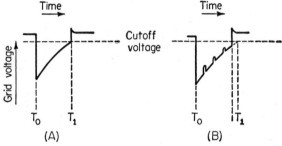

FIG. 20. Waveforms showing triggering of a free-running multivibrator.

chronizing pulses, one output pulse can be derived by taking the output from one of the plates of the multivibrator. The multivibrator operates at its free-running frequency between triggering pulses, but any deviation from the submultiple of the triggering frequency is compensated when the triggering pulses take charge of the flipping. In other words, in the example shown in Fig. 20 the whole period is "tied down" once for every eight input pulses.

In Fig. 20 the synchronizing pulses are applied to the grid of one of the multivibrator tubes. Actually, the synchronizing pulses may be applied to the plate or cathode. The requirement is that the desired pulse causes the multivibrator to flip slightly before it would under untriggered conditions.

Figure 21 shows several methods of injecting the synchronizing signal. Cathode synchronization is very similar to grid synchronization, whereas plate synchronization has the advantage that the impedance of the pulse source does not affect the operation of the multivibrator.

The amplitude of the triggering pulses must be just right, and amplitude control becomes more critical as the ratio of input to output frequency increases. This can be appreciated by studying Fig. 20. If the amplitude of the synchronizing signal in this

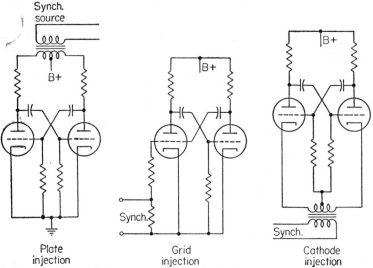

Plate
injection

Grid
injection

Cathode
injection

FIG. 21.   Three methods for applying synchronizing pulses to a multivibrator circuit.

case were slightly larger than shown, triggering might occur on the pulse preceding the desired pulse, and improper division would result.

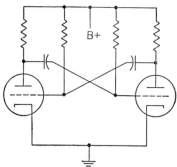

FIG. 22.   Connecting the grid to B+ creates more positive triggering action.

A multivibrator circuit often used is shown in Fig. 22. Here the grids are tied through a high-value resistance to B+; however, in operation the grid voltages never actually reach B+, because the tube triggers when the grid voltage reaches the cutoff value. Because of the strong pull toward B+ and the conducting value of the grid voltage, the free-running frequency of this circuit may be much higher than the other circuit shown, and the accuracy of control is improved. This may be explained by referring to Fig.

23.   Here are shown the normal grid voltage rise of the basic multivibrator and the steeper rise found in the circuit of Fig. 22. The reason for increased accuracy lies in the fact that the grid voltage approaches the cutoff value at a much steeper angle.

A similar circuit, with the grids returned to a separate voltage source, might be desirable for certain applications.

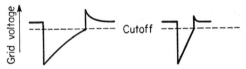

FIG. 23.   Waveforms illustrating differences of triggering for different rates of grid-voltage rise.

Another circuit frequently found in industrial counters and frequency dividers is the cathode-coupled multivibrator shown in Fig. 24.   Here V_2 is coupled to V_1 through a common cathode resistor R_k.   In explaining the operation of this circuit, assume V_1 to be conducting.   The circuit constants are chosen so that $I_k R_k$, the voltage drop across the common cathode resistor due to the current flowing through V_1, is sufficient to hold V_2 cut off.   As V_2 starts to conduct, because the capacitor between the

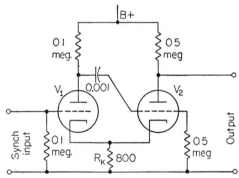

FIG. 24.   Cathode-coupled multivibrator circuit.

plate of V_1 and the grid of V_2 charges making the grid of V_2 positive, $I_k R_k$ increases reducing the plate current of V_1.   The voltage at the plate of V_1 increases bringing the grid voltage of V_2 up and increasing the current through V_2.   When the capacitor discharges, the plate current through V_2 drops and $I_k R_k$ drops until V_1 begins to conduct again.   The time constant is determined by the capacitor between the plate of V_1 and the grid of V_2 and the resistors through which it charges and discharges.

In this particular circuit the free-running frequency is somewhat erratic, because while the bias is dropping, the grid voltage is actually rising. This conducting combination is hard to control. Since the one time constant determines both halves of the cycle, the output is symmetrical.

Single-shot Multivibrators. A single-shot multivibrator is one which has one stable and one semistable set of operating conditions. An input pulse causes the circuit to flip, as in

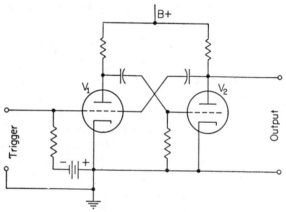

FIG. 25. Basic single-shot multivibrator undergoes one complete cycle for every pulse applied to the input.

regulator multivibrator circuits, but when the single-shot multivibrator reverts to its original condition, it remains in that state until the next synchronizing pulse is applied.

Probably the most obvious single-shot multivibrator would be that shown in Fig. 25, where one tube V_1 is held cut off by a separate negative voltage source. This type of circuit can be triggered by a positive pulse. The duration of the oscillation depends on the multivibrator circuit elements. The circuit flips itself back into its initial set of operating conditions as the capacitor to the grid of V_2 discharges.

The length of a period is determined in the same manner as that used in finding the half-cycle periods of the free-running multivibrator. The frequency-determining RC-network time constant is again limited and must be shorter than the period of the pulse so that triggering will occur.

The circuit shown in Fig. 26 is another single-shot multivibrator. Here the grid of V_2 is held high enough, by its connection to $+B$, to conduct strongly enough to hold V_1 cut off until a positive pulse arrives. The pulse makes V_1 conduct, its plate voltage drops, and this voltage drop is felt at the grid of V_2 and causes that side to cut off. As soon as C_1 charges and V_2 starts to conduct, the voltage drop across R_k, caused by the current through both tubes, is sufficient to cut off V_1. The circuit will

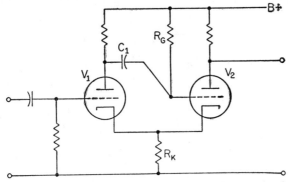

Fig. 26.   Cathode-coupled single-shot multivibrator circuit.

remain in this original condition until the next positive pulse is applied.

This circuit has the advantage of not requiring a separate bias supply. The steeper return of the grid of V_2 to conduction increases the accuracy. The major disadvantage of this type circuit is the short output pulse formed by the small value of R_G of V_2. This causes excessive grid current and short tube life.

Another single-shot circuit is shown in Fig. 27. Assume V_2 to be conducting. When it is cut off, its plate voltage rises. However, V_1 goes to cutoff bias voltage immediately, and the circuit is quickly returned to its original condition ready for the next pulse. The length of time the circuit spends in its triggered condition is determined by the values of R_{L_1}, C, and R_{G_2}. The waveshape is the same as in the other circuits, and the bias supply must be fairly large to overcome the divided plate voltage. For square-wave output a 250,000-ohm resistor may be placed in series with the grid, thereby increasing the positive grid time constant. Cathode coupling produces a low-impedance square-wave output.

Single-shot Applications. Single-shot multivibrators find many applications in industrial electronics where a specific time delay is required. For instance, imagine that some extremely short operation is to be started at a particular instant and stopped a few milliseconds after it is started. A pulse applied to a single-shot multivibrator would cause it to flip, and the time constants of the multivibrator would eventually return the circuit to its original condition. By differentiating (see Chap. 1) the output of the multivibrator, a pulse of one polarity may be derived at

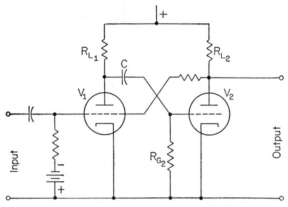

Fig. 27.   Alternate single-shot multivibrator circuit capable of square-wave output.

the beginning of the flipped condition and used to initiate the operation being controlled, and a pulse of the opposite polarity, which accompanies the return of the circuit to its original condition, could be used to terminate the operation.

These circuits are also extremely valuable in oscillographic applications where the beginning of the output voltage pulse is used to start the horizontal sweep, and the end initiates the operation the characteristics of which are to be viewed. The desired waveform is thus centered on the scope, and any delays which might otherwise be present in the starting of the sweep will not be objectionable.

Actually, the single-shot multivibrator is neither a counter nor a divider, but because of its similarity to the free-running multivibrator, it has been discussed here.

Step-type Counter. The step-type counter circuit shown in Fig. 28 is recommended for use in television applications but may be adapted to many industrial circuits. The repetition of pulses to this circuit may be interrupted momentarily or vary slightly in time, but they cannot be interrupted indefinitely, or the circuit will fall out of synchronization with the incoming pulses. Positive pulses of constant amplitude are required.

Operation is as follows: C_1 and C_2 are charged on the first pulse and C_1 discharges through V_1 between pulses. Succeeding

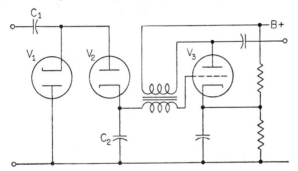

Fig. 28. Step-type counter circuit used in certain television applications.

pulses charge C_2 in steps until the cutoff voltage of the blocking oscillator V_3 is reached, at which point C_2 is discharged and the sequence repeated.

One of the outstanding advantages of this type of circuit is the sharp-pulsed output, which is particularly useful for timing operations or driving subsequent counters. Another of its advantages lies in the fact that it may be used in high division ratio applications. It has the disadvantage that input pulses must be of constant amplitude and then must be quite large in some cases.

Pulse Amplifiers. In describing individual counter circuits it has been pointed out that pulses of proper amplitude and shape were required. The voltage pulse produced by most detection devices is strong enough to trigger the counting circuit directly, but some use a multivibrator between the detecting device and the counter input as mentioned above.

However, when the detection device yields an impulse that is too small even for use as a trigger for a multivibrator or of the wrong polarity, one or more stages of pulse amplification may be necessary. It must be remembered that in conventional amplifiers a 180-deg phase shift occurs; that is, if a positive pulse is fed to a single-stage amplifier grid, the resulting pulse at the plate of the amplifier will be negative. Therefore if a positive pulse is desired for triggering the counting circuits, another stage of amplification is necessary. For most industrial applications, where pulse repetition rates are reasonably low, conventional amplifier circuits will usually work.

REFERENCES

Andrew, V. J., A Simplified Frequency Divider Circuit, *Proceedings of the Institute of Radio Engineers*, July, 1933.

Brown, Cyril H., Plug-in Scaler for Industrial Counting, *Electronics*, July, 1948, p. 90.

Kerst, D. W., A High Resolving Power Tenfold Thyratron Counter, *Review of Scientific Instruments*, April, 1938, p. 131.

Liftshutz, H., and J. L. Lawson, Triode Vacuum Tube Scale-of-two Circuits, *Review of Scientific Instruments*, March, 1938, p. 83.

Liftshutz, H., New Vacuum Tube Fractional Scaling Circuits of Arbitrary Integral of Fractional Scaling Ratio, *The Physical Review*, February, 1940, p. 243.

Meinheit, C. E., and W. W. Snyder, Electronic Counter and Divider Circuits, *Sylvania Technologist*, July, 1948, p. 5.

Phelps, B. E., Dual-triode Trigger Circuits, *Electronics*, July, 1945, p. 110.

Potter, J. T., A Four-tube Counter Decade, *Electronics*, June, 1944, p. 110.

Reich, H. J., Trigger Circuits, *Electronics*, August, 1939, p. 14.

Shenk, E. R., The Multivibrator Applied Theory and Design, *Electronics*, January, 1944, p. 136.

Weisman, R., Stable Ten-light Decade Scaler, *Electronics*, May, 1949, p. 84.

Wellman, B., Electronic Counter for Rapid Impulses, *Electronics*, October, 1942, p. 74.

CHAPTER 11

HIGH-FREQUENCY HEATING AND WELDING

High-frequency heating and welding equipments account for a major portion of the money that is spent in the industrial electronics field each year. Through these somewhat less glamorous branches of electronics, many industrial processes are made possible and profitable which would otherwise be unthinkable.

The circuits and techniques used in electronic heating and welding applications are quite specialized and of limited general interest. Therefore, only the general-interest aspects of this branch of electronics will be presented here. The bibliography at the end of this chapter will provide the reader with ample sources of additional, more thorough and specialized information.

ELECTRONIC HEATING

Basically there are two types of high-frequency heating: *induction* heating and *dielectric* heating. Both methods share a common principle: power in the form of alternating current is transferred from an electrical circuit, where it originates, into the material where it is converted into heat by the resistance of the material and raises the temperature of all or part of that material. The heat actually originates *inside* the body of the material being heated, but the energy which causes this heating is furnished externally.

There are two basic differences between these methods. Only conductors of electricity can be heated by induction heating, whereas dielectric heating applies only to nonconducting materials. The second difference lies in the apparatus used to transmit the energy from the electric circuit into the material. In the case of induction heating, the heating element is a coil of copper wire or tubing through which the alternating current flows. Energy is transferred by induction—thus the name induction heating. In dielectric heating, on the other hand, the material to be heated is placed between two metallic plates which are alternately charged to positive and negative voltages with respect to each other. The entire apparatus resembles a condenser with the material acting as the dielectric—thus the term dielectric heating.

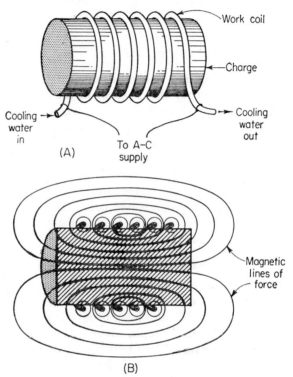

(A)

(B)

Fig. 1. Basic induction heating setup. High-frequency alternating current passed through the coil heats the metallic charge. The depth of heating depends on the frequency of the heater current.

Induction Heating. In induction heating apparatus the material to be heated is placed in an alternating electromagnetic field. The nature of the field required depends on the size, shape, and material of the work.

Figure 1A shows a typical case. A metallic bar is to be heated for purposes of hardening. The coil surrounding the bar is referred to as the work coil. Its function is analogous to the primary winding of a transformer.   The work or *charge*, being a conductor, acts as a short-circuited secondary.   When the primary, or work coil, is energized, a current is induced in the secondary, or work.   The magnitude of this induced current will depend on the amplitude and frequency of the alternating current flowing in the work coil.   It is the induced current that causes the heating of the material.

The lines of magnetic flux which are set up in the charge by the current-carrying coil are parallel to the charge axis in the case cited, as shown by the cutaway drawing in Fig. 1*B*.   The distribution of this flux (and thus the distribution of heating) within the work will depend on several factors: (1) the electric and magnetic properties of the material, (2) the dimensional cross section of the work itself, and (3) frequency of the applied alternating current.

Frequency.   The first two of these factors are usually fixed by the job at hand.   The remaining variable is the frequency of the alternating current which is made to flow in the work coil and which determines the rate at which the magnetic field within the charge builds up and collapses and then builds up in the other direction.

The selection of frequency for a particular job depends on the application.   If, for instance, a piece of metal is to be melted, it may be placed in a suitable crucible, which is surrounded by a fairly low-frequency work coil.   As the charge experiences the regularly reversing magnetic field, it begins to heat uniformly and continues until the desired temperature is attained.

If the frequency is raised, skin effect (in which the current tends to flow only in a thin shell on the charge surface) comes into play, and the secondary currents induced in the charge tend to remain on the outside.   Since more heating occurs in the vicinity of the high-flux density, only the outside is heated by induction. This sort of arrangement is advantageous where the outside of the material is to be heat-treated for high surface hardness and the interior is to remain soft.   Uniform hardening would cause the piece to be brittle, no hardening at all would cause the piece to be easily damaged.   Such a piece might be used in the bearing of a crankshaft.   By the same means, the cutting tip of a lathe tool may be hardened, while the main part is left soft and strong.

The induction heating effect may be noticed when frequencies as low as standard 60-cycle power line are used, but higher frequencies almost always are employed in actual practice. As might be expected, the production of relatively large amounts of power at middle-high frequencies usually presents a job for electron tubes. In some processes where only a few hundred cycles per second are required, frequency-multiplying rotating machinery operating from regular 60-cycle input can be used to better advantage.

Hysteresis Effect. In metal pieces containing iron an additional heating phenomenon will occur. The minute particles of which iron is composed become magnetized when the iron is brought into the influence of a magnetic field. These minute particles tend to align themselves with the magnetic field that charges them. In a rapidly alternating field the particles are in a continuous process of trying to realign themselves each time the direction of the field reverses. This particle motion generates heat within the material. The heating thus produced is described as the hysteresis effect.

The hysteresis effect disappears when the temperature of the iron reaches the point known as the *Curie temperature*. At that point the iron can no longer be magnetized. The temperature can be raised higher, however, since the eddy-current or straight induction heating continues as long as the alternating field is applied.

Work Coil Design. Induction-heating work coils may take on a number of shapes. The example shown in Fig. 1 is typical but by no means a standard form. The technique of designing a work coil that will produce just the right amount of heat in just the right portion or portions of the charge is a highly specialized science, and to explain all its fine points here would be impossible. A few typical configurations are illustrated in Fig. 2.

In A the induction heating coil passes inside the bearing shown. Thus the inner surface is heated by the flow of high-frequency current within the coil. In B the coil is concentrated around the corner of the piece of tool steel. Thus only that corner is heated. In C the surface of the piece immediately under the spiral-wound work coil is heated. A system for applying heat in two different portions of the piece simultaneously is shown in D. Here the induction heating current flows through two coils, and each coil imparts a certain amount of heating in the desired locations.

Very special work coils are sometimes required. In applications where induction heating is used in soldering or brazing, as in Fig. 3, it is usually important that only the portions which actually come in contact with the solder or brazing material be heated. Otherwise distortion of the assembly may occur. In

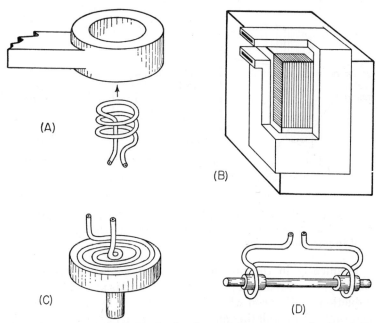

FIG. 2. Many special induction-heating coil forms are used. In *A* the inside of the connecting-rod bearing is to be heated. Drawings *B*, *C*, and *D* show other special cases for localized heating.

cases like these the work coil may take the form of a knife-edged single-turn loop, which fits snugly around but does not touch the immediate vicinity of the proposed joint.

Since the work coil is also part of an electrical circuit, its electrical properties must be considered. As a coil it has inductance—and, of course, resistance. These factors must be considered when choosing work coil shape and material. Low resistance is advantageous, since less power will be wasted in the work coil and the over-all operation will be more efficient.

Where moderately high frequencies are involved, the diameter of the wire or tubing used in the work coil should be large because of the skin effect.

In most high-powered induction-heating equipment provisions are made for circulating cooling water through the work coil tubing.   Care is taken to see that this does not hinder the operation of the device by shorting out the ends of the coil where the water enters and leaves.

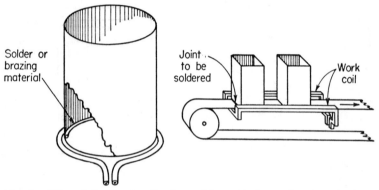

Fig. 3.   When induction heating is used for soldering or brazing, the heat produced must be concentrated in a small area surrounding the proposed joint to prevent distortion of the work.

Frequently in the production of strip materials where continuous processes are employed, the material is passed through an induction heating coil where it is brought up to the proper temperature.   In regulating and controlling this type of process the speed of travel through the coil may determine the amount of heating.

Dielectric Heating.   In dielectric heating nonconducting materials are placed between a pair of conducting plates which are electrically charged by a high-frequency a-c potential.   The basic setup is illustrated in Fig. 4.

The effects which are responsible for the heating of the nonconducting material were known for many years before the phenomenon was actually employed to do useful work.   It was noticed that condensers in high-powered radio stations heated in use and that as the frequency of operation increased, so did the amount of heat generated.

The first commercial use of dielectric heating had to do with introducing artificial fevers into various parts of the human body. The most desirable characteristic of the artificial fevers thus produced was that the fever spread uniformly and extended well below the surface of the body, which was not the case with simple heat-radiation devices.

Modern Applications. Dielectric heating is applicable to almost all nonconducting materials, such as wood, plastic, certain liquids, etc. The use of dielectric heating for jobs which could not otherwise be done is even more prevalent than in induction heating, though, at present, there is more induction heating equipment in existence.

One of the most common applications of dielectric heating is the preheating of plastic materials. By this means much time is saved in the plastics industry. Originally the material had to be heated very slowly in order that it be heated uniformly. By dielectric heating, only a few moments are required, instead of hours.

Dielectric heating is also widely used in the processing of both natural and synthetic rubber products. Again, even heating is required—and obtained—by this method. Where heat is required for drying, such as in the printing and dyeing industry, dielectric heating serves very well. In the lumber industry and its associated fields dielectric heating is often used to process lumber and to speed and perfect the drying of glued joints. In fact, the applications for dielectric heating are too numerous to compile, and their number is constantly increasing—even more so than for induction heating.

Fundamental Theory of Dielectric Heating. All matter is made up of tiny particles called molecules. These molecules are in turn composed of organized groups of the three fundamental subparticles: electrons, protons, and neutrons. The arrangement and number of these particles within the molecule determines the physical and electric characteristics of the material.

Nonconducting materials have no *free* electrons, in contrast to conducting materials whose molecules have free electrons. In the conductor these free electrons are the carriers of the electric current within the material. The nonconductor, not having them, obviously cannot conduct electrical currents.

This fact accounts for the dielectric heating effect. When the molecules of a nonconducting material are placed in an electric field, they tend to line up physically with the lines of force of that field. If the field is reversed, these particles tend to reverse themselves to line up with the field. If the field is periodically reversed at some fairly high rate, these particles will be constantly realigning themselves. In doing so, heat is created, and the temperature of the material rises.

The examples illustrated in Fig. 4 are typical of the dielectric heating work. Between the two plates is a homogenous piece of the nonconducting material. At any one time, when a certain voltage exists between the two plates, a share of the voltage difference is assumed by each minute section of the material. In other words if the top plate is positive with respect to the bottom, *the bottom half of each particle* will be slightly more positive than the top half.

When the material being heated is not homogenous, a different situation exists. Depending on the electrical characteristics of the different materials, a larger or smaller share of the voltage difference will be assumed by each material. The voltage that each material is responsible for determines the amount of heating that will occur in that material.

Figure 4 shows a system for applying even heat to speed the drying of a glued joint. The voltage change is gradual throughout the thickness of the material, since there is no change in the type of material between any two opposite points on the electrodes.

Where other than rectangular work is to be heated by the dielectric method, air gaps can be permitted, as long as their share of the voltage drop is taken into consideration and enough voltage is applied between the plates to allow sufficient drop across the material. Air acts just like another material (which it is) and must be treated as such.

High-frequency Generating Circuits. The electrical power required for both types of high frequency heating is usually provided by some sort of oscillator, although the power could be obtained from an amplifier driven by an oscillator. The basic theory of such oscillators is given in Chap. 3 and will not be repeated here.

What is needed in dielectric heating is a high voltage. This

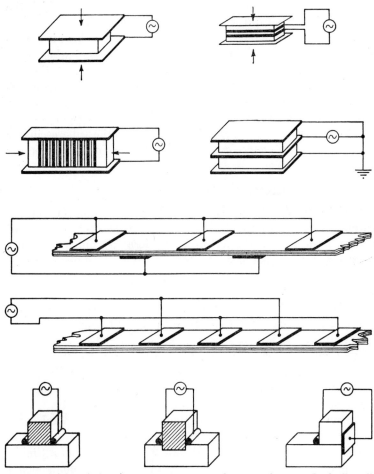

FIG. 4.   Dielectric heating apparatus may take many forms.   Basically, all
of these contain two metallic plates that are alternately charged at some
high rate.   Here glued joints are heated.

is provided at the terminals of the condenser in the tuned circuit
of an oscillator.   In inductive heating the need is for high current
at some desired frequency.   This high current is provided by the
current flowing through the inductance of the tuned circuit of an
oscillator.   Therefore, a tube oscillator provides both kinds of
electrical energy for high-frequency heating.   The major engineering is in the design of the oscillator circuit to provide the

proper energy and in the design of the applicators by which the energy is imparted to the work piece to be heated.

It is worth noting, however, that high-frequency heat is expensive heat and that it should not be employed except when more conventional methods are impossible to use or where the less economical tube method of supplying the heat is preferable. Tube-supplied heating power is expensive, because the losses in the system are high. The tube itself consumes much energy; energy is lost in transferring it from the tube oscillator to the work; and energy is lost in radiation from the connecting wires in the system.

ELECTRONIC WELDING CONTROL

Resistance Welding. Heat caused by the flow of current through materials is usually considered to be power lost and is, of course, undesirable. Many of our modern-day industrial processes depend on just such heating for the accomplishment of useful and productive work. Such an application is resistance welding.

Resistance welding is the process of joining two pieces of metal together by passing a heavy current through them in such a way that intense heat is generated at exactly the spot where the desired joint is to be formed. This heat causes a small portion of each piece to melt. The molten portions flow together, and when the current is turned off and the metal cools and solidifies, a permanent bond or weld is formed.

All resistance welding systems consist of three general components—a power source, a system of electrodes for applying power to the pieces being welded, and a control system for timing the application of power. The design of any of these components depends on the materials and type of weld.

Types of Welding. Spot welding, as its name implies, is a method of joining two metals by concentrating welding current on a relatively small area, using small electrodes. Such welding can be accomplished with portable tools, such as gun welders, in which the electrodes are connected to the power source by a pair of heavy conductors. There are many types of spot welders. A number of spot welder electrodes may be connected in series to form a series weld.

Seam welding is similar to spot welding except that current-carrying wheels replace the small spot-welder electrodes. The two pieces (usually sheet materials) are overlapped and fed through the welding electrodes at speeds varying from 2 to 100 ft per minute. Seam welding is illustrated in Fig. 5. The wheels are pulsed regularly with welding current, so the seam weld resembles an even series of closely-spaced spot welds.

A third type of resistance welding is the projection method. This is of two general kinds—butt and flash welding. In butt welding two pieces to be joined are held together firmly and current passes through the joint. When sufficiently heated the two are forced together under high pressure, giving a solid joint.

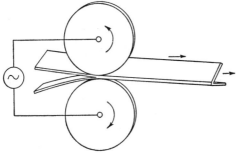

FIG. 5. Seam welding is accomplished by passing the two materials to be welded through a pair of alternately charged wheels which serve to apply welding pressure as well as welding current.

In flash welding the pieces are held together only lightly while current is passed through them. Owing to irregularities of the metal surfaces considerable flashing occurs and the surfaces are "burned" smooth, as well as heated. They are then joined under high pressure.

Power Source. The heat generated in any material may be determined by the simple mathematical formula $W = I^2Rt$, where W is the total amount of heat, I is the current flowing, R is the resistance of the material, and t the length of time the current flows. Since the current in this equation is squared, any change in current in a welding process will cause even more of a change in the heating. For instance, if the current is doubled, the heat generated will be four times as great.

In welding two pieces of metal, the resistance factor in the heating formula is very low—two pieces of metal brought together under pressure usually form a good contact. The time element is usually quite short, as determined by other considerations, so the remaining factor of the equation (the current) must be quite large if enough heat is to be generated to cause portions of each piece of metal to melt and run together. In practice welding currents run into hundreds of amperes, though the voltage required to cause such large currents need not be high—a fraction of a volt to 15 or 20 volts being typical values. The current is usually applied through a transformer which has a voltage step-down ratio from some readily available voltage to the desired welding voltage. The electrodes for connecting this low-voltage high-current power source must make extremely good contact with the materials to be joined. If more resistance appears at the electrodes than between the two pieces of material, more heating will take place at the electrodes, and they will melt and fuse before the proposed weld forms.

Mechanical pressure plays an important part in the operation. To be effective the application of pressure must be timed just right with respect to the application of the welding current. In a properly executed welding cycle full electrode pressure must be exerted before the welding current is turned on. This pressure must be maintained until after the current is interrupted and the molten "nugget" has cooled to a temperature at which it regains a large portion of the inherent strength of the metal from which the weld is formed. This delay in releasing pressure is called the *hold*, and it helps to prevent cracks and faulty welds. The period before welding current is applied, while the electrodes are approaching the proper pressure, is called the *squeeze time*.

Welder Control. Accurate timing of the squeeze, weld, and hold times is very important. Squeeze time must be sufficient to allow sufficient mechanical pressure to be built up but not unnecessarily long, for economic reasons. The weld time must be just enough to form the desired nugget, and the hold time must be right to prevent too rapid cooling and resulting flaws in the weld.

Resistance-welding control circuits are of two general types. The first type puts the equipment through its proper cycle at random times as initiated by the operator. In other words, as the operator positions the materials to his satisfaction, he actuates a device which initiates the welding cycle. The second type of control runs through squeeze, weld, and hold intervals

and then after a fixed period of "off" time, automatically initiates the next welding cycle. In this case some positive means
for positioning the proper areas between the welding electrodes
at the proper time is a necessity. In seam welding the second
type of control is used, and the electrode wheels are arranged to
move the materials a fixed amount during each off period.

Welding control circuits are nothing more than interval timing
circuits. Figure 6 shows a typical example. The time interval
is started by closing Sw_1, which connects the thyratron circuit
across the a-c supply line. The thyratron grid voltage at that
instant assumes a value depending on the position of the tap on
the resistor R across the line. The thyratron conducts on por-

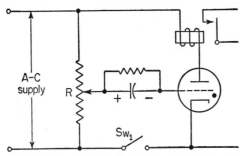

Fig. 6. Basic circuit of typical welder time-interval control.

tions of the a-c cycle when its anode is positive with respect to
its cathode, and a small amount of cathode current flows to the
thyratron grid, which is slightly more positive than the cathode.
This current flow charges the grid capacitor with a voltage of the
polarity shown. At a certain time, depending on the values of
grid resistor and capacitor, the voltage across the condenser will
make the grid sufficiently negative that on the next positive
excursion of the a-c supply voltage, the thyratron will no longer
conduct, thereby ending the interval. The smaller the grid
capacitor, the shorter the charging time required for the grid to
regain control, and vice versa.

The length of interval can easily be adjusted by setting the
tap on the resistance network, which determines the voltage at
the supply side of the grid capacitor. After the thyratron ceases
to conduct on positive half cycles of the supply voltage, there is
no longer any charging current in the grid circuit, and the capaci-

tor loses its charge by forcing current through the parallel resistor, which dissipates the charge in the form of heat. The time required for this discharging process depends on the value of the resistor—a high ohmic value offering more resistance to the discharging current and thus taking a longer time.

If the switch is still depressed when the capacitor discharges sufficiently to again allow thyratron conduction during positive excursions of supply voltage, the circuit will again operate, and so on. Relays in the anode circuit of the thyratron may be used

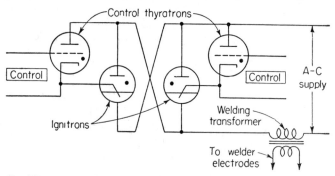

Fig. 7. Enormous values of welding current can be controlled by this circuit. Actual control is applied to the primary of the welding transformer by a combination of thyratron firing tubes and ignitrons.

to control the primary circuits of welding transformers, or as in the usual case, these smaller tubes are used to control the conduction in ignitrons, which in turn control the extremely heavy welding currents.

Ignitron Circuit. A typical circuit employing thyratrons as firing tubes for the larger ignitrons is shown in Fig. 7. The ignitrons are connected so that they will conduct current in both directions through the primary of the welding transformer. Each ignitron will conduct on half of the a-c cycle when its anode is positive with respect to its cathode, if the thyratron connected to its grid is conducting. The firing time of the thyratrons is easily controlled by circuits of the type discussed in the chapter on motor control. Some smaller types of welders use what might be called *half-wave controls*, which employ only one control tube, which conducts current only on every other half of the a-c cycle.

Synchronous and Asynchronous Control. Resistance welder circuits do not present a pure resistance load to their power

sources. In other words the current in the line does not reach
its maximum value at the same instant that the applied voltage
does. This is the result of a finite amount of reactance being
in the circuit.

If welding current is turned on at any random portion of the
a-c cycle, certain undesirable effects may take place. Most
serious of these is the production of unwanted voltage or current
surges known as transients. These transients can be eliminated
by making sure that the welding current is always applied at the
proper instant in the a-c cycle. In other words the current rises
from zero to maximum at a definite time relationship with the
voltage wave. This relationship depends on the amount of
reactance in the welding circuit.

Synchronous welder timers take this condition into consideration. In addition to controlling the amount of heat applied to
the weld, the control system delays the application of the current
(after the switch is closed) until the voltage wave is at the proper
point in its cycle. From that point at which the welder current
is applied the delay circuit loses control, and the interval timer
determines how long the current will flow.

The elimination of these transients is most important in large
size welders where, for economy, equipment must run very close
to its limit. Another factor that is taken into consideration in
designing control circuits is the fact that the core material in the
welder transformer will become saturated if a predominance of
current in a certain direction flows through its windings. This
effect is overcome by alternating the polarity of the first current
surge applied to the transformer.

Capacitor Discharge Welder. Most resistance welds are
accomplished in a relatively short period of time. The shortness
presents a rather difficult design problem. Whenever large
amounts of power must be delivered, certain precautions must
be taken to prevent equipment failure. In resistance welding
tremendous amounts of power may be required to flow during a
period which may be no longer than a fraction of a second. The
average power is low, but the equipment must be designed to
withstand the peak power.

The capacitor storage type of welder by-passes this difficulty
and is suitable for a great many industrial welding applications.
A typical capacitor storage circuit is shown in Fig. 8. There

are two phases to the welding operation. First, the switch is thrown (either automatically or manually) to the left, where it connects a capacitor, a d-c voltage source, and a resistor in series. The capacitor receives a charge from the power source through the resistor, which limits the current flow to a reasonable amount. In the welding step the switch is thrown to the right, and the capacitor dumps its slowly accumulated charge into the weld almost instantaneously.

The voltage source need supply only enough power to charge the capacitor slowly, while the weld still receives its extremely high power surge over the desired short period of time.

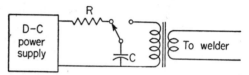

FIG. 8. Capacitor discharge welding equipment works on the principle shown. A capacitor is charged by a d-c power source and discharged through the welding transformer.

Electronics enters the welding picture chiefly through the control of welding time. A vast amount of engineering design has gone into this phase of the applications of tubes to industrial operations, and as a consequence the circuits developed may be highly complex. It is doubtful if the average individual in industry can effectively study and understand these complex circuits for his own use—it would be better to make use of the accumulated knowledge and techniques developed by the electronic-welding engineers. In other words seldom would it pay an engineer to try to develop a system for his own use; it would be cheaper in the long run to buy existing equipment.

An idea of the engineering involved in modern welding control systems may be gleaned from a brief perusal of a series of articles published in *Electronics* in 1942 and 1943 on the general subject of welding controls. These references will be found below in the list of articles and books which one interested in the general subject should see.

REFERENCES

Heating

Ackley, F. E., Control Equipments for Induction Heating, *General Electric Review*, March, 1944, p. 16.

Babat, George, Surface Hardening, A New Job for Transmitting Tubes, *Electronics*, June, 1938, p. 44.

Bichsel, H. J., Energy Storage Welding, *Mill and Factory*, January, 1945, p. 94.

Bivens, M. E., Special Welding Controls, *Electronics*, October, 1942, p. 62.

Boyd, Bruce, Grid-controlled Rectifiers for R-F Heating, *Electronics*, November, 1946, p. 125.

Briggs, Rufus, Precision Energy Storage Spot Welder, *Electronics*, June, 1947, p. 102.

Brown, G. H., C. N. Hoyler, and R. A. Bierwirth, "Theory and Applications of Radio-frequency Heating," D. Van Nostrand Company, Inc., New York, 1947.

Brown, A. W., Dummy Loads for Large Industrial Welders, *Electrical Engineering*, January, 1949, p. 12.

Chute, G. M., "Electronic Control of Resistance Welding," McGraw-Hill Book Company, Inc., New York, 1945.

Chute, G. M., "Electronic Motor and Welder Controls," McGraw-Hill Book Company, Inc., New York, 1951.

Clark, S. A., Timers for Welding Control, *Electronics*, November, 1942, p. 65.

Croco, C. P., Progress in Arc Welding, *Westinghouse Engineer*, March, 1949, p. 34.

Curtis, Frank W., "High-frequency Induction Heating," McGraw-Hill Book Company, Inc., New York, 1945.

Doolittle, H. D., Tube Trends in the Field of Industrial Heating, *Electronic Industries*, May, 1948, p. 4.

Durand, S. R., Mercury Arc Converter for Induction Heating, *Electrical Engineering*, April, 1949, p. 290.

Duryee, L. M., Economic Aspects of Radio-frequency Heating, *Electrical Engineering*, August, 1948, p. 747.

Fields, C. V., Electronic Heating Design Chart, *Electronics*, April, 1944, p. 143.

Gilbert, R. W., Automatic Tuning System for Preheating Plastics, *Electronics*, December, 1944, p. 115.

Gillsepie, H. C., Surface Hardening of Metals, *Electronics*, July, 1944, p. 102.

Guzzetti, A. J., Variables in High-frequency Preheating, *Modern Plastics*, April, 1949, p. 89.

Herbst, H. T., Characteristics of the Arc in Heliarc Welding, *Electrical Engineering*, January, 1949, p. 30.

Humphrey, H. C., Electronic Generators Extend Induction Heating Field, *Electronics*, January, 1943, p. 56.

Induction Heating Equipment, *Electronics*, August, 1945, p. 110.

Keithley, R., Heating by Centimeter Power, *Journal of the British Institution of Radio Engineers*, May, 1949, p. 97.

Kurtz, J., A Feedback Welding Timer, *Electronics*, April, 1940, p. 47.

Marcum, J., Heating With Microwaves, *Electronics*, March, 1947, p. 82.

Mittelman, Eugene, Design Chart for R-F Heating Treatment Generators, *Electronics*, 1941, p. 51.

Oestricher, S., Electrical vs. Mechanical Control of an A-C Arc Welder, *Electrical Manufacturing*, January, 1949, p. 82.

Palmer, H. L., Spot Welding Controls, *Electronics*, August, 1942, p. 36.

Penny, G. W., Induction Heating Comes of Age, *Electronics*, March, 1943, p. 123.

Pinder, K., Induction and Dielectric Heating, *Electrical Engineering*, February, 1947, p. 149.

Radio Frequency Heating Speeds Plywood Bonding, *Electronics*, November, 1942, p. 79.

Rogers, G. L., Energy Storage Welding Controls, *Electronics*, December, 1942, p. 63.

Rudd, W. C., High Frequency Heating in the Radio Spectrum, *Electrical Engineering*, June, 1947, p. 570.

Rudd, W. C., Duplex Operation of Induction Heaters, *Electronics*, November, 1946, p. 93.

Scott, G. W., Jr., Induction and Dielectric Heating, *Electrical Engineering*, September, 1948, p. 847.

Smith, C. E., Resistance-welding Equipment Considerations, *Electrical Engineering*, September, 1948, p. 865.

Stansel, N. R., Induction Heating Applications, *General Electric Review*, February, 1948, p. 45.

Stansel, N. R., Melting Metals by Induction Heating, *General Electric Review*, March, 1948, p. 35.

Storm, H. F., Induction Heating of Long Cylindrical Charges, *Electrical Engineering Transactions*, June, 1946, p. 369.

Taylor, J. P., R-F Heating Speeds Plastic Molding, *Electronics*, September, 1943, p. 102.

Venable, D., and T. P. Kinn, Radio-frequency Heating, p. 375, "Industrial Electronics Reference Book," John Wiley & Sons, Inc., New York, 1948.

Venable, D., Dielectric Heating Fundamentals, *Electronics*, November, 1945, p. 120.

Welch, A. V., Power Supply for A-C Arc Welding, *General Electric Review*, May, 1945, p. 41.

Winemiller, H. R., Experience with High-frequency Heating, *Electrical Engineering*, October, 1948, p. 981.

Winlund, E. S., Electronic Heating in the Furniture Industry, *Electronics*, May, 1946, p. 108.

Welding

Bivens, M. E., Seam and Pulsation Welding Controls, *Electronics*, September, 1942, p. 55.

Bivens, M. E., Special Welding Controls, *Electronics*, October, 1942, p. 62.

Garman, G. W., Resistance Welding Speeded, Improved by Tube Control, *Electronics*, March, 1943, p. 117.

Horton, H. L., Electronic Controls for Resistance Welding, November, 1944, p. 153.

Klemperer, H., Capacitor-discharge Welding Systems, *Electronics*, May, 1944, p. 118.

Palmer, H. L., Resistance-welding Controls, *General Electric Review*, September, 1943, p. 507.

Weller, B. L., Servicing Resistance Welding Controls, *Electronics*, January, 1943, p. 78.

INDEX